D1273513

TRIBUTE

Profile of San Diego County Fire Departments

Compiled by Pearl Ellis

Copyright © 2021

ISBN: 978-1-944891-71-8

Cover: Painting of Art Bale by Gloria Warren

Layout and Design by Tiffany Smith & Christopher Sturdevant

Published by HPN Books & Ledge Media, divisions of FRE-Enterprises

Jackson, Wyoming

www.hpnbooks.com

First printing, 2021.

Email: pearlaellis@gmail.com

CONTENTS

DEDICATION

To Art...

who uplifted me by his undaunted spirit and courage

to rebuild and recover after the Cedar Fire

&

To Kevin...

who added warmth and strength to me, his mother,

and a kind loving smile to all who knew him

TO ART

At the age of 17 Arthur "Art" Tarr Bale left New York City to search for a better life. While he was in high school he boxed as a 145-pound welterweight prizefighter to earn money. As soon as he had $40 in his pocket, he left the city.

During the next 14 years he struggled—working on a commercial fishing boat on the high seas; looking unsuccessfully for work in Canada; working on cattle ranches in Wyoming, Nevada, and Oregon; working in Northern California in logging camps; and doing underground construction work in Southern California. He said, "Life was hard. It wasn't an adventure. It was frustrating. Birthdays were just another day, and holidays were for other people."

When Art moved to Ramona in 1976 at the age of 33, he joined the Ramona Fire Department. After 14 months he was promoted to engineer and four years later he became a captain. He said, "It's a lucky person who considers his job his hobby, and I loved being a firefighter." Art not only found a family at the Ramona Fire Department but another one at a fire training session where we fell in love. We have been partners for 44 years.

Captain Bale said, "Firefighting is the most emotionally demanding thing I've ever done." One incident was the most spiritual experience in his life. "I was giving mouth-to-mouth resuscitation to an infant, and I caught hepatitis." He said, "I'd given mouth-to-mouth before, but, looking at that baby, I never felt so close to God. The baby died, but I feel like I carry a little bit of the infant around with me."

To Kevin

My son was brutally killed while riding his bicycle by a hit-and-run drunk driver at 10:43 a.m. on January 20, 2020, on a beautiful holiday morning in good weather on a country road. It is an injustice of fate that he should have been killed by a wretched criminal that did not even have the courage to give him assistance. The San Diego County Sheriff's Department used a helicopter to successfully capture the driver four hours later. The paramedics used all their skills to try to save Kevin, but life had left my precious son. My life has been crushed by this useless and unnecessary event.

How will I remember Kevin… my son?

Whenever I see babies, kittens, puppies and cubs, I will remember Kevin

For me, he was big and strong yet gentle, good and kind

Whenever I see raindrops or snowflakes, I will remember Kevin

His love of nature was boundless. When the winds come to whistle in my ear, I will remember Kevin

When I see Nancy, his wife … her smile, her caring and her love, I will remember Kevin

Kevin had a lifelong love with bicycles. While riding he enjoyed nature as it was intended to be

So when I see children playing with bicycles, I will remember Kevin

But most of all, when I see or hear love, kindness and goodness, I will feel the presence of Kevin… my son.

This book is dedicated to the first responders whose care and skill serve us all.

ABOUT THE AUTHOR

Pearl Ellis's childhood growing up in Brazil was a prelude to her becoming a firefighter. While living near an outlet of the Amazon River, she was a prey in a land of predators. She loved the beauty of the remote jungle but fully understood the reality of its dangers.

Responsibility came early for Pearl, at times living alone in a hotel in Sao Paulo while attending school because there were no schools in the interior areas of Brazil where her father worked for Morrison-Knudsen Construction Company. Her education included an eyewitness account of the improvised families and the threats to the Amazon's ecosystem by man burning the rain forest. These were harsh sights for the soft eyes of a child on her own. This would be Pearl's baptism of fire for her independent spirit, the same spirit her entire family inherited from her great-great-grandparents Zachariah and Eleanor Sales who crossed the plains of America in a covered wagon with John Bozeman to be among the first settlers in Montana.

And so, after spending many years living an adventure that most children can only read or dream about, Pearl left the jungle to graduate from Stetson University in Florida with a Bachelor of Science in Business Administration and to become an instructional media cataloger for San Diego Unified School District for 44 years.

In 1963 she settled in Ramona with her Bouvier des Flandres dogs in a quiet log cabin. Her self-reliance kept her from ever marrying. Every time she saw a fire it brought back impressions of the wild places and wildlife in Brazil. The appreciation of nature and an American patriotism instilled by living overseas and visiting over seventy countries steered Pearl to firefighting. It prepared her for the kinds of challenges encountered as chief of the Fernbrook Fire Company and as the first woman volunteer fire chief in the State of California.

FROM THE AUTHOR

As you open the door of this book, think of the world as a globe that rotates on its axis. Choose any continent you please, then any country, and there you will probably find volunteer and career firefighters.

This international brethren from all walks of life, with different languages and different cultures, share a common mission with each other. This mission to the community of public service, firefighting, medical aid and rescue is deeply rooted, with history and tradition dating back to the ancient Egyptians and the Roman Empire.

The volunteers, not unlike citizen soldiers, are citizen firefighters. The dentist, the mechanic, the homemaker, and the grocer all answer the alarm, the call for help, in any way they can, day or night, sometimes at great personal risk. The many hours committed to emergencies, training, education, maintenance of equipment, and even fundraising are donated by these dedicated men and women; they perform their duties without pay. Too often the sacrifices made by these people are taken for granted.

Now turn the globe to the western United States and stop at California. There are fifty-eight counties in this huge state. The vast, sprawling County of San Diego with many unincorporated communities has been served by volunteers as well as paid firefighters.

This book profiles the many fire departments that have existed in the past and those currently operating throughout San Diego County. As a former San Diego County volunteer firefighter who also served as fire chief of the Fernbrook Volunteer Fire Company in Ramona, I can attest to the twenty-four-hour demands that are many times necessary to get the job done. If the firefighters don't answer the call, who will? They are the first line of defense within the community.

I have spent many hours working beside people who were at their very best when things were at their very worse. The emergencies with which we were confronted stretched and challenged our physical and emotional limits—we were tested by fire, smoke, heat, cold, wind, rain, and long hours on the fire lines. There were also traumatic traffic accidents where we came face to face with reality—the victims screaming, their bloodied and mutilated bodies.

But, there were happy memories, too—the camaraderie, the friendships, the water fights. Most of all, there was a feeling of belonging, of being part of something that you could feel good about, or being proud, and of having a sense of purpose.

My time as a volunteer firefighter was a period of growing and learning for me. Of all the experiences in dealing with the injured and the sick, the fires and the rescues, one overriding lesson stands out—how frighteningly human and vulnerable we are!

DEPARTMENTS

Profile of San Diego County Fire Departments

Covering 27.5 square miles, with a population of 16,500, Alpine is bordered on the east by the Cleveland National Forest and on the west by Lakeside.

Over 12,000 years ago, the Kumeyaay lived in the area. In the 1780s, the Spanish missionaries forced the Kumeyaay to adopt their agricultural methods. In the 1850s, Governor Pio Pico gave ranchos in the area to his relatives and friends.

Highway 80 went through the center of Alpine until Interstate 8 was completed in 1968, passing the town about a quarter of a mile to the north. Now Highway 80 is called Alpine Boulevard.

The department was formed in 1948 by John Sheedy, John Jones, Sr., and Arthur Pratt. A war surplus truck was purchased with voluntary funds and parked at Grier Anderson's Standard Station in town.

Early fire commissioners were Rudolph Oeser, J.H. McKie, Johnny Friedenberg, Claude Young, C.E. Bennett, Frank Wilson, Henry Mumma, John Neely, and Paul Black.

Commander Rudolph Oeser, who served in the U.S. Navy for 32 years, was on the Alpine Fire Board for seven years. He donated his administrative skills to organize and set up a budget for the department. He was honored on April 12, 1962, by the Alpine Kiwanis Club for his important role in forming the fire department.

A bond issue was presented to the community in 1957 for $18,000 to build and equip a fire department. It passed six to one. Alpine was recorded as a fire protection district with the County of San Diego on December 19, 1957.

The fire commissioners secured a 99-year lease for $1 a year for property on Marshall Street where the Youth Center was located. The property was owned by Mrs. Hilton who was once Alpine's postmistress. A station was built by volunteers. The station had a meeting and recreation hall which also served as an office, space for four trucks, an apartment for the custodian, and a garage in the back. Grier Anderson, who lived next door to the station, took the calls and alerted the firemen.

In 1953, a fire engine was purchased. Whoever arrived at the station first drove the engine. The firemen were Archie Hill, Ron Justice, C.E. Bennet, Lee Roper, Sam Randozzo, Jack Hoisted, Weldon Wilson, and Jack Blankenship. Elmer Otto donated a new pickup to the department. Sam Randozzo was elected chief in 1952, and Lee Roper was appointed chief in 1958.

In 1962, the crew consisted of Jack Blankenship, chief; Malcolm Huey, Jr., assistant chief; Mace Bratt, captain; Robert D. Wilson, lieutenant; Clark M. Haney, secretary

and treasurer; and firemen Hazen Alkire, Robert Bostrom, Milton Cooper, Lonnie Dennis, John Findel, Phil Hall, Frank Hollett, John Hoistad, Harry Jennings, Henry Lengbridge, Jr., Frank Marino, Georgre Lutz, Lee Roper, and Leroy Wedel. The commissioners were Philip Hall, Alfred Hinkle, and Dick Robinson. On April 3, 1962, a special election was held adding two commissioners to the board of the fire department so there would be five instead of three commissioners. The new commissioners were Orville Palmer and John Saks.

When Rio San Diego Municipal Water Water District established service to Alpine in July 1962, fire hydrants were installed. By 1967, 23 hydrants had been installed at a cost of $700 each.

The first paid fireman, Dale Bennett, was hired in 1969. Bennett served as fire chief from 1969 to 1973.

The district is governed by a five-member board of directors who are elected at large from the residents of the district and serve a four-year term. The current board members are Jim Easterling, Jim Mann, Patrick Price, Steve Taylor, and Baron "Barry" Willis.

The Alpine firefighters who fought the Cedar Fire were Doug Naylor, deputy chief; Brad Rushing, Rick LaZelle, Bob Withers, captains; Bill Paskle and Cliff Crane, engineers; Scott Champlin, Patrick Dotson, Colby Ross and Brian Boggeln,

firefighter/paramedics; and Chip Howell, Mike Mead, Dave Archibald, and Mike Vacio, firefighters.

In 2018, the annual operating budget was $3.2 million.

In March 2012, Alpine Fire purchased Maximo RAD 57 carbon monoxide detectors and a roof ventilation prop with funds provided by grants from the San Diego County Indian Gaming Local Community Benefit Fund and the San Diego Regional Fire and Emergency Foundation. The roof ventilation prop is made up of rafters and plywood and allows firefighters to train in vertical ventilation.

It can be placed at different angles to simulate different roof pitches.

On February 18, 2014, the board of directors of the district approved buying a new KME pumper at a cost of $558,317. A San Diego County Indian Gaming Local Community Benefit Fund grant for $127,802 helped pay for the pumper. The rest of the money came from the fire district's accrued apparatus replacement funds.

In early 2015, Alpine received a grant from the San Diego Regional Fire Foundation to buy an AutoPulse, an automated, portable, battery-powered cardiopulmonary resuscitation device designed to take over from manual CPR while a patient is transported to the hospital. In 2016, the district was awarded a $35,000 grant from the California Office of Traffic Safety for rescue extrication equipment. In

September 2016, Alpine Fire received a $2,194 fire prevention grant from FM Global, a large commercial property insurer. The funds were used for roadway signs reminding the community that Alpine is in a very high fire hazard zone.

Effective September 1, 2016, Alpine had an ISO rating of 2/2Y, better than the ISO rating in 2012 of 3/8B and the rating of 4/9 in 1998. The first number of the rating is properties within five miles of a fire station and within 1,000 feet of a fire hydrant. The second number is for those properties within five miles of a fire station but beyond 1,000 feet of a fire hydrant. Properties more than five miles from a fire station receive a rating of 10.

The fire district has a staff of 16 personnel: Brian Boggeln, chief; Debbie Pinhero, payroll and accounting specialist; Erin Schick, administrative assistant; Jason McBroom, fire marshal; Patrick Dotson, Greg O'Gorman, and Mike Vacio, captains; Chip Howell, Broc Thorn, and Scott Champlin, engineers; Colby Ross, Aric Hiebing, Joe Laff, Shane Ozbirn, Joe Lavigne, and Sean Jackson, firefighter/paramedics.

Chief Bill Paskle began his fire career in Alpine in 1989 and was promoted to chief in January 2008. He graduated from El Capitan High School in 1983. He joined the Bostonia Fire Protection District in 1987 as a volunteer firefighter and in 1988 became a seasonal firefighter for CDF (now Cal Fire). In 2014 he was the honorary mayor of the community. Chief Paskle oversaw the annexation of areas to the district, increased the department's jurisdiction by 25%, initiated the 4-person crew policy, and decreased response times. Chief Paskle retired December 30, 2019.

Brian Boggeln was hired by the board of directors to be chief beginning on December 31, 2019. He was hired as a cadet firefighter by the Alpine Fire Protection District in 1997 and was promoted to firefighter/paramedic in August 1999. He was a fire captain for 13 years before becoming the division chief on October 1, 2018. Chief Boggeln was a 1994 graduate of San Pasqual High School and started his fire career as a volunteer for the San Pasqual Volunteer Fire Department. He has an Associate of Fire Science and a Bachelor of Science in Fire and Emergency Services Administration from Colorado State University. He is a California State Fire Marshal Certified Chief Officer.

Alpine's Station 17, located at 1364 Tavern Road, was dedicated on March 3, 2006. JKA Architecture designed and prepared construction documents for the station, and Ericson-Hall Construction built the 13,500-square-foot fire station that includes a three-engine apparatus bay, administrative offices, day room, dining area, kitchen, fitness center, and crew quarters. The station cost $3,600,000. A Mercy ALS transport ambulance, under contract with the County of San Diego, is housed at the fire station.

The department is dispatched by the Heartland Communication Facility Authority in El Cajon.

Most of the Alpine Fire Protection District is State Responsibility Area (SRA) except for the eastern third which is in the Cleveland National Forest. The District participates in automatic aid agreements with surrounding agencies including: Viejas, Lakeside, San Miguel, Heartland Fire & Rescue, Santee, San Diego Rural Fire Protection District, Cal Fire, and the U.S. Forest Service.

The motto of the Alpine Fire Protection District is "Service With Pride."

CALLS RECALLED:

*1904: The Alpine Store owned by Charles Emory was destroyed by fire in 1904.

*1955: The Ye Alpine Tavern was completely burned by a fire in 1955.

*1962: In October 1962, a fire in Dehesa spread by 20-mph winds burned 1,000 acres. The Alpine Volunteer Fire Department sent their two engines to the scene when it threatened homes in Alpine Heights. More than 200 firefighters, 17 engines, 7 planes, and 3 bulldozers were at the fire.

*1965: A brush fire in October 1965 broke out on Arnold Way near Foss Road. The Alpine Fire Department and the U.S. Forestry Service extinguished the fire.

*1970: The Laguna Fire was started by downed power lines in the Kitchen Creek area of the Laguna Mountains on September 26, 1970. Within 24 hours it had burned westward about 30 miles to the outskirts of El Cajon and Spring Valley. Eight people were killed, 382 homes were destroyed, and 175,425 acres were burned. Ten homes were destroyed in Alpine. The building that was the Japatul School in Alpine until 1947 was destroyed. Chief Dale Bennett of Alpine Fire said, "We had hard driving winds with gusts up to 85 miles per hour driving out of the northeast and changing around to the west. The driving fire storm reduced visibility to zero."

*2001: On January 3, 2001, the Viejas Fire in Alpine destroyed 10 homes and burned 10,000 acres. The fire was started when an eastbound car caught fire about 4:30 a.m. and then 65-mph winds pushed the blaze through the community. More than 1,500 firefighters from multiple agencies and six water-dropping aircraft from Cal Fire fought the fire.

*2003: The Cedar Fire destroyed 185 homes in Alpine on October 26, 2003. Firefighters started backfires on the north side of Victoria Drive on Sunday, October 26. There were 60-foot flames on both sides of Interstate 8. Christy-Anne Seiler Davis, 42, a resident of Peutz Valley in Alpine, died in her home during the fire. The fire killed 15 people, destroyed 2,232 homes, and burned 273,246 acres before being contained on November 3.

After the fire, a pickup arrived in Alpine from Home Depot. It was filled with buckets and sifters (wooden frames with screening) that had been constructed by Home Depot employees to help the fire victims. Home Depot employees made 500 sifters and delivered them to the Community Center.

*2012: In April 2012, two residents of Alpine helped save the life of a person who went into cardiac arrest while jogging along Victoria Drive. The Heartland dispatcher gave CPR instructions to the two residents while they were waiting for the paramedics to arrive.

*2012: In August 2012, a slow-moving brush fire burning near the intersection of Alpine Boulevard and Tavern Road was quickly extinguished by Alpine Fire Protection District and Cal Fire. There were three engines, two fire crews, one bulldozer, two helicopters, one water tender, two air tankers, and 75 firefighters at the fire.

*2015: In 2015, fire crews responded to 127 traffic collisions. Those injured numbered 140 with two fatalities.

*2018: The department responded to 1,607 calls, including structure fires, traffic collisions, vehicle fires, wildland fires, and medical aids.

*2018: In July, a truck driver was stranded 24 hours in a ravine. Alpine and Cal Fire personnel hiked down into the ravine and treated the driver for exposure and dehydration. He was rescued by the Sheriff's Search and Rescue Team.

*2018: The West Fire started on July 6, 2018, in 108-degree heat off West Willows Road and alongside Interstate 8 near the Alpine Oaks Mobile Estates at 11:15 a.m. Within 15 minutes the fire had spread over 15 acres. Over 3,000 people were evacuated. The fire destroyed 39 homes (including 10 homes in the Alpine Oaks Mobile Estates), damaged 15 homes, destroyed 29 buildings, damaged 6 buildings, and burned 504 acres.

*2020: On August 13, 2020, the Victoria Fire started near Interstate 8 and Victoria Drive about 4 p.m. Firefighters from Cal Fire, Alpine, and other departments responded to the 2-acre fire.

*2020: On September 5, 2020, the Valley Fire started at Japatul Road and Carveacre Road in the Japatul Valley, southeast of Alpine, at 2:15 p.m. The resources dedicated to battling the fire included 48 engines, 4 water-dropping helicopters, 2 bulldozers, 15 water tenders, 13 hand crews, and 609 personnel, San Diego Gas & Electric's Sky Maverick assisted with the air response. One air drop of the Sky Maverick is equivalent to 2,650 gallons of water. The Orange County Fire Authority dispatched a strike team of five engines and two battalion chiefs to assist with the fire. The fire was contained on September 24. The fire burned 16,390 acres, destroyed 30 homes and 31 other structures, and damaged 11 structures.

BARONA FIRE PROTECTION DISTRICT

The Barona Indian Reservation was established in 1932 and is home to the Barona Band of Mission Indians, which is recognized by the United States Government as a sovereign nation and is governed by a seven-member elected tribal council. It is located 30 miles east of San Diego and covers 5,900 acres.

Edwin "Thorpe" Romero was elected chairman of Barona's Tribal Council on January 1, 2017. He is a lifelong resident of the Barona Indian Reservation and has served three prior terms as a tribal council member, from 1983 to 1987, from 2001-2008, and chairman from 2009-2012. He is President of the Board of Trustees for the Barona Indian Charter School. Romero is chairman of the National Congress of American Indians. In 2010, The Daily Transcript named him as one of San Diego's most influential people. After attending an Indian boarding school in Arizona, he graduated from San Diego State University.

The Barona Resort and Casino opened on December 31, 2002, and employs more than 3,000 individuals. The Barona Museum at the Cultural Center opened January 26, 2000. The museum features more than 2,000 items showing the artistry, science, and skill of the Southern California Indians.

The resort and casino has made many charitable donations over the past 25 years. For over 20 years, Barona has been a partner with MADD San Diego, financially supporting its efforts to eliminate drunk driving, support victims, and prevent underage drinking.

Wesley John "Pee Wee" Peters organized the Barona Rural Fire Department, serving on it as a firefighter/EMT for 17 years. The department started with two volunteers and grew to five. Peters and the other volunteers handled incidents such as motor vehicle accidents and medical emergencies that occurred on the Barona Reservation during the 1980s and 1990s. Despite the fact that Peters was retired from rural fire duty, he put his jacket, pants and helmet back on and saved the homes of his uncle, cousin, and niece from burning during the Cedar Fire in October 2003. Jacque Whaley, his cousin, asked him, "'Did you see how close the fire came to my house?' He nodded and said to her, "'Do you know why that house didn't burn down? Because it was soaking wet!" Wesley Peters lived on the Barona Indian Reservation all his life. He died on September 17, 2004, at the age of 62.

The Barona Fire Protection District was established in 1998 to supply service to the residents of the Barona Reservation. The Indian gaming revenues has provided

for the fire department. It began with six members and now has 20 full-time fire personnel and one administrator.

Chiefs of the department include: Anthony Ravago (1998-2002), Randy Sandoval (2003-2012), and Ken Kremensky (2012-).

Anthony Ravago, a Pala tribal member, served as Barona's first fire chief. He is now chief of the Pala Fire Department.

Randy Sandoval was appointed chief in 2003. Previously he was a firefighter for the California Department of Forestry and Fire Protection from 1985 to 1991 and, after his service as chief of the Barona Fire Department, he served as chief of the Soboba Fire Department from October 2015 to 2019.

Ken Kremensky became head of the fire department in July 2012. As soon as Kremensky graduated from Granite Hills High School, he entered a fire academy and started working for the California Department of Forestry in 1976. He was a firefighter for Crest Volunteer Fire Department and assistant chief of the Julian Volunteer Fire Department. He was division chief for the Lakeside Fire Protection District from January 1981 to December 2007. From April 2009 to July 2012, he was the division chief for the Barona Fire Protection District.

Chief Kremensky's three brothers also joined the fire service. His brother Mark D. Kremensky retired from Borrego Springs Fire Department. John Kremensky is a battalion chief and training officer for Cal Fire. Burke Kremensky is a division chief for Cal Fire. This "band of brothers" have sons who are following in their boot steps.

Assistant Chief Ron Laff has been in the fire service for 40 years. He began his career at the age of 17 as a volunteer firefighter with the Descanso Fire Department. For six years he was a seasonal firefighter with the U.S. Forest Service Descanso Ranger District as a firefighter on both the engine and as a member of the Laguna Hotshots. In December 1986, he joined the El Centro Fire Department. In April 1989, Ron Laff was hired by the Lakeside Fire Department where he served for 27-1/2 years, retiring as a division chief. He has been involved with Incident Management Team as a Strike Team Leader, Division/Group Supervisor, Operation Branch Director, and Operation Section Chief responding to large incidents throughout the western United States.

Bob Pfohl has been the division chief for the Barona Fire Department since October 2012. Previously he was the division chief for Viejas Fire Department in 2011.

Barona has automatic aid agreements with Lakeside Fire Protection District, Ramona Fire Protection District, San Diego County Fire Department, and the Heartland Zone.

Station 27, located at 1112 Barona Road, was constructed beginning in 1998 and completed in 2000. The 9,000-square-foot station houses three double-deep drive-through apparatus bays, eight personnel, and four administrative offices.

Fighting fires is often physically demanding, working in heat and smoke, carrying equipment, and climbing steep terrain. Responding to critical illnesses and injuries is another important service of the fire department. The department reviews a new topic on each shift. The subjects rotate from emergency medical services (EMS) to fire every other shift. Some of the topics include: extrication, respiratory emergencies, cardiac arrest, pediatrics, ventilation, wildland safety, and communications. The department also sponsors numerous higher education level courses for its personnel and other departments of Southern California.

The equipment includes:

Engine 27 (E27) is a Pierce urban interface engine received on January 8, 2018. It has an Arrow XT chassis, Detroit diesel DD13 engine, 505 hp, Husky 3 foam system, 1,500-gpm Pierce PUC pump, foam and water tank, and 500-gallon tank. It has I-Zone bars for holding hose for interface fires along with T3 rear steer for a better turning radius and clearing.

A Type I Ferrara Inferno engine received in 2003 can seat six personnel. The engine responds to structure fires, medical aids, and vehicle accidents. It is capable of responding to the entire fire district within minutes with four personnel, 1,000 gallons of water, and 25 gallons of foam. It has a full complement of fire hose, ground ladders, and rescue equipment. The engine is staffed with a fire captain, engineer, firefighter/paramedic, and a firefighter 24 hours a day. The engine is able to provide advanced life support (ALS) in the event that the department's paramedic unit is unavailable.

Medic 227 (M227) is a Horton Type I paramedic ambulance used primarily as a reserve unit. It is placed in service when engine 27 is in for repairs and maintenance. It is also placed in service during events like the Barona Powwow.

Brush 27 (BR 27) is a 2003 Ferrara Type III, a state-of-art custom built piece of equipment. A brush engine is utilized to respond to wildland fires where a Type I engine cannot. Brush 27 is also a CAFS unit (compressed air foam system unit), which allows it the capability of pre-treating homes in the event of a wildland fire. Very few fire engines in the county have this capability.

Engine 227 (E227) is the department's reserve Type I engine. The 2000 Westates engine is available to the department for additional staffing in peak times or if the

primary engine is unavailable due to mechanical problems. This second engine provides a higher level of fire protection to ensure an additional or a backup Type I engine.

The chief's staff vehicles are capable of responding to large incidents requiring a command unit. A 2009 Ford F-250 diesel (4801) and 2012 Ford F-250 gasoline (4802) are 4x4 vehicles that feature custom-built command desks. The vehicles support the fire suppression units with documents, management, and communications.

The assistant fire chief's staff vehicle is a 2002 Chevrolet Tahoe (4802) that features a custom-built command desk in the rear.

The utility vehicle (Utility 27) a 2003 Chevy Suburban that serves as a back-up-duty vehicle for the chief and as a vehicle for the station personnel to attend training classes outside the area.

A 1985 International rescue vehicle (Rescue 27) carries a set of Amkus tools, stabilization struts, cribbing, extra breathing apparatus bottles, on-board generator for scene lighting, and swift water rescue equipment. This unit helps supports the engine company on vehicle accidents and is also used to respond to medical emergencies.

Truck 27 (T27) is a Type I Ferrara Inferno engine received in 2009 that carries 300 gallons of water, 25 gallons of foam, and has pump capability of 2,000 gpm. It can carry four personnel and is used to respond to structure fires, medical aids, and vehicle accidents. Staffed with a fire captain, engineer, firefighter/paramedic, and a firefighter, the truck is able to provide advanced life support (ALS).

Medic 27 (M27) is a Type I 2003 Road Rescue ambulance that is used to transport patients to the hospital. Medic 27 also responds with Engine 27 to incidents on the reservation providing two paramedics to those in need. It also responds to the communities of Lakeside, Santee, and Ramona for mutual aid.

The Barona Fire Protection District is committed to providing paramedic medical care and fire suppression to the reservation.

CALLS RECALLED:

*1913:   In September 1913, the Barona Fire burned 65,470 acres.

*1981:   More than 500 firefighters fought the Wildcat Fire in July 1981 that burned 2,400 acres. Six air tankers, 4 helicopters, 50 engine companies, and 12 hand crews battled the blaze. Many of the hand crews were comprised of inmates from the California Department of Corrections and the San Diego County Probation Department who earned 75 cents an hour. The fire was started by a bulldozer blade striking a spark on a rock. The area where the fire burned was bordered to the south by the San Diego River, to the west by Wildcat Canyon, and to the east by Lake Jennings. One house was destroyed.

*2003:   The Cedar Fire was reported on October 25, 2003, contained on November 4, and extinguished on December 5. Fifteen people perished, 2,232 homes were destroyed, and 273,246 acres burned. It was started by a lost hunter setting a signal fire.

In the fire, 39 of the 222 homes in the Barona Indian Reservation were destroyed. Twenty-six replacement homes were built. The residents who lost their homes were given a choice of five floor plans for three- or four-bedroom homes ranging from 1,500 to 1,900 square feet.

Sandra Millers Younger, who lives in Wildcat Canyon, describes how she and others survived the Cedar Fire in her book, "The Fire Outside My Window."

*2014:   The department responded to about 1,000 calls in 2014.

*2015:   The Wildcat Fire in June 2015 started off Wildcat Canyon Road and Akuunyaa Way east of the Barona Casino, burning 170 acres.

*2019:   In February, there was a swift water rescue on the Barona Indian Reservation. Due to the heavy amounts of rain that fell in the region, the small creek turned into a dangerous fast-moving river in minutes. A male was rescued with no injuries. Barona E27, E227, WT27, M 227, and chiefs 4801 and 4802 were assisted by Lakeside R3, E201, E2, and chief 4103 as well as Santee E4 and T4.

*2020:   In September 2020, Barona firefighters were assigned to the Valley Fire. When Chief Kremensky was asked about the hot spots on the line during the fire, he explained that the canopy is so thick that retardant does not always get down to the ground. The fire creeps through the retardant and causes the hot spots.

BONITA–SUNNYSIDE FIRE PROTECTION DISTRICT

Bonita is located between Chula Vista, National City, Spring Valley, and San Diego with a population of 12,538 (2010), covering 5.16 square miles. Sunnyside is located within the Bonita CDP (Census Designated Place) and has a population of 4,235 (2019), covering 1.84 square miles.

Henry Ernest Cooper, Sr. grew lemons on a ranch named Bonita in 1884. The Sweetwater Dam was built in 1888, creating the Sweetwater Reservoir.

In 1948, the temperatures fell to 19 degrees at night. The only fire protection in Bonita was by the California Division of Forestry. The closest fire station was on East J Street in Chula Vista. If more fire trucks were needed, they came from La Mesa.

A telephone was installed in the offices of the Sweetwater Fruit Company as well as at the La Tienda Cafe to receive an alarm. The person receiving the alarm rushed to the Old Red Barn, a landmark in the area, to ring the fire bell. The company employees hurried to the fire. A fruit sprayer truck owned by the Sweetwater Fruit Company was used to fight fires. If the truck was out in the orchard, its oil used to control insects on the fruit trees was dumped and filled with water before being taken to the fire.

On January 26, 1950, Scofield Bonnet suggested to the members of the Sweetwater Men's Club that a volunteer fire department be formed. On February 14, 1950, incorporation papers were signed forming the Upper Sweetwater Valley Volunteer Fire Department. Don Herron, a 6th grade teacher at Ellen B. Allen School, became the first fire chief and led a group of 15 volunteers.

The firemen used a sprayer truck from the Williams Ranch for firefighting. The fruit sprayer truck from the Sweetwater Fruit Company and the truck from the Williams Ranch each held 500 gallons of water and they each had spray nozzles. They were covered with tarps and parked near the Old Red Barn. The barn was torn down in 1960 to make way for the Bonita Village Shopping Center.

In June 1950, the department had a horse show that raised $1,300. The money was used to purchase a surplus 1931 Moreland engine from CDF for $750. A picnic and fundraiser was held to purchase equipment for the engine.

A. C. (Assistant Chief) was the only dog in a fire station in South Bay in the late 1970s. The 67-pound Dalmatian spent his free time chasing gophers and squirrels near the station. Years ago, when fire engines were pulled by horses, a Dalmatian would run between the horses to keep them apart.

Richard Yokley, who worked for Bonita Fire Department from 1972 to December 1999, is the author of "TV Firefighters" and "Emergency: Behind the Scene." He received Firehouse Magazine's Heroism and Community Service Award in 1987. Yokley works at Sea World San Diego as an EMT-D. He received the SeaWorld Excellence Award in 2000.

Firefighters left to right: Rich Faabort, Josh Krimston, Sonny Felkins, and Carl McAllister in front of the department's 1952 Mach.

The board of directors of the Bonita-Sunnyside Fire Protection District is comprised of three members elected at-large to serve four-year terms. Members of the fire board set district policy, annual budgets, and salaries. The current directors are Thomas Pockington, Mark Scott, and Jim Marugg.

Fire chiefs include Don Herron (1950), E. S. Bonnet (1950-1952), Bill King (1952-1953), Bill Waters (1953-1955), James Jones (1955-1966), Bill Cooke (1966-1967), Hal Miner (1967-1981), Orville "Butch" Lee Moody (1981-2001), Scott Walker (2001-2012), Tim Isbell (2012-2018), and Mike Sims (2019-).

Chief Orville "Butch" Lee Moody started his career with the Bonita Fire Department on January 1, 1967. He became fire chief on April 1, 1981. He worked with the State Fire Marshall's Office, San Diego County's Sheriff Department, and served as President and Treasurer of the San Diego County Fire Chiefs Association. He died on December 5, 2014, at the age of 79.

Chief Scott Walker spent 37 years with the Bonita-Sunnyside Fire Protection District. He was born in the Carolinas but moved to Chula Vista at the age of two. He attended Rosebank Elementary School and Hilltop High School. After high school, he had various jobs in the construction of houses until 1975 when he joined the Bonita fire district. He was employed by the National City Fire Department as a dispatcher before joining the Bonita Fire Department. He rose through the ranks, becoming chief in July 2001. Chief Walker retired in July 2012.

Chief Tim Isbell retired in December 2018 after nearly 30 years in the fire service in Bonita, serving as firefighter, engineer, captain, and chief. Over the years, he served on the boards of organizations in the county that provide support for fire departments.

Mike Sims was hired as a firefighter for the department in 1995 and worked through the ranks of captain and deputy fire chief and was selected as chief in January 2019. He has a Bachelor of Science in Public Administration from Columbia Southern University. Chief Sims has served as the San Diego County Fire Chiefs Association liaison to the County Training Officers Section and as a member-at-large for the executive board of the San Diego County Fire Chiefs Association. His experience includes working at the General Dynamics NASSCO Fire Department.

Annette Craven, the office manager, has been with the department for 19 years.

The department has 12 firefighters: in A Division/training are Michael Smith, captain/paramedic; Josh Krimston, engineer/paramedic; and Sonny Felkins and Halley Schmiz, firefighter/paramedics; in B Division/maintenance are Dan Genevicz, captain/paramedic; Robert Marcon, engineer/paramedic; and Cory Springett and Amado Rodrigues, firefighter/paramedics; and in C Division/fire prevention are Jason Oostrbaan, captain/paramedic; Goie Cosca, firefighter/paramedic, Goie Cosca, firefighter/paramedic and Richard Faaborg, firefighter/paramedic.

On June 9, 2019, the department had its 5th Annual Pancake Breakfast, organized by the Bonita Firefighters, Local 1827. Twice a month, the firefighters go to the Bonita-Sunnyside Branch Library to read books to the children that have been donated by Bonita Firefighters, Local 1827.

In December 2019, the district achieved an upgrade in its ISO rating from a Class 3 to a Class 2. (In 1972, the department had an ISO rating of Class 9.)

In July 2020, the department received a grant from the San Diego Regional Fire Foundation for breathing apparatuses. Chief Sims said, "Whether entering a burning building to rescue a person or treating a patient with COVID-19 or any other contagious disease, where six feet of separation is impossible, having a protective breathing apparatus is the best way to keep our firefighters safe and enable them to do their job."

The estimated revenue in 2019-20 was $2,791,827, salaries and benefits, $2,726,042, and operating expenses was $596,211.

Station 38, located at 4900 Bonita Road, was built in 1992. The 10,000-square-foot station houses E238 (2012 Pierce Quantum PUC); E38 (2007 Pierce Quantum with a TAK-4 system); 5101 (2016 Ford Explorer); 5109 (2012 Ford Explorer); 2006 Ford F250; and 5110 (1954 Mack parade engine). E38 is unique because it is black on top of gold and fire engine red, the only one of its colors in South Bay.

Station 2 at 4035 Bonita Road is home to an AMR ambulance.

In addition to saving lives and property, the firefighters at the Bonita Fire Department take an active role in the community.

CALLS RECALLED:

*1906:   When the wooden home of Mr. Allen caught fire, a bell was rung that was on the boarding house owned by the Sweetwater Fruit Company.

*1907:   The fire bell at the Old Red Barn was rung to call the hired hands in from the orchards to respond to a residential fire.

*1948:   In late 1948, a home on Willow Road was destroyed by fire.

*1967:   Poway recognized the department for its response to the Poway Fire.

*1988:   A resolution was made from Assemblyman Larry Stirling for the department's response to the Cowles Mountain Fire.

*1990:   A resolution was made from Assemblywoman Tricia Hunter for the department's response to the Dubbar Fire.

*1992:   Governor Pete Wilson recognized the firefighters for assisting in the Guejitio Fire.

*2003:   The department received recognition from Congressman Duncan Hunter for its response to the Cedar Fire.

*2015:   In February 2015, a brush fire broke out near Sweetwater Road off of Interstate 805 and Interstate 54. It started at a homeless encampment. It burned one acre.

*2015:   In February 2015, a drunk driver crashed into a median on Bonita Road. She kept her foot on the gas pedal, causing sparks from the spinning rim to set the tire's remnants ablaze. The fire personnel doused her burning Cadillac.

*2017:   In September 2017, a 3-acre fire that started at 10:30 p.m. threatened homes along Corral Canyon Road near Blacksmith Road. The Bonita crew, assisted by firefighters from San Diego, Chula Vista, and San Miguel, had the fire extinguished by 11:15 p.m.

*2018:   In November 2018, a man suffered burns on his back when his three-car garage was destroyed by fire in Bonita. He was taken to UCSD Burn Center.

*2018:   The crews responded to 1,663 calls in 2018, including 131 fires, 81 false alarms, 107 traffic collisions, 6 hazardous material conditions, 61 public assistance calls, and 6 move-ups.

*2020:   In January 2020, crews responded to a car fire which was spreading to a commercial building.

*2020:   In August 2020, E238 was part of Strike Team 6440A that was assigned to the LNU Complex Fire in Northern California. It was also sent to the Jones Fire in Nevada County, California.

*2020:   In September 2020, E38 in Strike Team 6441A was deployed to the Creek Fire near Shaver Lake northeast of Fresno. E38 was also assigned to the Valley Fire.

Borrego Springs Fire Protection District

Borrego Springs is a desert community located 85 miles northeast of San Diego and is surrounded by the more than 600,000-acre Anza-Borrego Desert State Park, the largest state preserve in the country. The community has a permanent population of 2,252. It also has a seasonal population of 4,500 as well as over a million visitors annually.

Cattlemen began homesteading the Borrego Valley in about 1875. The first successful well was dug in 1926.

The Borrego Springs Fire Protection District (BSFPD) encompasses 310.6 square miles, including the Borrego Springs town center and territory within the Anza-Borrego Desert State Park.

The nearest fire protection services were 60 miles away. In the fall of 1961, members of the Junior Chamber of Commerce organized a drive for fire protection. Edwin Eller, Ramona's first full-time chief, assisted in an advisory capacity in the development of the Borrego Springs Volunteer Fire Department. He offered information about the equipment needed and procedures to follow and helped in the training program for the firemen. He died on July 6, 1984, at the age of 74.

Residents formed a fire protection district under the California Health and Safety Code. A board of commissioners was appointed by the San Diego County Board of Supervisors. It was decided that a full-time paid fire chief should be hired to lead a volunteer staff. The Borrego Springs Fire Protection District became an official entity in January 1962.

Members of the board approved the purchase of a Homelite portable four-cycle pressure pump to be used on on a tanker truck, at a cost of $207. It pumped 150 gallons of water per minute at 45 pounds pressure with a draft of 28 feet and a total head of 95 feet.

In August 1962, J. Robert Baker was hired as the first chief of the district. He began his fire service experience at the age of 16 as a volunteer with the Upper St.

Left to right: Kevin Milleson, Tom Tomko

Clair Volunteer Fire Department and then as a paid member of the Mt. Lebanon Fire Department, both in suburban Pittsburgh. During that period he attained the rank of captain. He was secretary of the Upper St. Clair Volunteer Fire Department and president of the South Hills Firemen's Association.

Chief Baker hired 20 volunteers and three nurses, combining the firefighting and ambulance services. He bought used equipment from government surplus agencies. Only one apparatus was purchased new. The equipment included a 1947 Seagrave 750-gpm pumper, a 1956 International 500-gpm front-mount pumper; a 1954 Willys Jeep, a 1963 Apache Trailer; and a World War II model crash truck from San Diego County.

Raymond Tyler, 76, one of the original members of the Borrego Volunteer Fire Department, died on December 1, 1998. Tyler became a member of the Julian Volunteer Fire Department. He served in the Army during World War II in the South Pacific.

The board decided not to buy real estate and build a costly station. Instead a building that could be expanded was constructed and part of it rented to a business owner for income.

The district adopted the fire prevention and inspection ordinance of the National Board of Fire Underwriters. It requires all homeowners with wood shingle roofs to have the roofing treated with approved fire-retardants. Eighty hydrants were installed.

In 1988, a 4.1 earthquake shook the community.

The firefighters felt the jolt but there was no damage to the station. They moved all the equipment out of the station. In August 2000, a 3.7 quake was felt northeast of Borrego Springs.

In 1989 the temperature in Borrego got up to 122 degrees; the average temperature in July 2020 in Borrego was 108 degrees. In 1990, Battalion Chief Todd Smith said firefighters, although accustomed to hot weather, usually only go outside in the afternoons for emergency calls. "We have two things in our favor, the low humidity and the breezes," he said. "Still," he added, "hot is hot." About 80% of the calls are from senior citizens suffering from heat fatigue. In 1991, Chief Al Fehlberg said, "The only heat fatality we've had was a teacher visiting from New York, a high school football coach, who went out camping without adequate water. The people here know how to take care of themselves."

In 1992, about 80% of Borrego's annual fire budget of $800,000 went to personnel. The department had 12 full-time firefighters, 14 part-time reserves, and 6 volunteers.

The district has an elected five-member board of directors. The board of directors meets the second Thursday of each month. Meetings are open to the public. The fire board is dark in July and August each year. The operating budget for 2007 was $1.64 million and for 2012 $2.7 million. The revenue sources for the district are property tax, approved assessment, and San Diego County Fire Authority subsidies.

On August 31, 2020, the district had $787,800 available for operations. There is a 50% employee turnover rate. It is difficult to attract applicants because the compensation package is 29% lower than other agencies.

A parcel tax increase, measure PP, was on the ballot for Borrego Springs Fire Protection District on November 6, 2018. A yes vote was a vote in favor of increasing parcel tax rate at various levels, including $225 annually for single-family residences, to fund fire protection and emergency services. It was defeated.

The regular pay in 2018 for the fire chief was $129,955; captain, $70,988; engineer/paramedic, $63,855; firefighter II/paramedic, $56,689; firefighter I/paramedic, $44,407. There was a $600 per year allowance for uniforms. Personnel who were paramedics receive an additional $320 per month.

The maximum monthly base pay in 2020: chief, $10,961; administrative assistant, $5,256.09; captain, $5,292.97; engineer, $4,635.22; firefighter II, $4,324.55; firefighter I, $4,108.32.

In 2008, a bookkeeper who embezzled $276,867 from the fire district between 2001 and 2007 was sent to Las Colinas Detention and Reentry Facility in Santee for one year.

Chiefs include: J. Robert Baker (1962-1964), Jack Hansen, Sr. (1965-1985), Al Fehlberg (1988-1991), Gary Adams (1992-2008), James Thompson (2008-2009), and John W. Hardcastle (2009-).

John Hardcastle was appointed chief in 2009. Previously he was fire chief at Patton State Hospital from 1995 to 1997; Community Safety Officer for La Quinta from 1997-2004; Emergency Service Coordinator for Riverside County Fire Department, 2004; and Emergency Manager/Program Manager for the Palm Springs Fire Department from 2005 to 2008. He has a Bachelor of Business Administration from National University.

In 2012, the San Diego Regional Fire Foundation honored Cameron Beauchamps of Borrego Springs as one of the volunteer firefighters of the year for his service.

The Borrego Springs Fire Protection District has 12 paid personnel, augmented by 21 reserves. In addition to providing fire and rescue services, the district also provides paramedic ambulance service.

The district has one station located at 2324 Stirrup Road which houses a 2011 Pierce engine, a 1999 HME engine with 1,500-gpm, two wildland Type 3 engines, a 2010 Freightliner water tender that carries 2,000 gallons of water to supply to engines, and two paramedic ambulances that include 12-lead cardiac monitor/defibrillators, end-tidal CO_2 and oxygen saturation monitors, glucometers, endotracheal intubation, resuscitation equipment, and medications for treatment.

The district has a contract with Cal Fire for dispatch services. It participates in mutual aid with the U.S. Forest Service and Cal Fire.

In 2018, the Borrego Springs Fire Protection District received a $379,000 grant from the Alphonse A. Burn and Medical Education Foundation which was used to replace the deteriorated asphalt driveway with a cement driveway that goes around the station.

In July 2019, the San Diego Regional Fire Foundation awarded a grant to fund rope rescue equipment to the department.

The personnel are dedicated and committed to serving the residents and visitors of Borrego Springs and protecting the community each and every day.

CALLS RECALLED:

*1955:   In July 1955, heavy rain and strong winds destroyed a business and damaged two homes and a church.

*1977:   On January 29, 1977, Joe Booth and his son, Jerry, were salvaging old car bodies with their boom truck near Rancho Way when the truck hit an overhead high voltage wire. When the Borrego firefighters arrived, they found the older man about 25 feet from the boom and the younger man pinned down under the truck's front axle. The two men were rushed to the hospital in Brawley, then to the University Hospital's Burn Center. The father received second-degree burns over 70% of his body and the son had his right arm severely damaged and had to have his right leg amputated.

*1978:   In November 1978, seven-year-old Michelle Marie Edwards of Long Beach died in a dune buggy accident. She had been riding in the backseat without a seatbelt of a Volkswagen dune buggy driven by Richard Carey.

*1981:   In July 1981, a brush fire burned 1,000 acres southwest of Borrego Springs. More than 500 firefighters, including U.S. Forest and California Department of Forestry crews, battled the blaze.

*1982:   In September 1982, Brooks DeKock, a 26-year-old Ranchita jalapeno pepper farmer, lost control of his car on Montezuma Road and rolled 300 feet down a ravine. Dooley, a black Queensland heeder, found his way home seven miles away. The dog was bedraggled and barely breathing after the trek. The family realized something was wrong when they saw the dog as the dog was always with the young farmer. A fire crew found the man about 200 feet away from his car. A Life Flight helicopter took DeKock to a hospital. He suffered a broken collarbone, facial lacerations, and cracked vertebrae in his neck and back.

*2002:   There were 482 emergency calls in 2002.

*2010:   In June 2010, the Narrow Fire broke out off of State Route 78 near Highway S2. The fire burned 100 acres.

*2014:   On August 21, 2014, lightning struck a grove of palm trees. The Borrego Springs Fire Department arrived at the scene within six minutes. The T-70 and T-71 planes out of Ramona Air Base dropped retardant on the fire and San Diego County Sheriff's Department helicopters dropped water on it. The fire burned 10 acres.

*2015:   On March 17, 2015, Jack Bailey Godwin, 70, was killed and a 66-year-old woman was injured in a two-vehicle crash on Big Horn Road.

*2015:   On June 9, 2015, Shane Timothy Sluss, 27, was killed in a motorcycle crash on Montezuma Valley Road.

*2015:   In August 2015, a 27-year-old woman died in a crash on Borrego Springs Road. A 2-month-old infant who was in the car was airlifted to Rady Children's Hospital after the crash but died.

*2015:   On August 20, 2015, Erendyra Fiero, 27, was killed while attempting a U-turn and striking a car in Borrego Springs. Javier Salazar, 2 months, was killed in the crash.

*2016:   In May 2016, a rattlesnake at the home of Linda and Philip Canfield's house was caught by the Borrego fire personnel and taken to a less-inhabited location. The couple said, "The great services and the people who provide them are part of the reason we love living here."

*2017:   On October 4, 2017, a 67-year-old man was killed in a crash on Montezuma Valley Road when his 1997 Toyota Camry went off the edge and rolled down the rocks.

*2017:   In November 2017, a driver was trapped in a Honda for more than 30 minutes after a rollover crash on Borrego Salton Seaway.

*2018:   In February 2018, five people were injured when their car went over the brick wall at the lookout on Montezuma Valley Road and rolled down the bank. Paramedics and two helicopters quickly arrived at the crash.

*2018:   Paramedics responded to a crash on Borrego Springs Road north of State Route 78 on June 17, 2018, in which Douglas Russell Irons Jr., 24, was found dead.

*2019:   In August 2019, a spark from a grill at the home of the Borjorquez family resulted in the total loss of their home.

*2019:   In December 2019, a 66-year-old man was killed in a motorcycle accident near Tilting T Road.

*2020:   A 32-year-old man was killed when he lost control of his 2006 Kia Sorento on Borrego Springs Road.

*2020:   On September 4, 2020, a man was killed in a rollover crash on Borrego Springs Road near State Route 78 at 4:10 p.m.

BOULEVARD FIRE AND RESCUE DEPARTMENT

Boulevard is an area of 78 square miles with a population of 433. Its southern boundary runs up to the Mexican border; north, above Interstate 8 to Cottonwood Road; to the east, four miles on Highway 94; and to the west, one mile past Crestwood Road.

In the 1800s Boulevard was used as a trail by hunters and trappers. In 1913 Don Ruby built a resort in Boulevard with a post office, dance hall, reservoir, swimming pool, and garage. It was a popular place for people from Imperial Valley who wanted to escape the summer heat. Boulevard was sometimes called Eckener Pass in honor of Hugo Eckener who flew over the area in his Graf Zeppelin on August 27, 1929, on a round-the-world flight. One famous landmark in Boulevard is the Wisteria Candy Cottage which has been in operation since 1921.

In the late 1950s, volunteer firemen drove a flatbed truck with a water tank strapped to it. The first fire chief was Ray Aly, who served from July 1975 to July 1976. Other chiefs included Bob House, Paul Pinkham, Grace Jepsen, Lou Falconer, Bill Marshall, and Geoff Cogle.

Grace Jepsen became a volunteer firefighter in 1975 when she was 56. Breast cancer six years later was only a temporary setback, by the following summer she was back fighting fires. She served as chief for two years before retiring at the age of 67.

The Boulevard Volunteer Fire Department was formed in 1975. In 1984 it became a County Service Area, CSA 111. The fire department's budget for 1983-84 was $7,874, 1984-85, $17,220; 1985-86, $61,016 ; and 1987-88, $43,630.

Chief Lou Boucher was chosen to lead the department in March 1991. The 12 volunteers responded to about 200 calls in 1992 under his leadership.

The volunteers were local residents with a wide range of backgrounds, including two cowboys, one cowgirl, one mechanic, one heavy equipment operator, and several housewives, all who were trained as EMTs. The volunteers received mutual aid from personnel at the Jacumba Volunteer Fire Department and the Campo Indian Reservation Fire Department. During the summer months of the wildland fire season, the California Department of Forestry at the White Star station worked side by side with the Boulevard volunteers.

The first Boulevard fire station was built in 1983 at the intersection of Highway 94 and the old Highway 80. Next to the fire station stood the old East County courthouse that was later used as a sheriff's department substation. The station is now the Backcountry Resource Center.

The volunteers were well equipped to do the job that was asked of them. They had a 1988 Emergency One triple-combination pumper. It had a 1000-gpm pump with a 1000-gallon tank and 1-1/2 inch reconnect hose with class A foam pre-plumbed for initial attack on structure and wildland fires. A 1975 International Load Star was used for wildland fighting and was also complemented with prepped class A foam. The department had a 1991 Chevy quick attack that carried an assortment of rescue equipment, including the Jaws of Life.

The San Diego County Fire Authority built a station, San Diego County Fire Station 47, at 40080 Ribbonwood Road in 2014. The 7,866-square-foot station has sleeping quarters for 12 firefighters, a training room, and space for six apparatus. The facility has a well for water for the station and for holding tanks for water for the fire engines. A paramedic ambulance serves Boulevard and the area between Pine Valley and Jacumba. Station 47 houses Water Tender 7457 (2014 International 7400), Engine 7414 (Ferrara Igniter), and Engine 7415 (Ferrara Igniter).

The fire station is the result of a partnership between the San Diego County Fire Authority (SDCFA), which owns the station, and Cal Fire.

CALLS RECALLED:

*1991:   Chief Lou Falconer died in the line of duty on March 15, 1991, at the age of 62. He had a heart attack caused by stress and overexertion.

*2009:   A house fire in April 2009 resulted in $400,000 damages.

*2010:   An arsonist was sentenced to 15 years in prison for setting a fire in Boulevard in 2009.

*2012:   The department responded to a major fire, the Shockey Fire, in September 2012. The fire burned 2,850 acres, killed 1 man, and destroyed 11 homes on Tierra del Sol Road in Boulevard.

*2017:   The Ribbonwood Fire near Interstate 8 burned 25 acres. Eighty firefighters from Cal Fire and the U.S. Forest Service put out the fire within one hour. Two helicopters dropped water on the fire.

*2018:   Three people died and eight were injured when a pickup truck crashed near Crestwood Road while being chased by San Diego Border Patrol agents.

*2019:   In November 2019, the Crestwood Fire started near Old Highway 80 at Tierra Del Sol Road. The fire grew to 32 acres before 8 hand crews and 25 engines were used to extinguish it.

*2020:   On June 26, 2020, a driver was killed in a rollover crash on Interstate 8 near McCain Valley Road.

Big Jimmy: 1939 GMC Engine

The California Department of Forestry and Fire Protection is a statewide agency. In 2007 it became known as Cal Fire instead of CDF. It is the largest fire department in the Western United States. The department provides fire protection to wildland areas designated by the nine-member Board of Forestry as state land.

The Forest Protection Act of 1905 established an agency to protect and manage land designated as State Responsibility Area (SRA). Clifford Pinchot, a friend of President Theodore Roosevelt, served as Chief Forester from 1898 to 1905.

From 1927 to 1961, Cal Fire was part of the Department of Natural Resources; from 1961 to 1977, it was an agency of the California Department of Conservation; and since 1977, it has been part of the California Natural Resources Agency. In 1987, the name was changed from California Department of Forestry to California Department of Forestry and Fire Protection.

On May 13, 1938, the California Department of Forestry Employees Association (CDFEA) was formed to protect the welfare of firefighters. Now firefighters are represented by Cal Fire Local 2881.

The department's total fire protection responsibilities add up to over 42 million acres. This includes about 31 million acres of the state's woodland area and about 11 million acres under contract to local governments.

Cal Fire has an annual budget of $2.3 billion. It has 22 administrative units (ranger units) with 156 battalions. Within this organizational structure, Cal Fire operates 577 fire stations of which 354 are locally funded.

Cal Fire owns and operates 343 engines. The newest engine used by the agency is the Navistar Model 34 with a Type III engine, 500-gpm pump, and 500-gallon tank.

Cal Fire has 196 hand crews and 58 initial attack bulldozer units. This apparatus is staffed by 6,100 firefighting permanent personnel, 2,600 seasonal personnel, and 3,500 inmates. The agency responds to over 460,000 incidents a year.

Cal Fire has over 3,000 fire and emergency vehicles. To augment its firefighting resources statewide, Cal Fire operates a fleet of 23 Grumman S-2T airtankers, 2 Sikorsky S-70 helicopters, 12 UH-1H Super Huey helicopters, 15 Rockwell OV-10A airtactical, and 2 Air King A-20 airtactical. This includes the following types of airtankers that Cal Fire has used: McDonnell Douglas DC-10, Boeing 747, Martin Mars Type 1, Lockheed P-3, Orion Type 1, Lockheed P-2, Neptune, Douglas DC-6, Douglas DC-7, Canadair CL-215 and CL-415, and Grumman S-2T.

In 2017, Cal Fire purchased two Sikorsky S-70 helicopters to replace 12 Super Huey helicopters. In 2019, Cal Fire acquired 12 Hawk helicopters equipped to drop water on fires in the dark at a cost of $288 million. The helicopters are equipped with a hoist and 250-foot cable for rescues. Hawk CF-903 arrived in November and is at a 100,000-square-foot hangar at McClellan Airport for maintenance and pilot and crew training.

In 2019, Cal Fire got 7 C-130 airtankers through the National Defense Act. The airtankers were previously used by the Coast Guard. The C-130s take a three-person crew to operate, instead of the one pilot needed for the S-2T airtankers. They can each carry 4,000 gallons of water. They will begin to be put in use in the middle of 2021.

Cal Fire is a modern, professional organization with high standards. It has invested heavily and wisely in training and equipping its firefighting personnel.

The Cal Fire Training Center was established on 420 acres in Ione, near Sacramento, in 1967. It is one of the largest and most complex training facilities in the world. Each year over 2,000 Cal Fire personnel participate in an academic curriculum ranging from basic fire control and arson investigation to leadership development and forest practice enforcement. The training center can house and feed 86 students. It has two burn buildings, one of which is multistoried, an emergency vehicle operations driving course, and LPG and flammable liquid props. This facility also provides simulators for training captains, engineers, firefighters, and dispatchers. There is a four-wheel drive off-road driving course and a 60-yard small arms firing range. All classes are certified and can be used for college credit.

Cal Fire has an extensive cooperative fire protection program. Since the 1930s, Cal Fire has been providing fire protection services to various local governments. By contractual agreements Cal Fire has local agreements with 40 of the 58 counties in California. Cal Fire manages countywide fire departments in 12 counties and protects 20 incorporated cities. Cal Fire also provides dispatch to other fire departments.

The agency is involved in the use of microcomputer technology. The department is computerized to the station level and has the ability to network with other stations throughout the state.

A typical engine at a schedule A station (structure/rescue/brush) would be a custom Van Pelt, single stage 1,000-gpm pump with a 500-gallon tank. It carries large diameter supply hose and 1-3/4 in. reconnected attack lines. The engines have both front and side soft suction reconnects. Engine and truck companies use blowers to provide positive pressure ventilation on initial attack. There are also firefighter/paramedic squads that respond with private paramedic units. Some cities have civilian paramedic units that respond from Cal Fire stations.

Cal Fire protects 1-1/2 million acres of wildland in San Diego County. The agency is responsible for most of the land in San Diego County's rural areas and the structures on the land are the responsibility of local fire departments, although most in the unincorporated areas now have contracts with Cal Fire.

San Diego County contracted with Cal Fire for fire protection for nearly 50 years. In 1976, San Diego County terminated the contract because of the cost of the contract and an increase of structures in unincorporated areas. The county created the Office of Fire Services to establish volunteer fire departments.

The San Diego County Fire Authority has a Volunteer Reserve Firefighter Program for trained volunteers to respond to emergencies. They assist Cal Fire with services to about 460,000 residents in the 1.5 million acres of unincorporated areas of San Diego County.

Cal Fire operates Schedule "A" and Schedule "B" stations. Schedule "A" stations include fire departments and fire protection districts contracting with Cal Fire to staff stations. The San Diego County Authority has constructed 15 stations to be staffed by Cal Fire under contract. Firefighters in schedule "B" stations are responsible for protecting wildlands.

Cal Fire still provides brush protection throughout this vast county. Valley Center and Ramona were the first to contract with Cal Fire to provide structural as well as wildland protection. Presently Cal Fire contracts with most communities in the county.

Ken Pimlott was director of Cal Fire from 2011 to 2018. Chief Pimlott became a reserve firefighter at the age of 17 for Contra Costa County. When Chief Pimlott retired in December 2018, Mark Mohler was appointed chief. Chief Mohler began his career in 1971 as a reserve firefighter in Orange County. The chief joined Cal Fire in the San Bernardino Unit in June 2000.

The fire chiefs of the San Diego Unit include: Paul Q. Harvey (1921); Luther C. Gordon (1930-1932); W. Nevius (1932-1933); Luther C. Gordon (1934); Unknown (1935); Ed S. Miller (1936-1950); Jim Fenlon (1950-1968); Frank Crossfield (1968-1970); John M. Morrow (1970-1977); James G. Dykes (1977-1981); B. Neal (1981-1991); Tim Turner (1992-1996); K. Miller ((1996-2003); Chuck Maner (2003-2009); Thom Porter (2009-2014); and Tony Mecham (2014-).

Chuck Maner was appointed chief of the San Diego Unit in 2003, serving as the Cal Fire incident commander of the Cedar Fire. He said that there were so many fires going that they didn't have time to prepare the normal written briefing and maps. There was a unified command with the Cleveland National Forest and local fire departments for the Cedar Fire.

Chief Maner greeted Cal Fire archeologists on the first day they arrived at the incident base of the Coyote Fire in July 2003. He told the archaeologists to let him know if anything at all was needed to help them get the job done. This was the most welcome reception and most enthusiastic participation ever seen by Cal Fire archaeologists on any fire. His support made a positive impact on the unit's efforts toward protection of archaeology. On March 2, 2005, the 2004 Golden Trowel Award was given to the San Diego Unit for that team's innovation and leadership in protecting archaeological resources during wildland fire suppression activities.

Thom Porter was chief of the San Diego Unit from 2009 to 2014. His career with Cal Fire began in 1999 as a forester in the Southern Region. He worked his way through the ranks of Southern Region Forester, San Diego Unit Chief, Southern Region Chief, and Chief of Strategic Planning in Sacramento. In 2018 he managed the Camp Fire, which became the deadliest fire in California history at that time. On January 8, 2019, Chief Porter was appointed director of Cal Fire by Governor Gavin

Carl Murray, who retired from Cal Fire after 25 years of service, maintains the 1939 Big Jimmy.

Newsom. He holds a Bachelor of Science in Forest Management from the University of California, Berkeley and is a Registered Professional Forester.

Chief Tony Mecham took on the leadership role in 2014. He has been in the fire service for 33 years, starting in Goleta with the U.S. Forest Service while in high school. He began working for Cal Fire in 1987. He has held the ranks of dispatcher, firefighter, engineer, captain, battalion chief, and division chief. He has served in the San Diego, Sonoma, and Riverside Units. Chief Mecham's experience includes working in the Emergency Command Center and as a truck company captain and water rescue team leader and training chief. He served for eight years on a Cal Fire Incident Management Team as an Operations Section Chief and Incident Commander Trainee for IMT6. Mecham has been involved with the EMS program, strategic planning, and implementation of Mobile Date Computing. He holds an Associate Degree in Fire Science, a Bachelor of Arts in Public Administration, and a Graduate Certificate in Fire Protection Administration.

William R. "Bill" Clayton was the most decorated firefighter in the history of Cal Fire. He was a multiple winner of the Medal of Valor, the highest award given to firefighters in the state. He originally retired in 1998 after 40 years of service with the U.S. Forest Service and then Cal Fire. He soon returned to duty as a division chief and was one of the incident commanders for both the Paradise fire in Valley Center and then the Cedar fire a couple days later. Clayton retired again from Cal Fire in 2006. He then became the Sycuan Fire Department's chief from 2010 to 2012. He died in January 2018 at the age of 77.

In San Diego County, Cal Fire operates 27 engine companies, 2 air tankers, 4 bulldozers, 21 conservation camp crews, 19 fire stations, 4 conservation camps, and 1 air attack base.

Housed at the Ramona Air Attack Base is a 1939 GMC engine called the "Big Jimmy." Two of the fire trucks were built in the late 1930s by CDF personnel at the shop at the La Mesa headquarters. They were designated Units 296 and 300. Unit 296 was stationed at La Mesa and Unit 300 was stationed at Hilltop near Chula Vista. At the end of World War II, Hilltop was annexed to Chula Vista and Unit 300 was transferred to Carlsbad for the rest of its CDF service.

Unit 296, Big Jimmy, was sold to a lumber yard near Leggett, California, in 1952. When firefighter Ernest L. "Ernie" Balmforth saw the engine abandoned in the lumber yard, he purchased it. The inmates at the Parlin Fork Conservation Camp in Fort Bragg spent three years restoring the engine. The 1939 GMC fire truck specifications are engine: 308 CID; transmission: 5-speed manual; rear axle: 2 speed; electrical: 6 volt converted to 12 volt; crew capacity: 6; pump capacity: 150-gpm Edwards rotary gear front mount, 750-gpm Hale midship; tires: 8:25x20 tube type; water tank: 500 gallons; weight unladen: 12,800 lbs.; wheelbase: 144 in.; overall length: 258 in.; overall height: 105 in.

There are 39 conservation camps in California that provide 198 fire crews. These fire crews, also called hand crews, provide more than 2.3 million hours of emergency assistance each year. They are administrated cooperatively by Cal Fire which directs fire suppression and the California Department of Corrections and Rehabilitation which supervises the

inmates. The inmates at La Cima, McCain Valley, Puerta La Cruz, and Rainbow Conservation Camps in San Diego County provide assistance with fire suppression, conservation projects, and community services.

The La Cima Conservation Camp opened in 1966. The camp is 60 miles northeast of San Diego in the Cuyamaca Mountains. A staff of 20 supervises 84 inmates. Besides fighting fires, the inmates help with weed abatement, clearing brush, and restoration projects.

The McCain Valley Conservation Camp located in Boulevard, 70 miles east of San Diego, was established in 1986. A staff of 2 camp commanders, 1 division chief, 10 fire captains, 1 heavy equipment operator, 1 correctional lieutenant, and 7 correctional officers supervise 85 inmates. In 2013 the fire crews from the camp assisted in fighting a 23,000-acre fire at the border between California and Mexico. In the same year, the crews were at the Rim Fire in Yosemite National Park for 27 days.

The Puerta La Cruz Camp opened in 1959 on 25 acres in northeastern San Diego County in the Palomar Mountains. The male camp was converted to an all-female camp in 1986. It has 120 minimum custody inmates. The camp operates five 17-member fire crews. A mobile kitchen with inmate cooks provides food for personnel on emergency incidents. Other projects include work at the Anza-Borrego Desert State Park, San Diego Safari Park, and Palomar Observatory.

The Rainbow Conservation Camp was established on August 26, 1946, with six inmates from the California Institute for Men, one correctional officer, and two foremen from Cal Fire who were staying at the site. The camp is located west of the San Diego/Riverside County lines on 52 acres in a remote area of Rainbow. C. A. "Cab" Brown, a correctional officer, served as the first superintendent of the Rainbow Conservation Camp until his retirement in 1972. Gordon Fowler took his place and served until 1984. Bill Clayton followed him as superintendent. Now Harriet Woods is camp commander.

It eventually had 80 male inmates, but in October 1983 it was changed to a women's camp. The Rainbow Conservation Camp now has about 10 buildings to house 100 inmates, all selected for this facility because they have nonviolent histories. The average age of the inmates is 26.5 and the average stay in the camp is nine months. The camp has five 17-member fire crews. According to Captain John Loop, who worked at the camp for 18 years, many of the inmates do not want to leave. For some of the women, it is the only home they have ever known.

The first fire station for wildland protection in San Diego County was in Bostonia. It was followed by the Monte Vista Ranger District with the Grossmont-Mt. Helix Stations 1 and 2 and the Flinn Springs station; Red Mountain Ranger District with the Miller, De Luz, Lyons Valley, and Potrero stations; Dulzura Ranger District with the Dulzura station; Julian Ranger District with the Julian, Cuyamaca, and Witch Creek stations; Ramona Ranger District with the Ramona and Warner Springs stations; Campo Ranger District with the Campo and White Star stations; and Valley Center Ranger District with the Rincon, San Marcos, and Valley Center stations.

Cal Fire worked closely, hand-in-hand, with the San Diego County volunteer firefighters. The volunteer fire departments were considered viable organizations. Many volunteer departments trained with Cal Fire; and, in 1992, over a dozen departments signed contracts for Cal Fire dispatch services. Whether it was a rescue traffic accident, structure fire, or wildland fire, Cal Fire's arrival, actions, and resources were critical.

When a deadly wildland fire strikes anywhere in San Diego County, Cal Fire initiates an attack that can go from a medium to a massive show of force and resources. The incident command system is immediately initiated. Air attack from the Ramona Air Base is dispatched along with air command. Dozers, hand crews, brush and water tenders, strike teams, and support staff respond. A command post and a fire camp are established. The Cal Fire personnel work in unison with mutual aid agencies, providing water for apparatus, relief of personnel, and much needed logistical support.

Cal Fire stands ready, proud, and determined to protect Californians from the Oregon border to the Mexican border, from the Pacific Ocean to Death Valley. The firefighters have truly been tested by fire, wind, and smoke. Cal Fire personnel have earned the respect of the international fire service community.

CALLS RECALLED:

*1970: The Laguna Fire started September 26, 1970. It killed 8 people, destroyed 382 structures, and burned 175,425 acres. The fire spread at a rate of over 3,000 acres per hour.

*1981: The Southern California Fire Siege started on November 16 in San Bernardino. It killed 4 people, destroyed 370 acres, and burned 90,000 acres.

*1991: The Tunnel Fire started on October 19, 1991, in Oakland. It killed 25 people, destroyed 3,280 structures, and burned 1,520 acres.

*2001: In 2001, Larry Groff of Windsor and Lars Stratte of Redding were killed when their air tankers collided over a fire near Hopland.

*2003: The Cedar Fire started on October 25, 2003, in San Diego County. It killed 15 people, destroyed 2,820 structures, and burned 273,246 acres.

*2007: The Witch Creek Fire started on October 21, 2007, in Santa Ysabel. It killed 2 people, destroyed 1,265 homes, and burned 247,800 acres. It cost $1.339 billion.

*2007: The Harris Fire started on October 21, 2007, in Potrero and was extinguished on November 5, 2007. It killed 8 civilians, injured 21 civilians, and burned 90,440 acres.

*2012: In August 2012, the Rush Fire in Lassen County burned 271,911 acres in California and 43,666 acres in Nevada.

*2013: In August 2013, the Rim Fire in Tuolumne County burned 257,314 acres and destroyed 112 structures.

*2015: The Valley Fire started on September 12, 2015, in Lake County. It killed 4 people, destroyed 1,955 structures, and burned 76,067 acres.

*2017: The Tubbs Fire started October 8, 2017, in Sonoma, Napa, and Lake counties. It killed 22 people, destroyed 5,643 structures, and burned 36,807 acres.

*2017: On December 14, 2017, 32-year-old Cory Iverson died in the line of duty while working with Cal Fire's Monte Vista Unit at the Thomas Fire in Ventura County. He was overrun by fast moving flames and died of smoke inhalation and burn injuries. Iverson volunteered at the Elfin Forest/Harmony Grove Fire Department between 2008 and 2015. He received the Firefighter of the Year award in 2010 by his colleagues. In 2009, he accepted a position with the Riverside unit of Cal Fire's Riverside Unit. His assignments included time spent on a helicopter out of the Hemet-Ryan Air Attack Base and a season with the Bear Divide Hotshot Crew. He is survived by his wife, Ashley, and two daughters, one born in 2015 and another in 2017. The Thomas Fire burned 281,893 acres, destroyed 1,063 structures, and killed 2 people.

*2018: The Camp Fire started on November 8, 2018, in the town of Paradise in the foothills of California's Sierra Nevada Mountains. Tragically, it killed 86 people, destroyed 18,804 structures (13,850 homes), and burned 153,336 acres.

*2018: The Woolsey Fire started on November 8, 2018, in Los Angeles and Ventura Counties. Three lives were lost, 1,643 structures destroyed, and 96,949 acres burned.

*2019: On July 28, 2019, Yaroslav Igorevich Katkov, 28, a Cal Fire firefighter, collapsed during his second attempt at a 1.45-mile training hike near the De Luz Fire Station while wearing full gear and carrying 20 to 30 pounds of weight. He was flown in an air ambulance to Temecula

Hospital but suffered a two-minute seizure while en route. When he was admitted, his body temperature was 107.4 degrees. Fifteen hours later he was pronounced dead. Katkov was assigned to Station 16 in De Luz. He started his career with Cal Fire as a seasonal firefighter in August 2018. Governor Gavin Newsom said, "It's the work of brave firefighters like Yaroslav that keep our communities safe, and we are deeply grateful for his service."

*2019:   The Kincade Fire burned in Sonoma County from October 23, 2019, to November 6, 2019. It destroyed 174 homes, 11 commercial buildings, and 189 other structures, and burned 77,758 acres. The helicopters dropped 2 million gallons of water and the airtankers unleashed 1 million gallons of retardant on the fire.

*2020:   In August and September, firefighters fought the following California fires:

The North Complex Fire in Plumas and Butte Counties started August 17. It began with the Claremont, Bear, and Sheep Fires. It burned 318,930 acres, killed 15 people, and destroyed 2,471 structures. There were 1,239 personnel, 46 engines, 27 hand crews, 39 dozers, 4 helicopters, and 52 water tenders assigned to the fire. Those who died in the fire included: Jacob Albright, 72, was found inside a car close to Berry Creek, and Paul Winer, 68, was found a short distance away, 10 feet from his pickup, and a friend of his was discovered on a roadway nearby; Phillip Ruble, 68, burned to death inside his Toyota pickup truck on his property and his companion, Millicent Catarncuic, 77, was found on a nearby embankment; Sandra Butler, 75, died in the fire alongside her long-time husband, John Butler, 79; others who died in the fire were Randy Harrell, 67; Mark De La Gardie, 61; Ken Lee, 64; Jorge Hernandez-Juarez, 26; Khawar Bhatti, 58; and Josiah Williams, 16.

The August Complex Fire started as 38 separate fires started by lightning on August 16 in the Coast range of Northern California. It burned 1,029,605 acres, destroyed 160 structures, damaged 6 structures, and killed one firefighter. Cal Fire partnered with three other agencies to fight the fire. There were 1,002 personnel assigned to the fire and 4 crews. It is the largest complex fire in the state.

Diana Jones, the firefighter who died in the August Complex Fire, was a volunteer from Cresson, Texas. She had been with the Cresson Fire Department for five years. Jones and two other firefighters were working on the Tatham fire within the August Complex when a vehicle crash occurred.

The LNU Lightning Complex Fire in Sonoma, Lake, Napa, Yolo, and Solano Counties started on August 17. It burned 363,220 acres, destroyed 1,491 structures, damaged 232 structures, injured 5 people, and killed 5 people. LNU stands for Cal Fire's Sonoma, Lake, Napa Unit. A Vacaville-based Pacific Gas and Electric worker died while assisting first responders. Three people in Napa County died and one person in Solano County, Douglas Mai, 82, who would not evacuate, died.

The SCU Lightning Complex Fire started on August 18 and burned 396,624 acres and destroyed 222 structures. SCU stands for Cal Fire's Santa Clara Unit.

The CZU Lightning Complex Fire in the Santa Cruz Mountains started on August 17 and burned 86,509 acres, destroyed 1,490 structures, damaged 140 structures, injured 1 person, and killed Tad Jones, who was 73.

The Butte/Tehama/Glenn Fire started on August 19 and burned 19,609 acres, damaged 1 structure, destroyed 14 structures, and injured 1 person.

The Carmel Fire in Monterey County started on August 18. It burned 6,905 acres, destroyed 73 structures, and damaged 7 structures.

The Moc Fire in Tuolumne County started on August 20. It burned 2,857 acres and destroyed 2 structures. There were 686 personnel and 21 crews assigned to the fire.

The Glass Fire in Sonoma and Napa Counties started on September 27. The fire burned 67,484 acres, destroyed 1,555 structures including 600 single-family homes, and damaged 282 structures. At the peak of the fire, Cal Fire assigned more than 2,500 personnel to it.

The Zogg Fire started on September 27 north of Igo and was contained on October 13. It burned 56,338 acres, destroyed 244 structures, damaged 27 structures, and killed 4 civilians. Those who lost their lives in the fire were 79-year-old Karin King, 45-year-old Alaina Michelle Rowe, a minor, and 52-year-old Kenneth Vossen.

*2020: On September 20, 2020, there were 19,000 firefighters fighting 27 wildfires in California that have burned over 3 million acres. The state, local, tribal, and federal resources assigned to the active wildfires were more than 2,300 fire engines, 124 aircraft, 313 fire crews, 378 bulldozers, and 467 water tenders. As of October 2, 2020, 8,155 fires have burned 4,14,656 acres, 8,506 structures damaged or destroyed, 37 injuries, and 31 deaths. Many of the fires were caused by lightning strikes and climate change. More than 16,600 firefighters from 10 states and New Zealand, Israel, Mexico, and Australia fought the fires. The cost of the fires is $1.808 billion.

CAMP PENDLETON FIRE DEPARTMENT

The Marine Corps Base Camp Pendleton, located in North San Diego County, encompasses 200 square miles with 17 miles of coastline. Approximately 70,000 Marines and their families live on the base.

The Camp Pendleton Fire Department was established in 1942. It has 11 stations and 175 firefighters and emergency services personnel. The stations are all equipped with standard firefighting equipment, but some carry specialized gear strategically placed around the base.

Fire Chief William Frankel retired in February 2010 after serving 31 years in the department. He started his career in 1976 as a U.S. Forest Service firefighter in the Cleveland National Forest. Chief Frankel said, "The firefighters I tried to emulate were the old-time chiefs. Throughout my career I saw how they had such a strong willingness to work and how they always put the department, and more importantly, its firefighters first. Their leadership helped me to establish goals and work toward them every day."

Current leaders of the department are: Ken Helgerson, Fire Chief, John Cunfille-Owen, Assistant Fire Chief, John Crook, Deputy Fire Chief for Training, Robert Johnson, Deputy Fire Chief for Fire Prevention, Bruce Wathen, Division 2 Fire Chief, Bob Johnson, Division Chief, and Carlos Camarena, Division Chief.

To keep fires from running into surrounding communities, the department cuts 164 miles of firebreaks each year, created and maintained with bulldozers and road graders, In 2016, the fire department responded to more than 3,700 emergencies. The Marine Corps base averages approximately 185 training related vegetation fires annually.

Camp Pendleton Fire Department hosts an annual Wildland Fire School for firefighting agencies throughout Southern California. In June 2019, more than 300 firefighters from 20 agencies attended the fire school.

The firefighters work in 48-hour shifts. There are no active duty service members in the department, but there are veterans from all branches of service.

The Camp Pendleton Fire Department has seven Type I engines, ten Type III engines, one 75-foot aerial ladder truck, and one 105-foot aerial ladder truck.

In 2016, the fire department was named the Department of Defense Fire Department of the Year. In 2019, the department was selected as the Department of Defense's Large Fire Department of the Year.

When Rusty Duke was promoted from lieutenant to captain in 2018, he said, "I want my firefighters to be better than I am. That's the legacy I want to leave. Even if it's just one person, making a difference in that one person's life is a very rewarding feeling."

John Cook, the deputy chief of training, said, "The firefighters always come to work with a positive attitude. Every time we get a call to do our jobs, we do it the right way and I'm proud to be a part of that."

Chief Thomas C. Thompson has said, "We can see the impact we make every day—not every job is like that—and get satisfaction by helping our community and serving our warfighters and families."

In January 2020, Ken Helgerson became chief of the Camp Pendleton Fire Department. He served as a firefighter with the U.S. Air Force for 20 years. Since retirement in 2005, he has served as chief at four installations.

CALLS RECALLED:

*2017: On December 8, 2017, Marines and aircraft from the 3rd Marine Aircraft Wing coordinated with Cal Fire on the Lilac Fire in Northern San Diego County. Two UH-1Y Venons from Marine Light Helicopter Squadron 267 refilled their water buckets at Lake O'Neal. Also the Marine Corps Air Station sent two UH-1Y Venons that can carry up to 320 gallons of water.

*2018: In June 2018, the Puebitos Fire burned 42 acres in a training area on the southern side of Camp Pendleton Base.

*2018: In July 2018, the Pendleton Complex Fire burned 1,600 acres.

*2018: From July 27 to August 21, 2018, firefighters from Camp Pendleton assisted fighting the Mendocino Complex Fire in Mendocino County. The fire killed one firefighter, burned 459,123 acres, and destroyed 280 homes. Approximately 3,500 firefighters fought the complex of two wildfires.

*2019: In October, 2019, the Oak Fire burned 143 acres of brush in the northeastern portion of Camp Pendleton.

*2020: On June 9, 2020, the India Fire started on Marine Corps Base Camp Pendleton training areas. It burned 1,100 acres before it was extinguished on June 12. Over 175 firefighters from agencies such as the Cal Fire , Orange County Fire Authority, fire departments from neighboring cities such as Oceanside, Rancho Santa Fe, and Carlsbad, and the U.S. Forest Service assisted in the efforts.

*2020: On July 30, 2020, eight U.S. Marines and one U.S. Navy sailor were killed in a training session off the coast, including Bryan J. Baltierra, 18; Marco A. Barranco, 21; Evan A. Bath, 19; Christopher Gnem, 22; Jack-Ryan Ostrovsky, 20; Wesley A. Rodd, 22; Chase D, Sweetwood, 18; Cesar A, Villanueva, 21; and Guillermo S. Perez, 19.

CAMPO RESERVATION FIRE PROTECTION DISTRICT

Campo is located 60 miles east of downtown San Diego. The reservation of the Campo Kumeyaay Nation was established on 710 acres on February 10, 1893, following an Executive Order on January 12, 1891. Eighty acres were added on February 2, 1907, and 13,610 acres were added on December 14, 1911. Later additions brought the reservation to its current size of 16,512 acres.

The Kumeyaay have lived in the county for 12,000 years. In July 2020, members of the Kumeyaay Nation gathered at the Campo Indian Reservation to stop contractors from the U.S. Army Corps of Engineers from blasting for border-wall construction in the middle of Kumeyaay land and destroying an ancestral burial site.

An elected committee is the steering body of the Campo Kumeyaay Nation and a voting governing council consisting of all members aged 18 or over. The seven-member elected executive committee serve four-year terms. The council members in 2020 are: Marcus Cuero, Kerm Shipp, Johnathan Mesa, Annah Ceballos, Steven M. Cuero, Ronnie Lee Cuero, and Ronny Paipa.

Harry Paul Cuero Jr. was honored in October 2010 as a Local Hero by KPBS for his involvement in the governmental process of the Campo Kumeyaay Nation beginning at the age of 19. He was the cultural director in 2001, the chairman for four years beginning in 2004, and served on Campo's executive committee.

The reservation owns and operates the Golden Acorn Casino, which opened on August 25, 2001, the Golden Grill Restaurant, the Del Oro Deli, and a travel center, all located in Campo.

In 1997, the Campo Reservation Fire Protection District was formed, covering 27 square miles. In 2000, the fire department became completely paid, including advanced EMTs. It provides services for Campo, La Posta, Manzanita, and Ewiaapaayp Reservations. Chief Steven M. Cuero leads a crew of a district chief, a district clerk, and four firefighters. Fire personnel employ a three-platoon system of staffing, working 48 hours followed by 96 hours off.

The personnel includes Chief Steven M. Cuero; Division Chief Scott Timbs; District Clerk, Ashley Jones; "A" Shift Firefighter/EMTs Joshua Garcia and Jesse Spurdle; and "C" Shift personnel are Captain Eddie Flores and Firefighter/EMT Victor Parra. In October 2018, Joshua Garcia and Jesse Spurdle completed their probationary period.

Chief Steven Cuero has been with the Campo Reservation Fire Department since the early 1980s.

Division Chief Scott Timbs has worked for the department since April 2002. Previously he was at the Jacumba Fire Department.

Firefighter/EMT Jesse Spurdle was previously an EMT with Balboa Ambulance in 2014, an EMT with Lake Elsinore Storm from June 2014 to February 2016, and an EMT with Pala Casino Resort from February 2016 to October 2018. He has an Associate of Crisis/Emergency/Disaster Management from Palomar College.

The crew train to respond to a wide variety of calls. For example, in July 2018, the personnel practiced drafting skills. In September 2018, they participated in rescue training with Truck 46, using the 75-foot aerial ladder to perform a simulated rescue. The firefighters sometimes burn heavy vegetation in the winter to protect structures. On December 21, 2018, they burned some of the fuel near Church Road and

Visitor Antonia Cosentino in front of Campo Reservation Fire Protection District's fire danger rating sign.

Highway 94. Also the personnel are involved in the community. On February 19, 2019, they provided a presentation to the students at the Campo Elementary School, showing fire equipment and tools and discussing fire safety.

The station is located at 36210 Church Road.

Brush 46 is a 2002 Pierce Type III International 4800 4x4. It is the district's first-out engine to most incidents.

Patrol 46 is a 2004 Ford F-550 4x4 that serves as the primary rescue apparatus for vehicle accidents and rescues. It is currently used as a secondary apparatus for freeway incidents and for training purposes.

Truck 46 is a 2008 Pierce Quantum quint with an 75-foot aerial. It is primarily used for commercial structure fires and on freeway incidents.

Campo has a contract with Heartland Communications for 911 emergency dispatch services.

The fire department has two fire danger rating signs on the reservation: one on Buckman Springs Road and the other on Church Road in front of the fire station.

Only 100 of the 573 tribes in the United States have fire departments. Fortunately, the Campo Reservation and the nearby communities have dedicated first responders for protection.

CALLS RECALLED:

*2012:   In June 2012, the 995-acre Old Fire burned near Old Highway 80. The Golden Acre Casino was evacuated as well as many people in homes near the blaze. One home was destroyed.

*2012:   In September 2012, the Shockey Fire burned 2,556 acres, killing one man and destroying 11 homes. The fire started off of Shockey Truck Trail and State Route 94.

*2013:   In November 2013, the Campo personnel were deployed for 14 days to the Stanislaus National Forest in Northern California to assist with a fire caused by lightning.

*2016:   In December 2016, a mobile home and a recreational vehicle on Church Road caught fire while the owners were asleep. It took crews from four agencies three hours to extinguish the fire.

*2017:   In August 2017, a brush fire in Campo burned 200 acres.

*2017:   In October 2017, the Church Fire burned 100 acres near the Golden Acre Casino.

*2018:   On June 6, 2018, the Campo crew was first on the scene at the Recycle Fire which burned 265 acres.

*2018:   In June 2018, a 9-acre fire burned near the Golden Acre Casino. One structure was threatened. At the same time, there was a second 1-acre spot fire.

*2018:   On August 9, 2018, a large vehicle fire occurred on Interstate 8 East, west of Crestwood Road. Firefighters from Campo, Cal Fire, and San Diego County Fire Authority responded to the incident.

*2019:   On November 2, 2019, fire personnel were the first on the scene of the Crestwood Fire and initiated an aggressive attack on the left flank. The fire burned 32 acres.

*2020:   On August 23, 2020, a 1.9-acre fire threatened structures. The Campo crew worked with Cal Fire, San Diego County Fire Authority, and the U.S. Forest Service in stopping it.

CARLSBAD FIRE DEPARTMENT

Carlsbad is located along the coastline, 87 miles south of Los Angeles and 35 miles north of San Diego. It covers 37 square miles and has a population of 112,299.

Ranchers settled in the area in the late 1860s. In 1882, John Frazier dug a well near the coast and began offering his water to travelers at the train station. The community was first called Frazier's Station but was renamed Carlsbad in 1883 when its mineral waters were found to be similar to those of Karlsbad in Bohemia.

The Palomar Airport opened in 1959. It was annexed to Carlsbad in 1978 and renamed McClellan-Palomar Airport in 1982 after the civic leader, Gerald McClellan. In March 1999, Legoland opened.

A small truck mounted with a chemical sprayer and 250 feet of hose was purchased in November 1927 with a fund raised by public subscription. It was kept in the basement of the Twin Inns.

A volunteer fire department was organized in 1952. The firemen met at the California State Forestry and Fire Protection station located on the corner of Carlsbad Boulevard and Beech Avenue. They trained with the forestry firemen. They had fundraisers such as dances and barbecues to raise funds for equipment. The department was so good that Carlsbad's insurance rates were the same as cities with full-time departments.

In 1954 the department became funded by the city. In 1955, Bob Hardin was hired to lead the 21 volunteer firemen and oversee a $27,000 budget.

Carlsbad's first fire station shared a building with the police and city hall on Pio Pico Drive. When Interstate 5 was widened in the 1960s, the building was demolished and the station was moved to Carlsbad Village Drive.

In 1972, La Costa was annexed to Carlsbad and fire service was extended to the area. When Jim Thompson became chief in 1976 he had a staff of 73 people.

There were 1,385 applicants in 1991 to fill three firefighter positions that paid $31,000 a year. The applicants had to score 90% on the written test, spend a day physical testing, excel in an oral interview, and pass the background check, medical exam, and psychological exam.

Jeff, Dan, and Ed Sprague, who were all captains for the Carlsbad Fire Department at the same time, chose firefighting as their careers after seeing their father work for the Vista Fire Department in the 1960s. Dan Sprague said, "We were always amazed at the bravado required. He would come home and smell like smoke and we were impressed by that." Jeff Sprague retired from the Carlsbad Fire Department as a battalion chief. Ed Sprague worked

Cal OES engine stationed at Carlsbad Station 3

for the department from September 1986 to May 2012. Dan Sprague has worked for the Carlsbad Fire Department since July 1977.

Captain Dean Harrold, 36, died of cancer related to his work, in 1990. He served the department for 21 years, helping to launch the paramedic program and design three of the stations. His name is inscribed on the California Firefighters' Memorial in Sacramento.

Darrell Wayne Bennett, who worked for the Carlsbad Fire Department for 23 years, died on August 25, 1997. He began his career as a volunteer fireman.

Lois Klinischmidt, 71, who was a secretary for the Carlsbad Fire Department for 40 years, died on June 8, 1998.

Fire Marshal Michael E. Smith retired in August 2002 after a 34-year firefighting career. He was the fire marshal from 1986 to 2002 and helped lead the department in the Harmony Fire.

Rich Walton began his career with the Carlsbad Fire Department in June 1968. He was promoted to engineer in 1972 and to captain in 1976. Captain Walton retired in 2002. He worked in administration and was a training officer and paramedic coordinator. He helped buy the department's 13 engines and brush rigs and helped design Station 3. Walton said that the crew became like a second family, and he experienced their joys and tragedies like in any other family.

In 2004, Division Chief Brian Watson and Battalion Chiefs Sonny Hilliard and Tom Dana retired, each with the department nearly 30 years. Engineers Dan Zeller, who was hired in October 1975, and Jack Morgan, hired in 1974, also retired in 2004.

The fire chiefs of the department include: Bob Hardin (1955-1969), Scott Wolenchuk (1969-1976), James "Jim" Thompson (1976-1992), Dennis Van Der Maaten (1992-2001), Kevin Crawford (2002-2014), Michael Davis (2014-2018), and Michael D. Calderwood (2018-).

Bob Hardin was hired as Carlsbad's first chief in 1955. He oversaw a $27,000 budget and 21 volunteer firemen. Chief Hardin gradually converted those volunteer positions to full-time firemen.

Scott Wolenchuk saw the fire department grow in the 1970s. Each year the firemen had an elaborate Christmas display that over 30,000 visitors came to see. However, when the station moved to Carlsbad Village Drive, Chief Wolenchuk regretfully ended the displays in 1969.

Jim Thompson quickly worked his way up the ranks at the Escondido Fire Department and served as assistant chief of the department before becoming the chief of the Carlsbad Fire Department on October 1, 1976, a position he held for 16 years. The normal term of office for a fire chief is less than 10 years. In 1976, there were three fire stations and 27 uniformed personnel. Chief Thompson initiated automatic mutual aid with Carlsbad's neighboring cities, a strict commercial building code fire sprinkler ordinance, a noncombustible roof ordinance for the entire city, and utilization of civilian personnel in the Fire Prevention Bureau. He believed that the ingredients for a good fire department were top-notched trained personnel from the bottom to the top with well maintained modern equipment, and the support of the city council and city manager. He retired December 28, 1992.

Dennis Van Der Maaten retired from the department on August 3, 2001, after 33 years in the fire service, including 8 years as chief of the Carlsbad Fire Department. He spent 17 years with the San Diego Fire Department, departing with the rank of battalion chief, then assistant chief in Palo Alto and later the chief in Livermore before becoming the chief in Carlsbad on June 21, 1992. He helped to create the San Diego-Imperial Counties Regional Communications System. He was president of the San Diego County Fire Chiefs Association in 1998-99 and on the Burn Institute Board of Directors in 1998. Van Der Maaten was the League of California Cities Fire Chiefs' appointee to its administrative services policy committee for 10 years. Van Der Maaten said of firefighting, "It's all about people. What I'm going to miss is the camaraderie and the people."

In 2002, Kevin Crawford was selected as fire chief at the age of 44. He headed a department with 80 employees, 6 fire stations, and an annual budget of $10.5 million. Crawford, who joined the department in 1986, rose through the ranks of firefighter/paramedic, captain, and battalion chief. Crawford was with the department for 27 years, serving as fire chief of Carlsbad from 2002 to 2014. In 2014 he left the department to become president and CEO of the United Way of San Diego County. In December 2016 he returned to Carlsbad to become city manager. His annual salary in 2016 was $286,000. Chief Crawford began his career as a paramedic with Medivac Ambulance Inc., worked as a flight medic at UCSD Medical Center, and then was a firefighter/paramedic with the Poway Fire Department from 1984 to 1986.

Michael Davis worked for the El Cajon and San Diego Fire Departments before joining the Carlsbad Fire Department in 1990. He was promoted to fire captain in 2003, battalion chief in 2007, and division chief in 2013. He served as fire chief from 2014 to 2018. Chief Davis earned a Bachelor of Science in Occupational Studies from Long Beach State University and a Master of Public Administration from San Diego State University.

Michael Calderwood was sworn in as fire chief on July 10, 2018. He began his career as a firefighter/EMT in Pismo Beach from 1998 to 2000. He joined the Carlsbad Fire Department in 2003, advancing to captain, battalion chief from 2011 to 2013, and division chief from 2014 to 2018. As division chief, he oversaw the day-to-day administration and operations of the department under the direction of the fire chief. He has served in roles including executive leadership, resource management, labor/management relations, emergency planning, professional standards, mentoring, and employee wellness.

In 2017, Calderwood graduated from the John F. Kennedy School of Government at Harvard University's Senior Executives in State and Local Governments Program. He is also a 2013 graduate of LEAD San Diego. He earned a Bachelor of Arts in Law and Society at the University of California, Santa Barbara.

Chief Calderwood earned meritorious service awards for the 2007 San Diego County Firestorms and 2014 Poinsettia Fire. He has served as chair of the San Diego County Fire Operations Chiefs. He joined the Hospice of North Coast Board of Directors in 2017.

Each of the three shifts (A, B, and C) are on a 24-hour rotation. The shift changes at 7:30 a.m. The firefighters check out their personal protective gear, radios, breathing apparatus, and other equipment to ensure they are ready to respond to calls. The engineer inspects the apparatus. Firefighters eat lunch and dinner together The activities include maintenance, training, department projects, inspecting commercial properties, physical fitness, and, above all, responding to emergencies.

The department has five fire engines (two in reserve), one ladder truck, two brush engines, three paramedic ambulances (two in reserve), three chief command vehicles (one in reserve), and one urban search and rescue unit. Carlsbad purchases all its fire engines from Seagrave Fire Apparatus LLC, which is based in Wisconsin. In December 2012, Carlsbad purchased a Seagrave custom pumper for $593,000 to replace an engine with more than 110,000 miles and 6,500 hours of use. The city also purchased an ambulance on a Ford chassis for $200,000 in 2012. It replaced a 2006 Ford ambulance that had 105,000 hours on it.

In 2015, the department received a chartreuse engine from the California Office of Emergency Services (OES). The $242,000 engine is used primarily for fighting brush fires. The engine is owned by the state, but Carlsbad can use it as needed.

Station 1 is located at 1275 Carlsbad Village Drive. The service area covers the northwest side of the city (including downtown, Plaza Camino Real, Interstate 5, and Highway 78). It was built in 1968. It is staffed by a captain, an engineer, and three firefighter/paramedics. The station houses one engine and one ambulance. The firefighters respond to about 5,000 calls a year.

Station 2, located at 1906 Arenal Road, is located east of El Camino Real by the Omni La Costa Resort and Spa. It was constructed in 1969 with one full-time firefighter and less than 250 calls a year. Today it responds to about 4,100 calls a year. Now housing one engine and one ambulance, it is staffed by a captain, an engineer, and three firefighter/paramedics.

The station is too small to house the apparatus currently used and has inadequate storage space for fire hose, firefighting apparel, and medical supplies. It lacks the separation required by the current building code between the apparatus bays, the working and living quarters, and the medical supplies.

SchneiderCM, Inc. will provide construction management services of a two-story 10,782-square-foot building at the same site beginning in 2021 and take about a year to complete it. The contemporary Old Spanish design will have an exterior of white stucco, heavy wood timbers, and terra-cotta tile to blend in with the neighborhood and the nearby Omni La Costa Resort. Additional traffic signals controlled by the fire department will be installed on El Camino Real to clear the way for vehicles responding to an emergency. In November 2016, 71% of the voters in Carlsbad approved spending between $7.5 million and $10.5 million of existing general fund money to rebuild the station.

Firefighters will move into two trailers in the Dove Library parking lot while the new station is being built. A tent will shelter the fire apparatus. The area will be enclosed by a chain link fence.

Station 3 is located at 3465 Trailblazer Way adjacent to a future park in a residential area. The original Station 3 was built in 1976 and was located at 3701 Catalina Drive in the northwest area of the city. The new facility was completed in 2016 at a cost of $6.1 million. WLC Architects, Inc. designed the building. The 11,311-square-foot station can accommodate eight firefighters. It staffs a captain, an engineer, and three firefighter/paramedics. The station houses one fire engine, one ambulance, one wildland engine, and one heavy rescue truck. The personnel respond to about 4,200 calls a year.

The station has a two-story lobby space that includes enlarged historical fire department images as well as a demonstration fire pole. The pole is accessible through a hidden mezzanine area and can be easily accessed by firefighters for school tours and other demonstrations. It features individual sleeping quarters, a three-bay, double-deep apparatus room with 28-foot-high ceiling, administrative offices, kitchen, dining room, dayroom, and physical training room.

Station 3 is artistically designed using a combination of plaster, brick, and pre-cast concrete. A stand-alone hose tower is enclosed in an independent structure designed to reflect the historical architectural style of the building and is a focal point of the station. The work of a local artist, Betsy K. Schulz, is incorporated into the building. Lithocrete was used around the entrance of the fire station to represent the embers and ash that are left behind after a fire while the larger glass and ceramic pieces sprinkled throughout represent the small personal artifacts that are left behind once the fire is extinguished. The larger glass and ceramic pieces also feature images

and text from the 1970's firehouse log books which at the time were all handwritten. The entrance of the station also features heritage boxes that are permanently mounted to the fire station walls. These are inspired by the numerous boxes placed in the early 1900s at strategic points within wilderness areas. These historic boxes contained firefighting tools, cooking utensils, provisions, and even horse feed. The heritage boxes contain photos, articles about firefighting, and tools and equipment from the last 60 years of Carlsbad's firefighting history. The firefighters were consulted throughout the project to collect information and confirm facts. The jacket, hat, boots, hose and tools are hand-sculpted in high-relief ceramic. The images and text are screened onto tile and fused into glass. All ceramic and glass pieces are made using "controlled kiln fire" with temperatures of 1200°-2300° F. Incorporated seamlessly into the art are historical firefighting artifacts, such as the fire extinguisher, hose nozzle, and fire alarm. It is difficult to tell what is actual and sculpted.

Station 4 is located at 6885 Batiquitos Drive. It covers the southwest area of Carlsbad, including Legoland. Built in 1986, the station is staffed by a captain, an engineer, and a firefighter/paramedic, and houses one engine. The personnel respond to about 1,500 calls a year.

Station 5 is located at 2540 Orio Way. Covering the northeast area of Carlsbad, it also serves as a training ground and supply depot. The station was built in 1989. It is staffed by a duty battalion chief, a captain, an engineer, and a firefighter/paramedic. The personnel respond to about 1,200 calls a year.

Station 6, located at 7201 Rancho Santa Fe Road, covers the southeast area of Carlsbad. Built in 2009, it is staffed by one captain, one engineer, and one firefighter/paramedic, and houses one engine and one wildland brush rig. The personnel respond to about 875 calls a year.

The department has a budget of $18 million and 90 paid personnel. In 1990 the department responded to 3,000 calls a year. It responded to 13,000 calls in 2018. The firefighters respond to about 123 calls per month at each station and the paramedics respond to about 224 calls per month at each station.

The Carlsbad Fire Department Foundation was established in February 2014 by residents in the city to assist the fire department through supplemental funding, education, community outreach, and scholarships. Rancho Carlsbad Owners Association with the help of Community Connections hosted a fundraiser to thank the first responders who were called to a fire near Rancho Carlsbad on July 29, 2020, raising $2,200 for the department.

Versum Materials donated $2,500 to the fire personnel on September 23, 2020. Mr. and Mrs. Vineet Gupta of Vista donated $10,000 to the foundation's scholarship program. In 2019, the foundation provided over 200 bicycle helmets to youth in the community at the Pedal for a Purpose event, the Carlsbad Public Safety open house, and other community events; prepared and funded a grant to place 34 bleeding control kits in 20 city public buildings; supported the Youth Firesetter Intervention Program run by the Burn Institute through funding alongside 38 other cities within San Diego and Imperial Counties so that this program is offered free of charge to minors throughout those counties; and provided two scholarships to dependents of Carlsbad Fire Department personnel. In 2018, the foundation purchased three detox chamber units for the fire department. In 2017, the foundation awarded $21,500 in college (four) and vocational (one) scholarships for the upcoming school year to dependents of Carlsbad firefighters.

Both Robert Hollander, a probationary firefighter, and Andy Speare, a 16-year veteran firefighter/paramedic with the department, chose a career as emergency responders for a similar reason—to have a professionally rewarding career in which they can help people. Hollander was a life guard before joining the Carlsbad Fire Department. Speare said "ever since he was a little kid, he knew what he wanted to do."

As of October 23, 2018, lifeguard services in the north beach, the three-quarter-mile

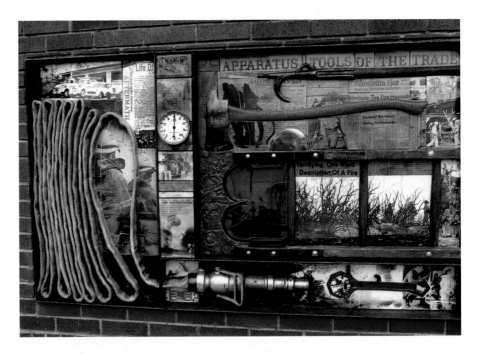

area from Oak Avenue to the city's northern border, is supervised by the fire department. Most of Carlsbad's nearly seven miles of coastline is owned and managed by California State Parks. Within a 10-minute timeframe on July 4, 2017, in Carlsbad, California State Lifeguards Cole Magro and Jeff Knapp headed into a massive rip current to rescue 19 people, many of whom were screaming for help and one who was unconscious and being held aloft by a friend. The two lifeguards prevented multiple fatalities.

Along with emergency calls, the fire department personnel participate in fire prevention activities and also focus on being community members throughout the year.

CALLS RECALLED:

*1967: In 1967, a brush fire consumed 25 acres southeast of Calaveras Lake. It took the Carlsbad Fire Department about three hours to extinguish it.

*1979: In August 1979, two men died in the crash of a Cessna 152 northeast of the Carlsbad Racetrack. Kris Kueneman, 56, was flying very low in heavy fog and hit a high-voltage powerline.

*1982: In October 1982, a 175-acre fire about a half mile northwest of the intersection of El Camino Real and Palomar Airport was fought by 40 firefighters from Carlsbad, Oceanside, Del Mar, Encinitas, and Rancho Santa Fe. The fire investigators suspect the fire was started by a cooking fire left by a farmworker living in Macarrio Canyon.

*1996: During the Harmony Grove Fire in 1996, fire climbed the slopes of Box Canyon. The fire descended from a 1,000-foot plume to ignite shake roofs. Fifty-two homes in Carlsbad were destroyed. The fire started at 2 p.m. on October 21, from Harmony Grove west of Escondido to La Costa. The cause of the fire is undetermined but it is believed that an arsonist started it. The fire consumed 8,600 acres in 24 hours, destroying nearly 110 homes, killing 1 man who was trapped in his car, and costing $1.25 million.

*2002: Jacqueline Beach, 37, died after her 1994 Toyota Corolla was hit by a driver in a 1995 Honda Accord at Cassia Road and El Camino Real. Her eight-month-old baby was delivered by Caesarean section at Scripps Memorial Hospital. The baby was unconscious at birth and had skull fracture and swelling.

*2003: In January 2003, a fire caused severe damage in a duplex on Corintia Street. About 33 firefighters from Carlsbad, San Marcos, and Encinitas battled the blaze.

*2003: On February 22, 2003, Mike Hornback saved his neighbor from a burning house. Chief Kevin Crawford presented the 38-year-old man with a commendation.

*2010: In August 2010, a brush fire started near Carlsbad Village Drive. It burned about an acre.

*2014: The Poinsettia Fire started on May 14, 2014, at 10:40 a.m. in Carlsbad. It started near the intersection of Poinsettia Lane and Alicante Road. After the fire crossed El Camino Real, evacuation orders were issued to 11,600 homes and businesses. The fire was 100% contained by May 17. Residents were assisted in finding housing through Carlsbad's Housing and Neighborhood Services collaboration with Ready Carlsbad, and clean-up efforts were made by Camp Pendleton Marines and trail volunteers. One man died 400 feet from where the fire started, 8 residences and 4 apartments were destroyed, and 600 acres burned. The cost of the fire was $24.5 million.

*2018: When a fire broke out at a home on Madison Street in March 2018, crews from Carlsbad, Oceanside, and Vista Fire Departments responded to the fire. No one was injured.

*2020: In September 2020, Brush 8640, part of Strike Team 6848C, was deployed to the North Complex Fire. BR 106 was assigned to the Valley Fire. The OES strike team spent over a month fighting the wildfires in Northern California.

*2020: Emergency Operations respond to more than 12,000 calls a year. Eighty percent of the calls for the department are for medical services.

CHULA VISTA FIRE DEPARTMENT

Chula Vista is located 7.5 miles from San Diego and 7.5 miles from Mexico. It covers an area of 52.1 square miles and has a population of 270,471 (2017). It is the 14th most populated city in California, the second largest city in San Diego County, and the seventh fastest growing city in the nation. The city is named Chula Vista because of its scenic location between San Diego Bay and coastal foothills.

In 1888, the Sweetwater Dam was completed to bring water to Chula Vista. The town was incorporated on October 11, 1911. The primary crop of the farmers was lemons. In 1931, the lemon orchards produced $1 million in revenue. Rohr Aircraft Corporation moved to Chula Vista in early 1941. The population tripled in 10 years, and the demand for housing reduced the number of orchard groves.

The city was originally protected by a group of 17 volunteers with a hand-drawn soda and acid cart. In 1919, a Model T fire truck was purchased. The Chula Vista Fire Department was founded on May 21, 1921. The soda and acid cart were stored at Helms Garage, present site of Security First National Bank. In front of the garage, a large iron ring from a locomotive wheel was rung to signal an alarm. The Model T fire truck was also housed in Helms Garage.

On the 50th anniversary of the fire department, the Star-News reported, "During those early years, the fire department also helped out the police. Firemen were responsible for custodial work in city hall and the police station. Care and feeding of prisoners was also under fire department scope and more than once, old firemen have said, a rambunctious prisoner was cooled off with a few shots of water from the fire hose."

Charles E. Smith was elected chief in May 1921, with Stewart Murch as assistant chief, Art Spencer as baseball captain, and H. B. Kindberg as secretary-treasurer. Chief Smith was born in Chula Vista in 1898. In 1931, he joined the California State Fire Marshal's Office. When World War II broke out, he developed new firefighting techniques for the government and instructed schools in firefighting. After the war, he returned to the California State Fire Marshal's Office where he served until 1955. He then went into private practice as a fire consultant for 13 years.

The station was moved to the city hall at 292 Third Avenue in 1923 and Howard Jordan became the first full-time paid firefighter. He lived at the fire station. The firemen won the San Diego County Baseball Championship of 1923. In 1924, the 1919 Model T fire truck was traded for a 1923 Seagrave pumper, the "Old Goose,"

Chula Vista, courtesy of San Diego History Center

which is still owned by the fire department. The "Old Goose" was retired in 1948 when the fire department moved to its new Station No. 1 at 447 F Street. It disappeared for two decades until it was discovered in the lemon orchard of a local dentist. In 1968, Dr. M. Brent Campbell offered it as a gift to the city, and efforts began to restore the antique engine and body.

When Wallace Armer became chief in 1931, he headed a department consisting of one fire engine, one station, one paid man, and 15 volunteers. The volunteers were paid $2 per meeting and $2 per fire.

In 1931, Louis Cook and George Lee became members of the volunteer fire department. Both later became paid firemen. In 1936, G. Hirst Perry joined the department as a volunteer, later becoming a paid fireman until his retirement in 1970.

When Bud Wooden became chief in 1941, a 1941 Chevrolet 3/4-ton truck with a water tank and pump was purchased to respond to calls and serve as the chief's car. The city bought a new 1941 Seagrave pumper to replace the 1916 Seagrave.

When the volunteers disbanded and became a social club, 11 full-time firemen were hired. In 1948, the department purchased a new fire engine and moved into a station at 447 F Street.

Chula Vista annexed the Montgomery Fire Protection District located in the southwestern part of the city in 1986. The Chula Vista Fire Department provided fire protection for the 22,000 residents living in the 5-square-mile area of the county. The station is at 391 Oxford Street.

In March 2008, the Chula Vista Fire Department contracted dispatch services with the San Diego Fire-Rescue Department. The contract upgraded response capabilities including automatic vehicle location and mutual aid capabilities. The Chula Vista Fire Department works closely with neighboring departments in providing and receiving mutual aid assistance.

In 2016, residents approved Measure P, a 10-year, half-cent sales tax for structural needs, like fire stations.

The department received a $15,000 Emergency Management Performance Grant in June 2011 to help educate the public about wildfire prevention. The grant was used to help with a Ready, Set, Go campaign with public service announcement videos, informational signs posted throughout the city, and a mailer sent to residents in high-risk wildlife areas.

A grant received in 2017 helped Chula Vista hire 15 new firefighters to keep up with the growth in the city.

In 2018, voters approved Measure A, a half-cent sales tax to hire police and fire personnel. The money went into the general fund. In January 2019, the city hired 12 firefighters with money from Measure A to improve response time to calls and to begin a captain and paramedic squad program to respond to emergencies. The squad trucks are used in the eastern part of the city.

With three firefighters on a rig, crews were only able to get to fires in less than 10 minutes 48.5% of the time. With four firefighters now on each engine because of Measure A, that percentage increased to 73%. A crew can deploy a hose at a fire in two and a half minutes. Previously, the same task took three firefighters six minutes. Chula Vista has a sales tax of 8.75%.

Chiefs include: Charles E. Smith (1921-1931), Wallace Armer (1931-1941), Francis "Bud" Wooden (1941-1942), George Lee (1942-1970), William M. "Bud" Smithey (1970-1977), Clyde "Bones" Longerbone (1978-1979), William "Bill" Winters (1979-1990), Sam Lopez (1990-1993), James Hardiman (1994-2002), Doug Perry (2002-2008), David Hannemann (2008-2014), Jim Geering (2014-2020), and Harry Muns (2021-).

Chula Vista, courtesy of San Diego History Center

When George Lee retired, William M. Smithey became chief of the department on August 26, 1970. Chief Smithey attended Southwest Junior High School and Sweetwater High School and then served three years in the Air Force before returning to Chula Vista and joining the Chula Vista Fire Department on April 16, 1947. He was promoted to engineer on October 31, 1950. On December 15, 1953, he became the city's first fire marshal. William M. Smithey was appointed assistant chief on February 16, 1968.

Dave Hanneman was chosen to lead the department in 2008. He had to cut 10% of the department's budget in 2008 as the city was in a $20 million deficit. He moved the Chula Vista Fire Department from basic life support to an advanced life support system. Chief Hanneman got a fire facility master plan adopted by city council and created a firefighter wellness program. His annual salary was $180,597. Previously he worked for the Boise Fire Department for 20 years. After retiring from the Chula Vista Fire Department on September 4, 2014, he taught at Idaho State University for 12 years before taking a position as chief of the Idaho Falls Fire Department until May 3, 2019.

After serving as interim fire chief from September 2014 to December 2014, Jim Geering was appointed chief in December 2014. In his 34 years with the Chula Vista

Fire Department, he has held the positions of firefighter, engineer, captain, training officer, fire inspector, fire investigator, fire marshal, deputy chief, assistant chief, and interim chief (2008). Chief Geering is a lifelong resident of Chula Vista and attended Chula Vista High School. He has been married for 25 years and has four daughters.

Chief Geering earned a Bachelor of Science in Occupational Studies from California State University, Long Beach, and he is a certified fire chief designated by the California State Fire Marshal. He was a founding member of the Chula Vista Firefighters Foundation and of the countywide Firefighters Advisory Council to the Burn Institute.

Harry Muns was appointed chief on December 31, 2020. He joined the department in 1996. Chief Muns has served as a firefighter, engineer, captain, training officer, battalion chief, and deputy fire chief in charge of operations. He is involved with the Department of Homeland Security/Federal Emergency Management Agency Urban Search and Rescue National Response System.

In January 2019 he was appointed deputy chief. Chief Peter began his career as a firefighter in 1991 with the Chula Vista Fire Department. He served as firefighter, engineer, and captain from 1991 to 2001; battalion chief of operations in 2001 and 2002; deputy chief of operations from 2002 to 2006; battalion chief of operations from 2006 to 2017; battalion chief of administration in 2017 and 2018; and battalion chief of training in 2018 and 2019. He is a member of FEMA's Urban Search & Rescue Task Force and was deployed to the World Trade Center Disaster in 2001 and Hurricane Sandy in 2012.

The department is divided into three divisions.

Fire Operations Division is responsible for emergency medical services (EMS), fire suppression, rescue, hazardous conditions, and all other emergency calls. This division responds to 85% medical calls, 10% firefighting calls, and 5% hazardous materials, rescues, and public assistance. Every day there are 49 firefighters on duty with an additional two firefighters per squad unit during the day. The battalion chiefs include: Brenden Burahura, Robert Nelson, Trevor Flores, Darrell Roberts, and Richard Brocchini. Engineer Mark "Big Mark" McDonald retired in September 2020 after serving the department for more than 30 years. He was an elected officer of Chula Vista Firefighters Local 2180.

The Fire Prevention Division enforces codes relative to fire and life safety issues, conducts new construction inspections, investigates fires, and develops a corridor between wildland and communities. The staff includes: Justin Gipson, fire marshal; Darin Golden and Derek Olivas, senior fire inspectors; Adam Beardsley, Fernando

Felix, Justin Berkley, Maggie Greene, Richard Garl, Marshall Castro, Christopher Smith, and Kelly Briers, fire inspectors; and Mariluz Zepeda, senior office specialist.

The Fire Training Division provides training for all personnel based on fire service standards, information analysis, and emergency response demands. Sean Lowery is the training chief and Grace Knepper is the training programs specialist. Chief Lowery was appointed battalion chief in April 2015. He is president of the Chula Vista Firefighters Foundation. From August 2013 to December 2018, he was an adjunct instructor at the Southwestern Community College District. Chief Lowery has an Associate of Fire Science.

The equipment includes:

Engines 51, 52, 54, 55, 56, 57, 58, 59, and 60—nine Type 1 engines. These front-line engines carry 500 gallons of water and various types of hoses, as well as rescue and emergency medical equipment. They are staffed with four firefighters each day. These engines respond from strategically placed fire stations around the city.

Truck 51 and Truck 57 are two aerial ladder trucks for rescue and ventilation operations. They respond to fires, rescues, and medical emergencies. They are staffed with four firefighters each day. The two ladder trucks are in service on the east and west side of the city respectively.

USAR (Urban Search and Rescue) 53 is a Type 1 heavy rescue apparatus; one Type 1 brush rig carrying 500 gallons of water and special hose packs and tools for woodland fire incidents. It is staffed with four firefighters each day. Crew members have received a high level of additional training in order to utilize the large number of specialized tools and equipment found on it.

Brush 56 is a Type III brush rig. It carries 500 gallons of water and a number of special hose packs and tools suited specifically for wildland fire incidents. This apparatus is at Station 6 and is "cross-staffed" by four firefighters assigned there. This means that based on the type of emergency call received, the crew can respond in either the front-line Type I engine or the Type III brush rig.

Battalion 51 and Battalion 52 are two heavy command vehicles for battalion chiefs. Every day there are two battalion chiefs on-duty, each covering one half of the city. These chiefs serve as supervisors for a number of fire stations and their respective crews and take command of major emergency incidents.

The reserve engines are utilized when front-line engines are placed out-of-service for routine maintenance or any other number of operational reasons.

In February 2019, the department implemented a squad (Strategic Quick Unit Apparatus Delivery) response unit. The squad unit serves areas of the city with high call volume or areas that are vacated due to another unit going out of district for fuel, mechanical repairs, or training. The squad unit supplements areas of the city known to have poor response times as indicated by data collected by the department.

The Chula Vista City Council voted to approve amendments to the 2020 expenditure plan and allocate more Measure P funds to replace fire station doors citywide. The fire station doors needed to be enlarged to accommodate new fire apparatus. A total of $1.5 million is allocated to replace fire station doors, with approximately $51.2 million being allocated to fire services overall.

The fire personnel operate out of the following stations:

Station 1 is located at 447 F Street. It covers downtown, Bayfront, Northwest, and Interstates 5, 54, and 805/north and serves as the battalion headquarters. The station at this site was built in 1948. The station has a remodeled kitchen and, in June 2019, it got a new roof funded by Measure P. Station 1 and Station 5 are the two busiest stations in the city. Station 1 houses Engine 51 (2015 Pierce Arrow XT); Truck 51; and Battalion 51.

Station 2 is located at 80 East J Street. It services central city, Interstate 805/central, Hilltop, and Country Club. Erickson-Hall Construction replaced a metal shed building with a new two-story masonry apparatus and maintenance facility. The project included the replacement of existing site paving and renovation of existing firehouse. It houses Engine 52 (2019 Pierce Arrow XT 6710) and OES 420.

Station 3 is located at 1410 Brandywine Avenue. It services Interstate 805, East Main Street, and south and east Chula Vista. It houses USAR 53 (2018 Pierce Arrow XT 6720, 26 ft. walk-around heavy rescue) and USAR 53 (tender/trailer).

Station 4, located at 850 Paseo Ranchero, services Rancho Del Rey, Bonita Long Canyon, and Southwestern College. Erickson-Hall Construction expanded the existing apparatus bay and added a new office to provide a training facility. The project included upgrades to the training tower and roof props. It houses Engine 54 (2018 Pierce Arrow XT 6710) and Brush 54 (Type III brush rig).

Station 5, located at 391 Oxford Street, services Montgomery, Harborside, Otay, Interstate 5/south southwest city, and west/Main Street. It was built in the early 1960s. It houses Engine 55 (2014 Pierce Arrow XT 6710).

A new station 5 will be opened at 341 Orange Avenue near Fourth Street in 2021. The 12,310-square-foot station will have eight bunk rooms and three apparatus bays. The new station is funded with Measure P, a sales tax increase passed in 2016. Station 6, located at 605 Mt. Miguel Road, services Eastlake, Rolling Hills Ranch, and San Miguel Ranch. In 1991, a temporary station was opened at 975 Lane Avenue in Eastlake, then in 2005, it was replaced by the station at 605 Mt. Miguel Road. The 6,493-square-foot station was built by Erickson-Hall Construction. The station includes a two-engine apparatus bay with a vehicle exhaust system, kitchen, dorm rooms, day room, exercise room, offices, and support facilities. It houses Engine 56, (2016 Pierce Arrow XT 6710) and Brush 56 (BME model 34).

Station 7 is located at 1640 Santa Venetia Street, near Otay Ranch High School. It services Otay Ranch, Village of Heritage, Heritage Hills, and Village of Countryside. It was opened on September 11, 2003. It has a statue and memorial to the 343 firefighters who died on September 11, 2001, including the names of all the New York fire personnel who gave their lives that day. The 14,000-square-foot facility was built by JKA Architecture at a cost of $4 million. The project was developed as a "design-build" project and was fast-tracked to provide complete design and construction of the station in a one-year time frame to house up to 10 firefighters and a battalion chief. Areas included an apparatus room with four drive-thru bays, bunk rooms, fitness area, kitchen, day room, shop, dispatch and administrative spaces. The station is the battalion headquarters for the eastern part of the city. It houses Engine 57 (2016 Pierce Arrow XT); Truck 57 (2017 Pierce Arrow XT 6710); Battalion 52; and Squad 62.

Truck 57 is a 2017 tractor-drawn Pierce tiller with a 100-foot long ladder capable of extending the length of seven stories. The truck includes the Jaws of Life and has safety features such as improved braking capabilities, reflective strips, and LED lighting. It meets emissions standards, making it safer for firefighters and the environment. It is nearly 58 feet long, weighing 37 tons. An engineer can steer the rear wheels, allowing the truck to make sharp turns. It cost about $1.4 million and was paid for with funds from Measure P. It replaced a 24-year-old truck.

Station 8, located at 1180 Woods Drive, opened in December 2006. It is at the intersection of Woods Drive and Hawthorne Creek. It services Eastlake Greens, Rolling Hills Ranch, and The Woods. It houses Engine 58 (2019 Pierce Arrow XT 6710).

Station 9 located at 266 East Oneida Street opened in the spring of 2006. It services Sunbow and Woodlawn Park. This station was the former station 3 built in the 1960s and had been closed after a new station 3 was built at 1410 Brandywine Avenue. The former fire station was closed fo years until its reopening as station 9. It houses Engine 59.

A new Station 9 will open at 100 Moss Street in 2021. The 13,080-square-foot station will have eight bunk rooms and four apparatus bays. The cost of the new Station 5 and Station 9 will be $17.9 million. The construction projects are funded with Measure P, a sales tax increase passed in 2016.

Station 10, located at the corner of Millenia Avenue and Stylus Street, serves Southeast Otay Ranch, Winding Walk, and Millennia communities of eastern Chula Vista. It houses Engine 60 (2019 Pierce Arrow XT 6710). On March 29, 2019, a Pierce rescue rig was delivered to the Chula Vista Fire Department. Engine 60 has an Arrow XT chassis, Detroit diesel DD13, 525 horsepower, TAK-4 independent front and rear suspensions, and a Command Zone electrical system.

On March 29, 2019, ground was broken for this new station, and it opened on May 20, 2020. The cost of $8.1 million was funded by Development Impact Fees. The two-story, 13,435-square-foot station has three bays equipped with high-speed roll-up doors. The station also includes safety features for firefighters including a Plymovent vehicle exhaust extraction system which removes carcinogens and prevents exhaust from entering the living areas. The station has a traffic light-controlled intersection for safe and swift exit when responding to calls. It can house 10 firefighters.

The personnel of the Chula Vista Fire Department are "people who care about people."

CALLS RECALLED:

*1923:   On February 1, 1923, the Randolph Lemon Packing Plant on K Street between 3rd and 4th Streets burned. The firemen fought the blaze with their Model T for 12 hours. A heavy rain helped to save the south end of the city. The loss of the packing plant was valued at $19,768.

*1923:   On November 29, 1923, a fire occurred in four buildings used for cottonseed storage at the San Diego Oil Products Company at the San Diego Oil Products Company on D Street. The fire was fought by one engine company from Chula Vista, one from San Diego, one from National City, and one fire boat from San Diego. It is the only time a fireboat has been used on a fire in Chula Vista. The fire loss for the buildings was $331,135.

*1926:   On April 6, 1926, a cyclone wrecked homes, causing a loss of $40,000.

*1927:   In February 1927, a flood kept firemen busy rescuing persons trapped by the water.

*1934:   On May 30, 1934, a fire was caused at the Fredericka home due to an iron being left on.

*1956:   The home of the Davies was destroyed by fire on October 8, 1956. The loss was $52,000.

*1960:   The processing buildings of Tyce Engineering were damaged on October 7, 1960. The loss was valued at $46,500.

*1963:   The sales area of the Mayfair Market was destroyed in a blaze on July 5, 1963. The cost was $62,000.

*1964:   The maternity wing of the Bay General Hospital caught on fire on April 7, 1964, causing $50,000 worth of damaged.

*1965:   When a commercial aircraft with 65 passengers aboard was not able to lower the landing gear, Chula Vista personnel assisted.

*1967:   Chula Vista Fire Department responded to a brush fire in Poway that burned 30,000 acres. Forty-six homes were destroyed.

*1968:   The residence of Walter Bowering burned on May 23, 1968, at a loss of $25,000.

*1968:   A paint factory in the Tijuana business district was destroyed. Chula Vista assisted the Tijuana Fire Department.

*1968:   Three classrooms at Feaster Elementary School were destroyed by fire on October 20, 1968. The damage was estimated at $54,000.

*1969:   On March 14, 1969, four classrooms at Rosebank Elementary School burned. The cost was $123,000.

*1970:   Fire departments worked together during the Laguna Fire in 1970.

*1970:   On January 20, 1971, the residence of Curtis L. Price suffered damages totaling $36,000.

*2013:   In August 2013, a five-man regional strike team from Station 1 was deployed to the Rim Fire, spending 11 days protecting the Hetch Hetchy Reservoir, San Francisco's main water source. The team first worked 12-hour shifts, then, as the fire grew, 24-hour shifts. They kept the structures around the reservoir protected.

*2014:   Sadly, Fire Investigator Samuel "Sam" Escalante died of a heart attack at the age of 43 on June 21, 2014. He died within 24 hours of his last work day. Escalante began working for the department in February 2006 as Chula Vista's first fire prevention engineer. He was a manager within the Fire Prevention Division. Prior to joining the department, he was a fire protection engineer in the U.S. Navy. He is survived by his wife and three small children.

*2016:   In August 16, a fire destroyed up to 25 vehicles in a storage yard on Main Street and damaged about a third of a neighboring upholstery business.

*2016:   In September 2016, a 58-year-old man suffered burns over 30% of his body in a motor home fire on Main Street. He was taken to the UCSD Medical Center burn unit in critical condition.

*2016:   In 2016, there were 13,573 rescue and medical emergency calls, accounting for 68% of all responses. Fires made up 2% of emergency calls.

*2018:   In November 2018, Firefighter Jed Burt went down a manhole and crawled through an 18-inch drainage pipe to reach a 30-pound dog, Sammy, which had been missing from his Eastlake home for four days. When the dog refused to come out on his own, Burt pushed the dog through the pipe to another manhole nearby. Firefighters had located where the dog was by his barks. The dog suffered no injuries.

*2019:   On January 12, 2019, a Chula Vista fire engine was involved in a collision when it spun out of control on a wet Interstate 805 in the South Bay.

*2019:   In February 2019, a 6,000-square-foot building belonging to wholesale business Santa's Toys was destroyed by a blaze. Firefighters from Imperial Beach, National City, San Diego, and Coronado assisted the Chula Vista firefighters.

*2019:   Two unrelated fires broke out in Chula Vista on March 18, 2019, one at a mobile home park which destroyed two trailers and another at an apartment building, where two people were injured.

*2019:   Thirteen ducklings were stuck in a storm drain on April 14, 2019. It took the Chula Vista Fire Department about 45 minutes to rescue them.

*2019:   On November 19, 2019, Battalion Chief Darrell Roberts was part of the San Diego Urban Search & Rescue California Task Force 8 deployed to Butte County to perform searches of structures and locate missing people.

*2020:   On January 13, 2020, a fire started about 8:32 a.m. in the Victorian roof at the Hancil Cordrey House at 210 Davidson Street near 2nd Avenue and F Street in central Chula Vista, causing extensive damage in the corner of the second floor. The three-story home was built about 1889 and received historic designation in 1987. It is one of the few remaining original Victorian homes built during Chula Vista's early development. Crews had the fire extinguished in 20 minutes. One firefighter suffered 1st- and 2nd-degree burns to his calves and was taken to UCSD Medical Center where he was treated and released.

*2020:   In August 2020, Chula Vista had 23 personnel deployed as REMS (Rapid Extraction Model Support)d to the SCU Lightening Complex Fire. (REMS is a pre-staged rescue team assigned to a wildland fire to provide firefighters a safe, effective and efficient method of egress off the fireline in the event of injury or illness incurred during firefighting operations.)

*2020:   In September 2020, a 33-year-old arsonist was arrested after seen walking away from a brush fire. The man admitted to intentionally setting several brush fires in the Otay River bottom over five months.

*2020:   On September 25, 2020, a Chula Vista resident was killed when his Lexus SUV went off of State Route 54 into the Sweetwater River. Chula Vista and National City crews went into the water in an attempt to save him.

*2020:   September and October, fire crews assisted in seven California wildfires.

*2020:   Chula Vista Fire Department responds to nearly 23,000 calls a year.

CORONADO FIRE DEPARTMENT

Coronado is across the bay from San Diego. The island is surrounded by the Pacific Ocean and San Diego Bay. The city land area covers approximately 8 square miles with over 24 square miles of water. There is a population of about 27,000.

The famous Coronado Hotel was opened in 1888 and is listed on the register of National Historic Landmarks. The Victorian hotel is the second largest wooden structure in the United States and one of the first to have fire sprinklers. In 1969 the Coronado Bridge was opened. There are more than two million visitors a year to Coronado.

On May 30, 1887, the Veteran Hose Company was organized by R. H. Bierce. The company failed due to lack of equipment and hydrants. A second hose company was formed in January 1889 with a hose, hose cart, and a horse that was kept harnessed every night in the event of a fire.

When a third fire company was formed in 1892, a grand ball was held at the Orange Avenue Hotel on May 7 to raise money. E. S. Babcock offered the fire company the use of the former Catholic Chapel at 1st Street and 124 Orange Avenue as Coronado's first firehouse. The rent was $60 a year. The Coronado board of trustees furnished two 35-gallon Champion chemical engines. Coronado was divided into two hose cart precincts. In 1900, the city purchased a Seagrave gasoline-powered fire truck with inflated tires. The driver was paid $25 per year and the firemen received $10 per year.

A fire house was built in 1906. In 1908, alarm boxes were fastened to the poles of the Consolidated Gas & Electric Company. The wheel rim used as an alarm was raised on a bell tower that the Union Iron Works constructed in 1909. It was connected to a mechanical striking system. When a fire occurred, it was struck the number of times for the alarm box pull station activated. A bronze bell from Meneely and Company was purchased in 1911. The locomotive wheel was later given to the Lakeside Volunteer Fire Department.

The city bought a Knox gasoline motor driven engine with two bucket seats in 1912. John D. Spreckels gave a Cadillac converted into an ambulance to the firemen in 1915. The city purchased a 1916 Seagrave pumper from San Diego Fire Department in 1916 for $8,700. It became a reserve pumper in 1928.

Courtesy of Coronado Historical Society

In 1916, the fire chief was paid $100 per month. The engineer lived at the station and was paid $85 a month. The firemen made $49 per year. They received silver badges in 1914 and wore rubber hats and coats. Adolph Johnson was hired as a part-time chief

Coronado Fire Chief J.W. Waller, 1892, courtesy of Coronado Historical Society

Coronado Volunteer Fire Department
Mar. 30. 1895 — Wright Photo.

in 1919. Louis Bandel was the last volunteer chief of the department. In September 1919 John D. Spreckels gave the department a new ambulance.

A station was built by Alfred Laing of Coronado in 1923 for $27,415.90 to house a Seagrave pumper, Dodge chemical truck, and Cadillac ambulance. A contract between J. D. and A. B. Spreckels Securities Company and Coronado was made in August 1924 to lease property for the fire station for 10 years at a cost of $5,871.11 the first year then $3,327.11 annually thereafter.

A 1927 Mack quad combination pumper was purchased in 1928 for $13,400. The pumper was given to the Tijuana Fire Department in 1954.

In 1930, a Studebaker Eight and an ambulance were purchased from J. B. Townsend Company.

In 1938, the fire truck No. 80, called "Little Mac," a 750-gpm pumper was purchased. It was in service in reserve status until 1976 when it was sold. In 1998, the pumper was found parked in a field in Jamul. A group of residents led by Patty Schmidt brought it back to Coronado. It was restored by Bill Gise and volunteers from the fire department and is used in parades.

In October 1940, Kenneth Pedler, the chief mechanic for the fire department for eight years, took a year's leave of absence to go to Pearl Harbor as a mechanic in civil service.

At a council meeting in 1941, it was decided that the Coronado Fire Department would cooperate with the North Island Naval Air Station for mutual aid in the case of emergencies.

The National Fire Protection Association stated that Coronado was second lowest in structural fire losses per 1,000 population and third lowest in per capita fire losses in the United States for the five year period ending in 1948. Coronado averaged 1.2 structural fires per 1,000 population and $.43 per capita fire loss from 1943 to 1948.

In July 1955, the city council ordered a new switchboard made by Gamewell Company for the fire department. The old switchboard was originally installed in the Hotel Del Coronado. It was moved to the fire department during World War I.

A Mack quad combination pumper and a Willy's jeep were purchased in 1951. In 1954, a Crown pumper with 1,250 gpm was purchased. In 1957, a REO civil defense rescue truck was bought. In 1959, a Chevrolet pickup truck was purchased. In 1960, a Cadillac ambulance was received. In 1964, a Crown Triple combination pumper with 1,250 gpm was purchased. In 1968, a Chevrolet STP wagon was delivered and a year later the department got a Crown fire truck with a 100-ft. aerial ladder. In 1970, a Chevrolet 4-door sedan was ordered. In 1980, a Crown TeleSquirt with a 50-foot aerial ladder, 500-gallon tank and 1,000-gpm pump was purchased.

Chiefs of the department include: J. W. Waller (1892), Adolph Johnson (1919), Louis Bandel (1920-1923), George Sanven (1923-1926), G. E. Zimmerman (1926-1931), L. W. "Tommy" Thompson (1934-1943), Frank H. Welch (1948-1951), F. W. McCarty (1951-1953), Charles N. Damren (1953-1958), Edward "Ted" Kohl, Sr. (1964-1966), Walter L. Nettlehorst (1967-1972), Robert Shanahan (1972-1987), John Traylor (1997-2003), Kim Raddatz (2004-2009), John Traylor (2009-2010), Mike Blood (2011-2017), and Jim Lydon (2017-).

G. E. Zimmerman became chief on October 4, 1926. He started his fire service career in Selma, Alabama, where he was born in 1896. His father had hoped his son would become a railroad engineer, but his son became a member of Fire Company No. 2 of the Birmingham Fire Department on July 3, 1913. On a trip to California, Chief Zimmerman fell in love with sunny Coronado and moved to the city.

F. W. McCarty resigned as chief in 1953 to take a position as chief in Globe, Arizona.

Charles N. Damren served the Coronado Fire Department for 29 years, retiring on January 31, 1958. He worked for the Chula Vista Volunteer Fire Department for 10 years. Damren moved to Coronado in 1928 and worked for the police department for nine years. He transferred in 1937 as a sergeant on the police force to a lieutenant in the fire department. He was a fire captain for eight years. Chief Damren died at the age of 58 in 1961.

Edward "Ted" Kohl, Sr. was appointed chief in 1964. He was a 28-year veteran of the Chula Vista Fire Department. He was born in Massachusetts and became a resident of Coronado in 1923. He died on October 17, 1986, at the age of 79.

Robert Shanahan accepted the position of chief in 1972. He hired the first fire marshal, Clarence White, in April 1981 because he found that handling fire prevention took 40% of his time. White previously worked for 16 years for the National City Fire Department, working in fire prevention for seven years, three of them as fire marshal. In December 1985, Clarence Wright retired and Jim Walker took his place as fire marshal.

John Traylor served as chief from 1997 to December 24, 2003, and served as acting chief in 2009 and 2010 when Kim Raddatz retired. He made the move to the regional Heartland Fire Dispatch, upgraded to 800MHz radios, joined the county's Regional Communications System (RCS), brought paramedic service to the city, and formalized mutual aid and automatic aid agreements between Coronado, Federal Fire (Navy), and the South Bay cities. Chief Traylor served as a consultant to the Local Area Formation Commission and for the City of Solana Beach on fire service consolidation. He worked for the El Cajon Fire Department for 27 years before joining the Coronado Fire Department, working his way up the ranks to become battalion chief for eight years. Chief Traylor was an incident commander during the 2003 Cedar Fire. He served in the Air Force as a firefighter from 1965 to 1970.

Courtesy of Coronado Historical Society

Coronado Fire Station, 1948
Courtesy of Coronado Historical Society

He spent 32 years with the San Rafael Fire Department as firefighter, captain, and battalion chief before becoming chief of the Benecia Fire Department in 2013. He has a Master of Organizational Leadership from Gonzaga University and a Bachelor of Science in Fire Service Administration from Cogswell Polytechnical College. He maintains an active paramedic license and possesses multiple professional certifications in the fields of emergency response and incident management.

When the department recruited for five firefighter/paramedic openings in 2009, there were more than 60 applicants. The five hired as probationary firefighter/paramedics were: Nathan Ramos, who started his fire service in 2002 and worked for the Borrego Fire Department; Larry Hogueisson, who taught elementary school for 12 years before becoming a reserve firefighter for San Miguel Fire Protection District in 2006; Ted Porter, who attended Palomar College's Fire Academy and worked for the Del Mar Fire Department for almost a year; Chris Balke, who started his fire training as a cadet for the San Diego Fire-Rescue Department in 2002; and Brian Standing, who began his training while still in high school as a cadet for the San Diego Fire-Rescue Department. The recruits were put through an intense three-week in-house fire academy by the Coronado personnel.

Captain Darren Hall was named California Training Officer of the Year in March 2011. Hall credited one of his Hilltop High School teachers in Chula Vista for suggesting a firefighting career. He joined the Chula Vista Fire Department Explorer Program, which was when he helped on a hose line the night an arsonist torched four classrooms at Castle Park Elementary School in Chula Vista in 1991.

In December 2017, Firefighter/paramedic Brian Phan joined the department. Phan, who is from San Jose, studied human biology at University of California San Diego and attended paramedic training at Palomar College. He worked for seven years for San Diego City EMS.

In May 2018, Firefighter Ted Porter, who has been with the department since 2008, was promoted to captain. The same day, Firefighter Brandon Ihde, who has been with the department since 2012, was also promoted to captain. On December 18, 2019, Engineer Eric Hingeley was honored by the mayor and council for his years of service to the Coronado Fire Department. He retired on December 26.

Kim Raddatz became chief on February 28, 2004, after serving as the division chief in charge of operations and training in 2002 and 2003. He left in March 2009 to take a position as chief of the Salinas Fire Department. He joined the Lakeside Fire Protection District in 1977 where he was promoted from firefighter to engineer to captain and training office and then acting division chief. He holds a Bachelor of Science in Business Administration and Organizational Management from the University of Phoenix.

Michael "Mike" Blood was appointed chief on July 2, 2011, at the age of 49. He was the first Coronado fire chief who progressed up the entire organizational ladder. He began working for the Coronado Fire Department in March 1989. He spent six years as a fireman, eight years as an engineer, three years as a captain, and four years as a division chief. In 2001, Chief Blood was a member of the Urban Search and Rescue team that responded to the 9/11 terrorist attack in New York City. He started his career in the fire service by working for one year for the U.S. Forest Service and then one year for the Solana Beach Fire Department. He has a Bachelor of Science degree from California State University, Long Beach.

Jim Lydon succeeded Chief Mike Blood on October 10, 2017. There were 48 applicants for the position. He oversees two fire stations and a beach lifeguard facility.

The department has 40 personnel, two stations, and one beach lifeguard facility. It has a budget of $8.1 million. The battalion chiefs are Joshua Scarboro (fire marshal/training), Perry Peake (operations/emergency preparedness), and Jayson Summers (EMS/logistics).

Battalion Chief Perry Peake wanted to be a fireman from the age of three. When he reached the age of 16, he became a volunteer with the Annapolis Fire Department in Maryland. When he first came to San Diego County, he was a volunteer fireman for the Ramona and Poway Fire Departments. He worked at the San Diego Fire-Rescue Department for 31 years before becoming the chief of operations for Coronado Fire Department in 2011. Chief Peake is a senior leader of California Task Force 8, which is one of 28 urban search and rescue units in the United States. Peake is one of the original members of the task force, joining it in 1991.

In 2000, a Pierce Quantum model fire engine was purchased for $319,000 to replace an open-cab 1975 Crown. In 2009, a Spartan Gladiator 100-foot tractor-drawn aerial was purchased to be stationed at the Cays. The quintuple combination pumper provides five functions: pump, water tank, fire hose, aerial device and ground ladders. Those functions allow it to serve in place of two vehicles: an engine and a ladder truck. Its cost, including equipment and taxes, was $1.1 million.

Station 1 is located at 1001 6th Street. In 1970, a fire station was built across the alley from the old fire station for $248,000. It houses Engine 36 (2016 Pierce Arrow XT 6710); Engine 236 (2009 Spartan Gladiator Evolution LFD); Medic 36; and Battalion 253.

Station 2 is located at 101 Grand Caribe Causeway near the Coronado Cays and Silver Strand Natural Preserve. In May 1971, Station 2 was built at a cost of $170,000. In 2008, the station was expanded to accommodate longer fire apparatus. It houses Engine 37 (2000 Pierce Quantum) and Truck 37 (2018 Pierce Arrow XT /107' Ascendant rear-mount, 525 hp, TAK-4 Independent front suspension and rear suspension, foam, water tank, 1,500 gpm pump, 500-gallon tank).

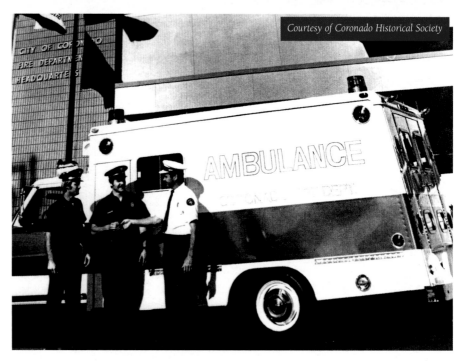

Courtesy of Coronado Historical Society

The beach lifeguard station is located at 920 Ocean Boulevard. The captain is Sean Carey.

The first metal badge was given to the firemen in 1914. The second badge was updated in 1950 and worn by Coronado firefighters for 60 years. The modernized badge was larger as medal was not in as high of demand as it was when the original badge was designed. The members of the department created a new badge in 2010. They designed a badge that preserved the history of the Coronado Fire Department and incorporated the elements of the two previous badges.

Coronado firemen, left to right: Arnold Bone, Kohl Brub.
Courtesy of Coronado Historical Society

The Coronado Community Emergency Response Team (CERT) helps residents know how to prepare for a disaster.

The Coronado Fire Department Open House is an event that takes place every October. Fire Prevention Week is observed throughout the United States to commemorate the Great Chicago Fire of 1871. The department has an annual spaghetti dinner in July to benefit the Burn Institute.

The mission of the Coronado Fire Department is to maintain a highly trained, professional organization providing excellent service to the community, region, state and each other through duty, honor, respect, and family.

CALLS RECALLED:

*1888: In December, 1888, a fire burned the home of H. M. Reynolds at 1st Street and I Avenue. The home was valued at $1,500.

*1913: The Orange Avenue Hotel on the northeast corner of Orange Avenue and Third Street was destroyed by fire in 1913.

*1931: In 1931 there were 44 fires, seven of which were in buildings. The total fire loss was $465. Less than 10% of the taxes was spent on the upkeep of the fire department and equipment.

*1932: The per capita fire loss in 1932 was 4 cents, total fire loss was $268.

*1948: During 1948 there were 30 building fires and 12 automobile fires with a total fire loss of $7,373. The department responded to 119 calls, 10 of which were false alarms.

*1967: The fire personnel responded to 498 calls in 1967, including 101 fires. The fire loss were under $20,000.

*1970: There were 525 calls in 1970 with a total fire loss of $32,000.

*1984: On Thursday, November 8, 1984, at 6:10 p.m., a blaze destroyed a 92-unit condominium that was under construction. The flames were 500 feet high and could be seen 40 miles away. It took almost three hours for 90 units and over 200 firefighters to extinguish the fire. The damage cost over $20 million. In 1986 the condos were rebuilt.

*2004: The crews had about 1,500 calls in 2004.

*2007: In June 2007, a fire in the gym at Coronado High School caused $250,000 damage.

*2008: A condominium fire on F Street was extinguished in March 2008. The Coronado Fire Department received aid from Imperial Beach Fire Department, National City Fire Department, and San Diego Fire-Rescue Department.

*2010: Personnel responded to 2,261 calls in 2010.

*2011: Of the 1,850 calls during 2011, 66% of them were medical aids.

*2012: Three residences were severely damaged on A Avenue. Crews from Coronado, San Diego, Federal Fire, and National City fought the two-alarm fire.

*2012: In October 2012, the fire personnel rescued a man stuck on a 40-foot-long maintenance platform that malfunctioned and was hanging from the side of a high-rise beachfront condominium building.

*2013: Lifeguards William "Pepper" Lang, Jacob Bender, and Blair Geiss were awarded commendations from the City of Coronado on January 15, 2013, for saving a man with life-threatening injuries in the water.

*2015: On December 2, 2015, a residential fire was caused by fluctuating electrical currents from the main breaker. Captain Josh Scarboro led a crew who quickly extinguished the blaze.

*2016: In June 2016, five people were hospitalized after being overcome by chemical fumes at a construction site in Coronado.

*2017: Battalion Chief Perry Peake was deployed with the Urban Search and Rescue California Task Force 8 to Hurricane Harvey in Texas.

*2018: In July 2018, Engine 36 with four personnel was dispatched to the West Fire burning near Alpine.

*2018:   In November 2018, the crew on Engine 36 was deployed to Ventura County to assist in fighting the fires there.

*2019:   On January 14, 2019, a two-alarm fire damaged the historic El Cordova Hotel on Orange Avenue near Adella Avenue shorty before 11:30 p.m. The fire started within the hood system ventilation duct area over the cooking surface in the kitchen. The fire caused $450,000 damage. The building was built as a retirement home in 1902 and converted into a hotel in 1930. The fire also damaged Miguel's Cocina, one of four restaurants in the hotel complex.

*2019:   In October 2019, a crew from Coronado was assigned to fight the Kincade Fire in Sonoma County.

*2020:   When the USS Bonhomme Richard, an 844-foot-long marine assault vessel, caught fire on July 12, 2020, at the Naval Base San Diego, local firefighters assisted the US Navy personnel in extinguishing the blaze. The fire burned for four days, devastating the $4 billion ship, damaging 11 of its 14 decks. Some areas of the ship had temperatures as high as 1,200 degrees.

CREST FIRE DEPARTMENT

Crest is a mountain community situated between El Cajon and Alpine covering 6.5 square miles with a population of 2,746 (2018). It is located 1,620 feet above sea level.

The Crestridge Ecological Reserve is a 3,000-acre reserve bordered by Crest on the south and east and Interstate 8 on the north and west. It is managed by the Endangered Habitats Conservancy and the California Department of Fish and Game. Once the site of a Kumeyaay Indian village. it has three prehistoric archaeological sites. During the 1990s, the San Diego County had approved the property for residential development. The residents of Crest formed the Crest Open Space Supporters and the Back Country Land Trust to advocate for conservation of the property. The property was sold to the California Department of Fish and Game in 2000.

Crest was originally known as Suncrest (in the southern part of the community) and La Cresta (in the northern part of the community) from 1928 to the early 1960s. Some of the earliest settlers in the area were John and Dena Dodson, Barney and Dollie Cornelius, Albert and Nettie Wilder, the LaFrance clan, and the Macpherson clan.

Crest fire station
Courtesy of Crest Historical Society

In 1942, the residents used barrels of water hauled on a trailer attached to an automobile to take to fires. The trailer was a car body frame from a Ford. The trailer also carried three back pumps, one fireman's ax, one brush hook, one McLeod rake, four buckets, and three canteens. It was parked to the left of the Suncrest Store.

The volunteer fire department had a great impact on bringing the community together. The residents worked together to raise funds to purchase equipment for the town. Soon a pumper unit from government surplus was purchased for $276. It was installed on a Corbett crash truck purchased from North Island Naval Air Station. In October 1947, a volunteer fire department was chartered. A board of directors was elected and Tom Jump was appointed chief. There were 40 volunteers in the department including a social fundraising committee called the "Smoke Eaters." Twelve teenagers became junior firemen.

In September 1947, the Ladies Auxiliary of the Crest Volunteer Fire Association was formed. In addition to planning fundraising events, cooking meals, and obtaining supplies in emergencies, the women were trained on the equipment. Three of the women were qualified to drive the fire truck. They were the only insured group of firewomen in the country at that time. From 1947 to 1951, a horse show became an annual event. The money raised was used to start the construction of a firehouse and to purchase a second truck.

In 1954, the residents supported the fire department by membership to support the yearly budget of $2,223. However, only 50% of the residents contributed to the budget. In 1957, the Crest Volunteer Fire Association recommended a tax be levied to operate the fire department. The Crest Volunteer Fire Protection District, a taxing body, was formed to cover the cost of the department.

The water district leased a building site to the fire department, and volunteers built the first station. The Crest Public Utility District and the Crest Volunteer Fire Department shared the site for many years.

Chief Roger Dutton announced the appointment of new officers on February 1, 1964. They were James Younghusband, assistant chief; Robert Nelson, captain in charge of training; Jim Fransway, in charge of the junior department; Jim Pere, junior chief; and Paul Mondragon, Don Coleman, and Ronnie Hunter, lieutenants in the junior department. New volunteers in the senior department were George Lacey and Jack Dyer.

On February 15, 1964, the women's auxiliary participated in their first practice control burn. They manned the hoses and learned other firemen duties during the clearing of property located on La Cresta Boulevard.

Eleven false alarms were turned in by pranksters during the first three weeks of February 1964. Chief Roger Dutton stressed the threat imposed when a false alarm tied up the only resuscitator in town.

In the 1970s, the volunteer fire department relied on a small budget from county funds, grant writing, and fundraisers to operate the department. In 1976, the budget for the Crest Volunteer Fire Department was $95,088. In 1979, the budget was $112,528.

On April 8, 1980, a special benefit tax for fire suppression and emergency services initiative was passed by two-thirds of the voters. The $40 tax funded operating expenses, capital improvement expenditures, and debt repayment. In 1984, the Crest Volunteer Fire Department had a budget of $159,640. The volunteer firefighters were replaced by paid positions. The fire chief in 1983-1984 was paid $16,800.

On July 1, 1994, Crest and Bostonia merged to form the East County Fire Protection District.

On November 5, 2002, a special benefit tax to provide paramedic/firefighters within the East County Fire Protection District was approved by 71.5% of the voters. The tax ensured advanced life support for the residents.

After 290 homes in Crest were lost in the Cedar Fire in 2003, a double-wide trailer was set up in Nancy Jones Park as a resource recovery center for the community. Many volunteers were at the center every day to help those who had lost their homes. Local residents created the Crest Coordinating Committee for Fire Recovery. Organizations utilizing the trailer included the Crest Community Association, Friends of Crest, the Crest Sub-regional Community Planning Group, Kiwanis, the Christian Reform World Relief Committee (volunteers rebuilding houses), San Diego Youth and Community Services, and the Salvation Army. The Crest Kiwanis was established in 2003 to help the community.

In October 2004, about 300 people gathered at the Nancy Jane Park to reflect on the Cedar Fire. Twenty-three of the 290 homes lost in the fire had been rebuilt. One resident said, "Most of the town's residents have helped in some way with the rebuilding efforts. A tighter sense of community is seen in the already close-knit town."

On October 24, 2004, a groundbreaking ceremony was held to rebuild the Crest Community Association Clubhouse. Phil and Debbie Goettsch led the volunteer effort. The residents had monetary assistance from Supervisor Dianne Jacob's office, Crest Kiwanis, and the Sycuan Band of the Kumeyaay Nation. The building was obtained from Cascade Joinery out of Bellingham, Washington. The roof structure was a timber frame with a tongue and groove wood ceiling. It was installed in the beginning of November 2005. Over 90% of the volunteers who worked on the clubhouse were from Palomar College. The clubhouse was dedicated on July 7, 2008.

The Crest Fire Safe Council was established in 2003 to implement an emergency call system, install a fire siren behind the Crest Community Association building, secure a grant of $208,000 in 2008 from the U.S. Forest Service for fuel reduction and training sessions, and find other ways to prevent fires.

By 2007, the East County Fire Protection District needed a tax base. On September 25, 2007, residents approved Proposition E to provide funds to operate the fire department. The tax passed with a vote of 73.2%. Several agencies then became interested in taking over the district for the revenue. It became a very controversial issue for the community.

Crest merged with the San Miguel Consolidated Fire Protection District in July 2008. It was the elected fire board's responsibility to make the decision and residents did not vote on the merger.

San Miguel Fire & Rescue hosted its annual Wildland Urban Interface training in Crest from May 5 through May 27, 2020. Due to the requirements of COVID-19 social

Courtesy of Crest Historical Society

Courtesy of Crest Historical Society

distancing, the training was minimized to preplanning briefings and tactical discussions only. The participating fire departments were: Heartland Fire & Rescue, Alpine Fire Protection District, Bonita-Sunnyside Fire Protection District, Santee Fire Department, Lakeside Fire Protection District, Viejas Fire Department, and Barona Fire Department.

The San Miguel Station No. 18 is located at 1811 Suncrest Boulevard.

CALLS RECALLED:

*1946:   In September 1946, a brush fire burned 40 acres.

*1948:   On July 11, 1948, a fire with flames as high as 100 feet spread through the community of Suncrest. Crest Volunteer Fire Department was the first unit at the fire. One hundred homes were saved.

*1950:   On June 28, 1950, a fire on the Jarrett property destroyed a barn and moved up the north side of Lilac Drive. The fire was caused by children playing with matches. Crest volunteers and U.S. Forest Service firemen saved 25 houses.

*1950:   In July 1950, 300 firemen and 18 fire trucks fought a fire that covered 3,000 acres. The fire went up Rios Canyon to Oakridge and past Crest, then along the east side of Mountain View Road.

*1950:   On July 10, 1951, a fire broke out near South Lane in Suncrest and spread over 250 acres. Firemen from La Mesa, El Cajon, Crest, Harbison Canyon, Riverside, Valley Center, Elsinore, San Bernardino, Cuyamaca, Lyons Valley, Ramona, San Marcos, and the California Department of Forestry had the fire under control in four hours.

*1951:   In June 1951, more than 100 state, federal, and volunteer firefighters fought a 500-acre fire south of Suncrest.

*1965:   John W, (Jack) Dyer died at the age of 49 in October 1965 from being burned in a fire. He was a lieutenant in the Crest Volunteer Fire Department. He was working with Chief George B. Behrens, whose hands were badly burned in the fire.

*1970:   The Laguna Fire in 1970 devastated the community of Crest. Tragically, 117 homes were lost in Crest. The Laguna fire started on September 26, 1970, from downed power lines during Santa Ana winds near the intersection of Kitchen Creek Road and the Sunrise Highway in the Laguna Mountains. The fire killed eight people, destroyed 382 homes, and burned 175,425 acres.

*2003:   The Cedar Fire, from October 25 to November 4, 2003, burned 290 homes of the 1,100 homes in Crest. Twenty-seven families were uninsured and many were underinsured.

Betty Lucas, editor of the Crest Sun, wrote:

"Early on that Sunday morning, smoke was visible from the fire that started in the Ramona area. It spread to Scripps Ranch area, and many of us thought it was far away. We watched the news, and as the sky darkened, we became concerned. We conferred with neighbors and started packing our cars with what was important to us. Or, we thought, we will only be gone for a few hours and packed very little. Horses and house pets were gathered. From 2 p.m. to 3 p.m neighbors with motorhomes and cars or trucks towing boats paraded by. There was a steady stream of traffic, two lanes, going down the hill backed up as far as St. Louise Church. It took about an hour, more in some cases, to get 'down the hill.' Some people stayed, foolish or brave? You decide; they worked with garden hoses or water trucks that they used in their businesses and fought to save neighbors' houses. Our house was one of them.

"In the late afternoon, Crest was on fire. Those of us leaving the hill moved in with family and friends or went from motel to motel looking for a place to stay. Some went to shelters. We watch anxiously while fire moved from the east to the south then the west side of the mountain.

"Monday morning we were scrambling for news of our homes and our friends. Some people came up through trails; others tried to get up La Cresta Road but were turned back by sheriffs and CHP officers. The air was smoky and full of falling ashes. We were advised to wear masks to protect our lungs. Cell phone contact with people that we knew were on the hill gave reports of houses saved and houses burned. On Tuesday morning, when it was announced that La Cresta Road was opened to residents, there was a caravan of anxious people returning to homes or no homes. What we saw for the first time was destruction. Whole streets of houses were reduced to ashes. Father Robert Irwin, pastor of St. Louise Church, while staying in a model in El Cajon, had been busy contacting people and organizations and by Tuesday afternoon, had a relief area set up at the Parish Hall. They brought in hot meals and grief counselors to talk to residents. Shadow Mountain Church appeared within a day to provide clothing for those who lost homes. Crest Elementary School and Community Church were distribution centers for donated items. Within days dozens of agencies were on hand to lend a helping hand. The rebuilding process was incredibly emotional, complicated, and slow. Over 180 children immediately disappeared from the Crest School rosters having to relocate with their families to other communities."

In the Cedar Fire, 15 people were killed, 2,232 homes destroyed, 22 commercial structures destroyed, 566 other structures destroyed, and 273,246 acres burned in the fire countywide. The suppression cost was $29,880,826. Firefighters assigned at the peak of the fire were 4,275. Steven Rucker, a Novato firefighter, lost his life defending Julian. The communities evacuated: Ramona, Pine Hills, Barona Mesa, San Diego Country Estates, Poway, Descano, Flynn Springs, Jamul, Pine Valley, El Cajon, Santee, Lakeside, San Diego, Julian, Mt. Laguna, Escondido, Crest, Cuyamaca, Alpine, Guatay, Ranchita, Wynola, and Santa Ysabel. Chief Tim Turner, a member of the San Diego Area Coordination Team, said, "The Cedar Fire burned 80,000 acres in 10 hours. That's over two acres per second." In memoriam: Galen Blacklidge, 50, Wildcat Canyon Road; Christy-Anne Seiler Davis, 42, Alpine; Gary Edward Downs, 50, Wildcat Canyon Road; Nancy Morphew, 51, Valley Center; Steven Rucker, 38, Novato; Stephen Shacklett, 55, Lake View Hills Estates; James Shohara, 63, Solange Shohara, 58, and Randy Shohara, 32, Lake View Hills Estates; Robin Sloan, 45, and Jennifer Sloan, 17, Wildcat Canyon Road, and Ralph Westly, 77, Wildcat Canyon Road.

*2018:   A fire that started in the garage of a home on Lilac Drive caused $200,000 damage. Crews from Heartland Fire & Rescue and the Lakeside Fire Protection District assisted San Miguel firefighters.

*2020:   In January 2020, Raul Valderrama Jr., 46 years old, was killed when he lost control of his pickup on La Cresta Road east of Forester Creek Road and it went down an embankment and hit a large boulder.

*2020:   During the Valley Fire in September 2020, San Miguel Fire & Rescue had apparatus covering Crest.

DE LUZ SPRINGS VOLUNTEER FIRE DEPARTMENT

De Luz is located 6 miles northwest of Fallbrook and west of Temecula. It is about 15 miles from the Pacific Ocean. It covers 36 square miles and has a population of about 1,500.

In the late 1870s, homesteaders ranched and raised cattle in De Luz. A store and a post office were built to serve the ranchers. The mail was delivered three times a week by horse and buggy from the Fallbrook Post Office. The 10-foot square post office in De Luz was said to be the smallest operational post office in the United States. Lemon Judson ran a mineral hot springs resort in the 1880s and 1890s in the small community.

When the California Southern Railroad was opened for operation from National City to Fallbrook on January 2, 1882, the De Luz Station was built. However, the railroad washed out in the 1890s and was rebuilt closer to the coast.

In 1976, San Diego County provided funding, equipment, and training to rural volunteer fire departments for a period of five years. The San Diego County Office of Fire Services assigned five used fire engines to De Luz. In 1981, the community decided the cost per household would be too great to maintain the volunteer department and returned the engines to the county. The residents then relied on the seasonal crew who were at the California Department of Forestry (CDF) station in De Luz. However, Deluzians continued to respond to fires with only shovels and garden hoses.

Ross Daily (1916-2008) was a member of the original De Luz Volunteer Fire Department. Daily's son-in-law, Bill Rose, was the first fire chief, while Daily participated in the fire department and also built the first fire station on the end of the Rose's property.

The original members of the fire department were Chief Bill Rose, Ross Daily, Virgil Harding, Ernie Kuhn, Ben Stevens, and George Shippey.

In 1994, residents voted not to approve higher property taxes to keep the CDF station open all year.

In the spring of 1997, Mike Manchor, Rick Burch, Ted Von Hirsch, and several other residents bought a used 1963 Ford pickup for $200. They refitted it with 400 feet of fire hose, a pump, a 110-gallon water tank, and a CB radio. They devised a siren by rigging a car alarm with an on/off switch. By the end of 1997, the truck had been used on seven fires.

The volunteer firefighters included: Mike Manchor, chief; John Beemer, deputy chief; Mike King and Dick Wright, captains; Dan Spruill and Ted Von Hirsch, engineers; and

A 1963 Ford pickup was refitted with 400 feet of fire hose, a pump, a 110-gallon water tank, and a CB radio to use on fires.

Dan Spears, Matt Hudson, Rick WIlliams, Scott Robbins, George Robbins, Carlos Ramos, Brandon De Shields, Andrew Mathews, Tina Timonian, Emily Kapitanski, Gilbert Jimenoz, Dan Fry, Leonard Phillips, Mike Kittle, Kraig Wright, Mark Weaver, Ed Shields, Glen Cutler, Rich Burch, Dan Marin, Juan Marin, Mike Mendahl, Will Evans, Christina Murphy, Bob Marcus, Roger Milner, Paul Schaden, El Fego Covarrusbias, Phiul Hernandez, Wally Jurkiewicz, Bill Collins, Dick Marcon, Wade Foos, Gary Schultez, Howard Wright, Jesse Sanchez, Paul Andrews, and Steve Richie, firefighters.

In June 1998, Chief Mike Manchor found a used CDF International Model One brush engine for $4,300. He used a mail fundraising drive to pay for it. On July 4, it arrived at Ross Lake in De Luz.

In 1999, the San Diego Regional Fire Foundation donated $5,000 and two 27-year-old SDG&E utility trucks which were converted into fire trucks.

Between 1997 and 2002, the De Luz Volunteer Fire Department fought 31 fires in the De Luz area, nearly always arriving first on the scene within 15 minutes of a call. In 2002, the department had 33 trained volunteer firefighters and 11 fire engines.

In the fall of 2001, FEMA gave the department a $27,300 grant to be used for new protective gear. FEMA paid $9 for every one dollar the department raised. There were 19,000 departments that applied for the grant, but only 30 received funds.

In 2002, the county awarded the department with a $150,000 grant. Chief Manchor bought five used engines, 30 new VHF radios, and a 30 x 50-foot steel building to house the engines.

In 2012, the San Diego Regional Fire Foundation honored Paul Andrews of De Luz as one of the volunteer firefighters of the year for his service.

Cal Fire Division Chief Nick Shuler met with the volunteer firefighters and residents in June 2015 to explain the fire authority policies that would take place in July 2015 when the De Luz Volunteer Fire Department would merge with the San Diego County Fire Authority. The department was mostly concerned about what Chief Manchor's position would be. He is a hero to the people of De Luz and was referred to as the "community caretaker" at the meeting.

Mike Manchor tried to enlist in the Marine Corps at the age of 16 but was sent home. At 17, he enlisted in the Navy and worked to earn his officer's commission. On his first ship he trained for close-quarter firefighting–flight deck and engine rooms. He spent time as a surface warfare officer, then volunteered for a tour as officer in charge on a 710-foot fleet oiler. He then volunteered as a Marine Corps naval gunfire and artillery forward observer/forward air controller with the First Marine Division. He led a team of ten Marines as forward observers assigned to a Marine combat infantry battalion during Operation Desert Storm. He said, "We were in the task force that went into the Kuwait desert through the burning oil fields all the way to Kuwait City ... the Paradise Fire reminded me a lot of that."

In 1991, Manchor and his wife Catherine bought a small avocado grove by Ross Lake in De Luz. He was an unpaid volunteer, never receiving pay for all he did for the community for 19 years. As a farmer, he spends three days a week tending to his 1,500 fruit trees and selling his crops at the local markets. He said, ""This community keeps me going, and when you find a community that fits you, stay there. " He said the De Luz Volunteer Fire Department saved a total of 218 homes since its inception.

The San Diego County Fire Authority has improved the De Luz Fire Station (Station 18) at 39524 Daily Road. It contracts with Cal Fire to provide staffing. The station houses Engine 7118 (2012 Ferrara inferno), Water tender 7158 (2006 International 4400), and Patrol 18 (2016 Ford F-550).

CALLS RECALLED:

*1997:   In September 1997, the De Luz volunteer firefighters responded to a blaze with 15-foot flames that was threatening five homes. They took their pickup and hose to a hydrant maintained by the Fallbrook Public Utility District but found themselves too far away to have much impact on the fire. CDF arrived and extinguished the flames before any homes were lost.

*1997:   In 1997, the De Luz Volunteer Fire Department fought five fires and were able to contain a 2-acre brush fire.

*2002:   During the Gavilin Fire in 2002, twenty-four De Luz firefighters used six emergency apparatus to save five homes.

*2003:   In 2003, the incident commander of the Paradise Fire sent the De Luz five-engine quick response task force to the North Lake Wolford area. The De Luz crews spent 11 hours in that neighborhood. The fire approached the crews three times from three different directions but the firefighters were able to save 23 homes. County Supervisor Bill Horn recognized the De Luz firefighters during his annual State of North County Address, and Valley Center awarded them and the other firefighters there that day the Meritorious Fire Service Medal.

*2007:   The Rice Fire burned from October 22, 2007, until November 1, 2007, in Fallbrook. The fire destroyed 248 structures and burned 9,472 acres.

The incident commander of the fire assigned three De Luz engines to Steward Canyon and a De Luz water tender, a small patrol engine, and six volunteer firefighters to the Valley Oaks Mobile Home Park. The six De Luz volunteers and engines spread out across the eastern perimeter of the large mobile park in two-man teams. For eight hours they battled the fire and saved 112 homes.

*2019:   On July 28, 2019, Yaroslav Igorevich Katkov, 28, a Cal Fire firefighter, collapsed during his second attempt at a 1.45-mile training hike near the De Luz Fire Station while wearing full gear and carrying 20 to 30 pounds of weight. He was flown in an air ambulance to Temecula Hospital but suffered a two-minute seizure while en route. When he was admitted, his body temperature was 107.4 degrees. Fifteen hours later he was pronounced dead. Katkov was assigned to Station 16 in De Luz. He started his career with Cal Fire as a seasonal firefighter in August 2018. Governor Gavin Newsom said, "It's the work of brave firefighters like Yaroslav that keep our communities safe, and we are deeply grateful for his service."

*2020:   In August 2020, the Volcano Fire ignited near De Luz Road and Tenaja Truck Trail, burning about 50 acres. Five air tankers and two water-dropping helicopters were the first to reach the fire. Crews from Riverside County, San Diego County, and Cleveland National Forest were also dispatched. Under a mutual-aid agreement, crews from both San Diego County and Riverside County conduct a joint response whenever a fire is within five miles of the county line.

DEER SPRINGS FIRE PROTECTION DISTRICT

Deer Springs covers 47 square miles from northern Escondido to Route 76. It is approximately 12 miles long and 7 miles wide with a population of 13,000.

The fire district provides service to parts of Valley Center, near Circle R Drive and Old Castle Road, and parts of unincorporated Escondido, along the I-15 Corridor.

The Deer Springs Fire Protection District was formed in December 1981. Revenue was limited because the district was formed after the property tax freeze of Proposition 13. In 1992-93, the annual budget was $844,300.

In 1994, the district contracted with CDF to provide full time protection. Initially only one crew of two firefighters was hired but eventually two crews were hired. In 2004, the district could afford three firefighters on each engine. The crews were supplemented by a contracted ambulance service.

In 1999, the district purchased the lot next to the Meadows Deli with the intent to build a third station on it. Residents voted in favor of increasing the fire protection assessment. The new station was dedicated in 2008 and the staff increased from four to nine firefighters. The Board President Dr. Peter Omer spearheaded the drive to build the station. The fire crews were headed by Cal Fire Battalion Chief Chris Amestoy.

In 2016, Moon Nursery in San Marcos provided the landscaping for Station 2 as a gift. The nursery removed about 7,000 square feet of grass and replaced it with drought tolerate landscape; plants, herbs, river rock, and a walkway.

In 2011, Captain Tim Irwin wrote a successful FEMA grant application on behalf of the district. The district received $120,000 which was used to purchase four defibrillators.

The San Diego County Fire Authority contracts with Cal Fire to provide fire protection services to the district. The district has a contract from July 1, 2018, through June 30, 2023, with Cal Fire for emergency services at a cost of $27,945,103. The Cal Fire contract for 2020-21 costs $5,335,708.

The board of directors of the district are: Bret Sealey, Jean Slaughter, Brian Holley, Mark Jackson, and James Gordon.

Cal Fire Battalion Chief Nick Brown served as the head of the department from June 2015 to October 2019. Chief Brown was given the President's Award by the Deer Springs Fire Safe Council in March 2017. Only four other recipients have received the award since the council was formed in 2007.

Chief Brown received a call on October 9, 2017, to go to the Sonoma-Napa wildfires to serve as a branch director. He was assigned to be the incident commander for the Patrick Fire in Napa. He said the rural-urban-suburban features of the Sonoma-Napa area are almost identical to those in the Deer Springs district. In October 2019 Chief Brown was appointed Unit Aviation Officer. He oversees the aviation program for Cal Fire/San Diego County Fire.

Rick Johnson was appointed Deer Springs battalion chief in November 2019. Previously he worked as a Cal Fire captain in Hemet.

In May 2020, the San Diego Fire Foundation gave a $25,716 grant to the department which was used to purchase EMS jackets and Scott respirators.

Two engines are housed at Station 1, one engine at Station 2, and two engines at Station 3. In 2017, the district ordered an engine that cost $530,000, a Spartan Metro Dtaqr MFD 10" RR; Hale QMax-XS 1,500 gpm; 500 gallon tank; and 25 gallon foam tank. The engine is housed at Station 2. It replaced a 12-year-old engine which is used as a backup. Engines usually last for 10 years but the 1995 KME Renegade Excel was used for 12 years. Engine 7111 is a 2008 KME Severe Service Predator with a Hale Q-Max pump.

There are three stations:

Station 1 (Station 11) is located at 8709 Circle R Drive, Escondido, in the central portion of the district. The station was opened in April 1987. The response area of Station 1 includes West Lilac, Castle Creek, Circle R, Gopher Canyon, Welk Resort, Champagne Village, and a large portion of Interstate 15. It houses fire personnel and administration staff. The personnel at the station are: Rick Johnson, chief; Liz Heaton, administrator; Sid Morel, fire marshal; Miguel Garcia, fire inspector; Freddy Arambula, captain; Shavawn Johnson, Trevor Whitehead and Cody Dunn, engineers; Dan Geary, Mike Metzger, Mike Hannaberry, Carlos Montenegro, and Rose Valek, firefighters II.

Station 2 (Station 12) is located at 1321 Deer Springs Road, San Marcos, in the southern portion of the district. It serves the communities of Deer Springs, North Broadway, Jesmond Dene, and a large portion of Interstate 15. The personnel at the station are: Anthony Watters, captain; Jeremy Pazienza and T. J. Mellon, engineers; Jiri Dostal, Jesse Rivera, James Heaton, and Justin Gevedon, firefighters II.

Station 3 (Station 13) is located at 10308 Meadow Glen Way East, Escondido, in the southeastern portion of the district. It provides service to the communities of Hidden Meadows and Rimrock. The personnel at the station are: Cory Costa, captain; Todd Daley, engineer; Eric Anderson, Jon Hamblin, Matt Alcorn, and Eric Norwood, firefighters II.

Miller Station 15 is located at 9127 West Lilac Road. Captain John Clays is in charge of the station. This station is operated by Cal Fire and is not under the operational control of the Deer Springs Fire Protection District but whose crews respond to local emergencies when available.

As so often happens in the fire service, careers as firefighters are passed from one generation to the next. Ostin Thomas, a Deer Springs reserve firefighter, says he is "carrying the torch" from his father, who retired from the fire service.

The volunteer Deer Springs Fire Safe Council was formed after the October 2003 wildfires. It serves North Broadway, Jesmond Dene, Hidden Meadows, Rimrock, Champagne Village, Welk Resort, and West Lilac in North County. Craig Cook has served as president of the council since 2005. In partnership with San Diego Gas & Electric, the council publishes an e-newsletter called Fire Safety News with articles

on chipping, creating defensible space, hardening structures against wildfire, and evacuating large animals. It hosts neighborhood seminars throughout the year.

During its more than 15 years of community involvement, the council has received nearly $1 million in grant funds from federal, state and local sources. In 2019, the council received $50,000 from SDG&E for Moosa Canyon fuel break. In 2018, it received $61,288 from San Diego County Neighborhood Reinvestment Program for purchase of 4 Zoll Autopulse CPR systems for the fire department. Also in 2018, $189,525 ($93,230 from Cal Fire with $96,295 match from multiple sources) for hazardous fuels reduction and $5,000 from Deer Springs Fire Protection District for education and communication. In 2016, it received $41,568 from the California Fire Safe Council for education and fuel treatment project and $5,000 from the Deer Springs Fire Protection District for education programs. In 2015, it received $29,610 from Cal Fire SRA fees for the chipping program and community education; $7,000 from the Deer Springs Fire Protection District for ongoing community education programs; and $15,000 from SDG&E for equipment for Cal Fire public information officer vehicles.

In 2014, the council obtained a $169,000 Neighborhood Reinvestment Grant that was used to purchase communication and computer systems that were donated to eight Cal Fire battalion chief vehicles in North County. "They understand that wildland fire pays no attention to political boundaries or jurisdictions," Chief Amestoy said. "They have branched out beyond their mandate and looked at how they can assist in ways that are regional and cooperative and integrated."

In 2016, the Deer Springs Fire Safe Council honored Captain Anthony Watters as the Deer Springs Firefighter of the Year. He joined Cal Fire in 1998 and has worked at the Deer Springs Fire Department for seven years.

The district works with the Deer Springs Fire Safe Council in the implementation of a U.S. Forest Service grant to reduce dangerous vegetation along the Moosa Canyon ridgeline. Moosa Canyon is a deep gorge separating Hidden Meadows from Valley Center. Cal Fire constructed a 100-foot-wide fire break on the canyon's west rim to protect Hidden Meadows in 2009.

The fire personnel at the Deer Springs Fire Protection District who protect lives and property are respected by the community.

CALLS RECALLED:

*1993: In September 1993, an arsonist set fire to a home on Meadow Glen Way West. The damage was $120,000.

*1995: In December 1995, a house on Covey Lane was destroyed. The cost of the damage was $75,000.

*1996: In March 1996, Martin Silva-Carrillo, 31, died when he lost control of his Hyundi and struck a pole.

*2003: In 2003, the Paradise Fire came close to homes on Alps Way. The fire stated in Valley Center on October 26. It burned 57,000 acres, destroyed 176 residences and 192 outbuildings, and killed 2 civilians. More than 25 civilians and firefighters were injured.

*2016: In March 2016, an 11-year-old boy was killed in a vehicle accident on I-15 near Gopher Canyon Road. He was a passenger in the rear seat of his family's SUV. The vehicle was struck from behind by a Dodge Challenger which caused the SUV to roll over.

*2016: In August 2016, two fires burned 35 acres on the west side of Interstate 15 near Gopher Canyon Road. Ground crews and personnel aboard five air tankers and four water-dropping helicopters worked to control the flames.

*2016: The crews responded to 2,815 calls in 2016.

*2019: Deer Springs Engine 11 crashed into a ditch at N. Old Highway 395 between Gopher Canyon and Lilac roads at 6:13 a.m. in February 2019. Three firefighters were taken to a hospital to be evaluated but were released at 10:00 a.m.

*2020: On June 9, 2020, crews extinguished a one-acre vegetation fire near Mesa Rock and Deer Springs Roads.

*2020: In July 2020, the personnel responded to 126 calls, including two vegetation fires, RV fire, and three vehicle accidents.

*2020: On July 25, 2020, a motorist was killed in a crash near Old Highway 395 and Interstate 15. The vehicle went over the side of the road at about 4:35 p.m.

*2020: In September 2020, crews and equipment were assigned to fires throughout San Diego County.

*2020: On October 31, 2020, a man died in a fire that destroyed two residential trailers and one detached garage near Rocky Ridge Road and Sage Glen Trail.

DEERHORN VALLEY VOLUNTEER FIRE DEPARTMENT

Deerhorn Valley is in San Diego's East County at the base of Lyons Peak. It is 3 miles west of Barrett Lake and 4 miles northeast of Dulzura. Deerhorn Valley is east of Jamul and only 7 miles from the U.S. border with Mexico. It has a population of about 600.

In 1975, the Deerhorn Valley Volunteer Fire Department and its Ladies' Auxiliary were established. The only equipment was an old triple action pumper. For four years it was housed in a garage belonging to Floyd and Emily Bennett. In 1979, the pumper was moved to Paul and Dianne Jacob's brown barn off of Honey Springs Road. In 1984, the residents in the community donated money to purchase a 1975 Ford attack pumper.

In 1987, Paul and Dianne Jacob donated land on Honey Springs Road to the fire department for a station and community center. Paul Ernest Jacob (1937-2018) improved fire safety in Deerhorn Valley. He provided his ranch for use as an emergency shelter and fire operations center during wildfires. He was a founding member of the Jamul Dulzura Community Planning Group and also was devoted to helping the East County YMCA. Dianne Jacob was elected to the San Diego County Board of Supervisors in 1992, serving seven consecutive terms. Supervisor Jacob has served as a member of the Heartland Fire Training Facility Authority Commission. She has had a tremendous impact on fire protection in the county. The county has spent $500 million on providing fire protection and emergency medical services in 1.5 million rural areas. In January 2021, she will leave her position representing District 2 because of term limits.

By 1988, residents had contributed $40,000 for a fire station. There were 250 households that donated to the building fund.

In 1988, a new engine (E-22) was assigned by the Rural Fire Protection District to the Deerhorn Valley Volunteer Fire Department. In 2016, the restored engine was donated to the California Fire Museum.

The Deerhorn Valley Volunteer Fire Department Board placed a proposition on the November 1990 ballot to maintain the station and provide support for the volunteer firefighters. Over 80% of Deerhorn Valley's registered voters turned out to vote, and 76% supported the proposition. It was the highest voter turnout ever in a San Diego County Special Election!

In 1992, a ground-breaking ceremony was held at 2383 Honey Springs Road for the new fire station. On May 4, 1993, construction began on the station. On September 26, 1993, a dedication ceremony was held for the station, named "Don Payne Fire Station."

The original volunteers were: Chief Don Payne, Assistant Chief Floyd Bennett, and firefighters Larry Ballard, Dan Bennett, Lee Bennett, Leanard Blaisdall, George Boyle, Ron Edwards, Ray Elmer, Ron Gilmore, Rollie Heckathorn, Herb Honegger, Dean Larsen, Leslie Locken, Lon Ann McDaniel, Rod McKinley, Al Merwin, Forest Olsen, Bill Parker, Bill Reed, Gene Reif, Janice Rines, Doug Shorter, Ester Sims, Will Smith, and Dennis Thompson.

Nowadays, the San Diego County Fire Authority provides funding for the department (Station 37) and contracts with Cal Fire for staffing. The county retains ownership and maintains apparatus through the County Department of General Services Fleet Management.

Fire services are better prepared than they were in the fires that occurred in 2003 and 2007. Cal Fire Chief Issac Sanchez said there is better coordination with other

Honey Springs Fire was started July 2010 because of a vehicle accident.

Brush fire on July 19, 2010

departments in the city, as well as with state and federal agencies. He states "It's more of a regional preparedness than one particular fire department. It's a recognition by all departments in the county that it's not an East County problem or a backcountry problem, it's a community problem. A countywide problem."

CALLS RECALLED:

*2007:   The Harris Fire in October 2007 killed 8 people, burned 253 homes, destroyed 90,440 acres, and injured 21 civilians and 40 firefighters. The fire burned more than 150 homes in Deerhorn Valley. It began on October 21 in Potrero during hot weather, low humidity, and 100-mile Santa Ana winds. It was the driest rain season since records began over 130 years ago. By October 23 it had moved west/southwest to reach Chula Vista and Otay Lake and north to the south end of Barrett Lake. The fire was fully contained on November 5. It cost $21 million.

*2010:   In September 2010, a vehicle accident on Honey Springs Road started a brush fire that burned 20 acres. There were 10 engines, 4 fire crews, 2 bulldozers, 2 helicopters, 2 airtankers, 1 water tender, and 150 firefighters at the fire.

*2019:   In May 2019, a brush fire burned 30 acres.

*2020:   On September 6, 2020, residents in Deerhorn Valley had to evacuate from their homes because of the Valley Fire. They escaped to two temporary evacuation centers, where they received water and snacks before being placed in hotels. By September 7, the Valley Fire had burned 17,345 acres and destroyed 11 structures and was 3% contained. There were 56 engines, 14 helicopters, 8 airtankers, 6 bulldozers, 7 water tankers, and 424 firefighters and 121 overhead personnel at the fire.

DEL DIOS VOLUNTEER FIRE DEPARTMENT

Thirty miles northeast of San Diego, Del Dios is a 30-square-mile lakeside community near Lake Hodges with a population of about 4,370 people.

Lake Hodges Dam was built in 1918 to conserve water from the San Dieguito watershed. The dam has 14 concrete piers, an open spillway, and is 137 feet high. When full, the dam has a reservoir of 12 billion gallons of water, creating a lake about two miles long and four miles wide. Del Dios began as a hamlet with cottages for San Diego fishermen. Now it is a neighborhood with $900,000 homes.

In the early days, a brigade extinguished fires with hand tools and buckets. Shortly after World War II, a jeep with a water tank was put in service. A portable pump was used to take water out of the lake to fill the tank.

While Frank Watson was chief in the 1960s, the department had a 1934 Ford engine. A station was built at 20155 Elm Lane with community funds and volunteer local labor. John Sherman, who joined the department in 1968, became a battalion chief and has good memories of those days.

When Frank Watson retired in 1972, Lee Parent became the chief. Under his leadership, from 1972 to 1987, the department flourished with the addition of an equipment bay added to the firehouse in 1978, including fire apparatus from the San Diego County and an improved dispatch system.

The Del Dios Volunteer Fire Department received funds as a CSA (Community Service Agency). When the CSA was dissolved in 1987, the volunteer fire department became a subsidiary (Station 4) of the Rancho Santa Fe Fire Protection District with a paid captain to lead the volunteers. Rancho Santa Fe personnel dispatch the firefighters and the medics and respond to Del Dios.

Station 4, located at 18040 Calle Ambiente in Rancho Santa Fe, serves Del Dios.

Cal Fire has primary responsibility for wildfires around Lake Hodges. Cal Fire Station 77 is located at 2323 Felicita Avenue.

Captain Richard Foster of the Rancho Santa Fe Fire Department had a crew of 15 firefighters. Five of the volunteers were women; Nannette Waggoner was an engineer for five years. The firefighters drilled every Monday night from 5:30 to 9:00 p.m.

The department had a 1988 1,100-gpm Peterbilt with 500 gallons of water; a 1976 Ford with 500 gallons of water; a 2,000-gallon water tender; and a rescue truck.

The crew responded to about 75 calls a year. Many of the calls were related to the recreational activities at Lake Hodges and also automobile accidents on the mountainous roads.

It is obvious to outsiders that the firefighters were proud of their department, rescuing cats out of trees and skunks out of basements. They even rented two dumpsters and drove through town picking up junk. They prepared food for the elderly. They let one man take showers at the firehouse while the plumbing in his house was being repaired. For many years the firefighters had a yearly pit barbecue and two yearly pancake breakfasts (one in October and one in April). The proceeds from the breakfasts were not only used for the fire department but for town projects. Coffee and donuts were available for purchase every morning from 6 to 8 a.m. to people who came by the station.

Two typical firefighters were Claudia Foster and Socorro Musselman. Foster, who was with the department for six years, was a dispatcher at the Ramona Air Attack Base. During the off-season she spent her time on community projects. Musselman, who joined the department in 1985, went to Palomar College to become the first E.M.T.-1 on the force. She said, "Richard Foster is the reason I joined the fire department. You cannot beat our team. There's not one person in the department who is not liked."

Captain Richard Foster stressed that the Del Dios Volunteer Fire Department "is not only a fire department. We view ourselves as a community service base."

CALLS RECALLED:

*1990:   The Paint Fire of September 1990 started at a target shooting range off of Via de las Flores, a backcountry road. More than 600 firefighters, five air tankers, and two helicopters fought the 2,400-acre fire. By the time the brush fire was extinguished, 1,800 acres burned, 200 people evacuated, and five homes damaged.

After the, fire some of the residents of Del Dios and Mt. Israel sent notes to the firefighters. Following are some of their comments:

Al and Helena Hernandez: "What those firemen and evacuation crews did was a very incredible job. We watched the vans moving animals, the firemen setting backfires to keep the main fire from crossing the highway. It was simply unbelievable! They are all heroes to us."

Buddy Ashbrook: "It never hit me until early Wednesday morning, while I was taking my morning walk by the lake, what the firefighters had done for me. They were just getting out of their sleeping bags, cleaning up, or eating breakfast in the park before leaving… their job mostly finished. It brought tears to my eyes to realize these total strangers had saved my precious home and mementos, Everything could be gone now, except for these brave people. I'll be forever grateful."

Renee Porte: "Del Dios is, I think, already unique in its sense of community purpose and participation, and this was never more clearly demonstrated than it was during the "Burning Hill" days we all suffered through last week. Arranging potluck dinners is one thing, but putting your life on the line—well, that's something special. I, for one, shall never forget it. Bravo to all, but especially those brave firefighters."

Nancy Nordstrom and staff: "On behalf of Blue Fox Farms, we would like to thank the firemen for the excellent job they did. We would also like to thank the volunteers who helped us evacuate all our horses. We would never have gotten them out without your assistance."

The Lewis Family: "Important to me was to see the firefighters still sitting all around the hot spots in the hills along the highway all Tuesday night. To be able to go to bed for a decent night's sleep after seeing the twinkling lights on their helmets as they turned their heads to talk to each other. To get up on Wednesday morning and see them coming slowly down the mountain, picking their way around and over the rocks. I'd been asleep all night and they had been up there watching over it all night for my family. We can't thank them enough for everything."

Mike Brown: "The immediate response, the bravery, the precision of action, and coordination of manpower, in real life bigger than TV drama, was impressive to watch and endearing to my soul. I presently owe most of what I "have" to these men and women. "What else can I say? So I'll say thank you and hope that some day in some way, I can serve them in the same way they have served us."

Mark and Jackie Portman: "We're expecting a baby in three weeks and are so thankful we have a place to bring the baby home to."

The Hawkins Family: "We were in Europe when the Paint Mountain Fire roared over Mt. Israel. With shock and disbelief we viewed the result of the fire from our deck on Thursday morning. We are struck with chilling certainly that it is not just luck or fate that our house is standing today. It is because of your courage, strength, and vigilance in the path of a fierce and potentially deadly inferno! Thank you, dear people."

Marie Barden: "Their devotion was just wonderful, and they protected us when our fragile sense of security was trembling in the balance."

ADDITIONAL CALLS RECALLED:

*1986: Richard Foster was the first on the scene of a brush fire off of Del Dios Highway on July 23, 1986. The firefighters spent 28 hours fighting the blaze.

*1987: During September 1987 the sparks from a truck's brakes caused a 250-acre brush fire north of Lake Hodges. Del Dios Highway was closed for eight hours.

*1987: Also in September 1987, a home was destroyed in a fire caused by an electrical malfunction. The firefighters were notified of the fire at 1:10 p.m. They were at the scene at 1:16 p.m. and had controlled the fire within 20 minutes.

*1987: A call in December 1987 was particularly hard for the Del Dios firefighters. Lee Stevens, a 78-year-old man, died in a house fire. He was one of the founders of the Del Dios Volunteer Fire Department and a former firefighter. As so frequently happens, volunteer firefighters respond to calls that involve their family and friends.

*1990: While a deputy sheriff was searching for a reported prowler at a nursery in November 1990, his $24,000 patrol car and radio equipment burned up.

*1992: In February 1992, an Illinois man was killed when his car went over the side of Del Dios Highway.

*1992: In January 1992, the Del Dios fire volunteers hiked over 1,000 feet of difficult terrain west of Lake Hodges Dam to put out a trash fire in a migrant camp.

*1992: On January 11, 1992, a driver traveling at 50 mph lost control of his motorcycle on Del Dios Highway.

*2007: Del Dios was hit hard by the Witch Creek Fire which started on October 21, 2007, near Santa Ysabel. On October 23, the fire crossed Lake Drive into Del Dios with separate fires going uphill toward Ash Street and westward toward Elm Street. Firefighters from Rancho Santa Fe, Oceanside, Carlsbad, Escondido, and Alameda County fought back the fire the best they could. Five federal helicopters dropped water on the ridges north of Lake Hodges as bulldozers cut a 20-foot fireline through the brush. More than a dozen homes in Del Dios were engulfed in flames. Helicopters from Cal Fire, San Diego Fire-Rescue Department, and San Diego Sheriff's Department filled their buckets with water from Lake Hodges. The fire burned 247,800 acres, destroyed 1,265 homes and 587 outbuildings, and killed two people.

*2014: In May 2014, the Cocos Fire, which began in San Marcos, headed east toward Del Dios. People in Del Dios were told to evacuate, and both Harmony Grove Road and Del Dios Highway were closed during the fire.

*2019: On August 29, 2019, a vegetation fire near Del Dios Highway and Toyon Canyon Road burned about three acres and threatened two homes.

DEL MAR FIRE DEPARTMENT

Del Mar is located just west of Interstate 5 with a population of 4,347 (2018) and an area of 2.5 square miles. It has about 1,600 structures. In this city "where the turf meets the surf," the median home value is $2.5 million. In 2020, Bill Gates bought a home in the community for $46 million! There are over three million visitors to the Del Mar Fairgrounds annually.

In 1882, Theodore M. Loop, a contractor, built a tent city on the beach. His wife called it Del Mar—from a poem, "The Fight on Paseo Del Mar." In 1885, Jacob Taylor purchased 338 acres for $1,000. Taylor built a grand hotel called Case del Mar. After the hotel burned in 1889, it took 15 years before Del Mar flourished again. Then in the early 1900s, the South Coast Land Company began to develop Del Mar. When the city received electricity in the 1920s from San Diego Gas and Electric, people rushed to build in the beautiful area. The company built the Stratford Inn which brought many Hollywood celebrities to the area.

On October 8, 1939, the Del Mar Fairgrounds opened on a 186-acre site. It now has 340 acres. After a racetrack was built on the fairgrounds, the Del Mar Turf Club was opened under the leadership of Bing Crosby. Soon Del Mar became even more popular. During World War II, the racetrack was closed and the grandstand became a bomber tail assembly production facility. On August 14, 1945, Pat O'Brien announced to those at the racetrack that Japan had surrendered.

The city was incorporated on July 15, 1959. The vote for incorporation was 555 to 479. The late 1960s to the early 1980s became known as the "open space decade." There was an emphasis on protecting the environment and beautifying Del Mar.

The Don Diego Alvarado family had a large land grant in the 1800s. The Don Diego Clock Tower at the Del Mar Fairgrounds was restored in 2017 and moved to in front of the O'Brien Gate. Don Diego, as portrayed by Tommy Hernandez, is a symbol of hospitality.

Retired Fire Chief David Holmerud said, "My very first job ever, at age 15, was for the 22nd Ag District (fairgrounds), and I worked in the building north of the clock tower in front of the old grandstand. My job was to walk around in a blue vest telling people not to touch the woodworking exhibits from high school students, and the clock tower was very important to us as it was the official time we used for our shifts. I also got to meet Tommy Hernandez one time in the offices. Very big deal at that age!"

Retired Del Mar Fire Captain Tom Wolf and his wife, Lori, said, "It was always the place to meet. The bathrooms were awful and it was where we found out what time it was. Tom and I both still work the fair every year, Tom with EMT/First Aid and I as an ambassador."

The Del Mar Fire Department was established in 1960 with James Kavanaugh as chief and two firefighters. In 1962, Betty Bossert, a member of the Del Mar City Council, organized 10 women to serve as the Ladies of Del Mar Fire Brigade. In 1974, Sue Merstens was hired as the first woman firefighter for the department.

Fire chiefs include: James Kavanaugh (1960-1963), Bill Tripp (1963-1982), Larry Jones (1982-1991), James Baker (1991-1996), Jack Gosney (1996-2003), David Ott (2003-2009), Mark Muir (2009-2011), Scott Henry (2011-2013), Mike Daigle (2013-2015), and Mike Stein (2016-).

After Chief Kavanaugh's retirement in 1963, Bill Tripp was appointed to lead the department. His fire service career spanned 35 years, until 1982. Chief Tripp served in the U.S. Army during World War II. He died on March 1, 2013.

Larry Jones was chief from 1982 to 1991. He retired to Rogue River, Oregon. James Baker served as chief from 1991 to 1996. After his retirement to Pine Hills, he became renown for helping people in that community. Chief Baker was a U.S. Marine before working for General Dynamics and serving as a firefighter at Lindbergh Field.

Jack Gosney served as chief from April 1996 until October 2003. He grew up in Rancho Santa Fe, attending Earl Warren Junior High and San Dieguito High School. When he was in elementary school, he listened to stories his uncle told about his career as a firefighter in Newport Beach. When he was in high school, he became a volunteer firefighter. Chief Gosney worked his way through the ranks in Del Mar.

David Ott was chief of Del Mar and Solana Beach from July 2003 to October 2009. In 2005 Chief Ott also became deputy city manager for Solana Beach and city manager in 2006. Ott was a firefighter in the U.S. Forest Service, at Camp Pendleton and in Coronado. Beginning in 2000, he worked in leadership in Imperial Beach before coming to Solana Beach. He retired as city manager of Solana Beach on November 28, 2014.

Chief Ott earned a certificate in Public Administration from San Diego State University; Bachelor of Science in Fire Administration and Bachelor of Science in Fire Prevention Technology from Cogswell Polytechnical College in Sunnyvale, California; Masters of Human Resource Management from the University of Redlands; and a Masters of Organizational Management from Grand Canyon University in Arizona. In 2004, he graduated from the National Fire Academy's four-year Executive Fire Officer Program.

In October 2009, Del Mar, Encinitas, Solana Beach, and the Rancho Santa Fe Fire Protection District entered into a two-year cooperative agreement to share management functions for their fire departments to avoid duplicate positions. The Rancho Santa Fe Fire Protection District withdrew from the agreement in 2013. Del Mar, Encinitas, and Solana Beach share the cost of a fire chief, deputy chief, and three battalion chiefs. In addition to serving Del Mar, the department provides mutual aid to Solana Beach, Encinitas, and portions of San Diego.

Mark Muir became chief of Del Mar, Encinitas, and Solana Beach in 2009. Chief Mark Muir, who served in the fire service for 35 years and the Encinitas City Council for seven years, was chief of the Encinitas Fire Department from 2006 to 2011. He joined the Lemon Grove Fire Department when he was 18 years old, then became a firefighter in Encinitas for most of his career.

Scott Henry was chosen to lead the Del Mar, Encinitas, and Solana Beach Fire Departments in December 2011 after serving as deputy chief. He joined the Encinitas

Fire Department in 1980, promoting to captain in 1987. He was active in the Burn Institute. He retired in October 2013.

Jon Canavan served as chief from October 14, 2013, to December 5, 2013. He decided not to keep the job because of the time and energy commitment needed in the position. Previously he served as the Poway Fire Department division chief. He joined the Poway Fire Department in 2003 after spending 13 years with the San Marcos Fire Department.

On December 19, 2013, Deputy Chief Mike Daigle was promoted to chief. He replaced Jon Canavan, who resigned after holding the position for only two months and returned to Poway as fire marshal. Chief Daigle, who was in the fire service for over 30 years, retired in late 2015.

After serving as acting chief for eight months, Mike Stein was promoted to chief of Del Mar, Solana Beach, and Encinitas in 2016. Chief Stein was hired by Encinitas in September 2013. During his 30-year career in the fire service, he has moved up the ranks from reserve firefighter to chief.

In 2009 as a battalion chief, Stein was assigned to San Diego's Office of Homeland Security where he managed a regional training program for both fire and law enforcement personnel from around the entire county. In 2013, he was given the Major's Award from the U.S. Army Sergeant of the California Emergency Management Agency for his work in Homeland Security.

Chief Stein holds a Bachelor of Science in Business Administration from San Diego State University and a Master of Public Administration from Cal State Dominguez Hills. He is a third generation firefighter with his grandfather serving with the Los Angeles Fire Department and his father serving with the Santa Monica Fire Department for 31 years.

The Del Mar CERT (Community Emergency Response Team) members attend a 25-hour training course, free to residents or local employees who are at least 18 years old. They are trained in how to save lives and property during a major disaster to supplement first responders. On July 11, 2013, the Del Mar CERT received a $2,500 SAFE grant from the San Diego Gas and Electric. The volunteers have been helping to enforce public health orders during the coronavirus pandemic.

The Del Mar firefighters and lifeguards host an annual pancake breakfast.

Joel Carrington is president and Giovanni Maniscalco is vice president of the Del Mar Firefighters Association, IAFF Local 4163. After working part-time as a student firefighter and paramedic with Del Mar Fire Department, Giovanni Maniscalco was promoted to full-time firefighter/paramedic in 2008 and to captain in 2016. Captain Maniscalco has a Bachelor of Arts in Political Science from University of California, Santa Barbara, and he attended fire academy and paramedic school at Palomar College. He worked as a paramedic for a private ambulance before joining the Del Mar Fire Department.

Battalion Chief Dismas Abelman retired on September 19, 2014, after serving Solana Beach, Del Mar, and Encinitas for 10 years. He previously worked at the Coronado Fire Department for 17 years. Chief David Ott said, ""His value to the fire service—I have never questioned. He understands what it means to be in the fire service, what a privilege it is to be in the fire service—the ability to help people in sometimes their darkest hour. Dis has always understood that."

Captain Patrick McNeil retired on July 5, 2015 after being with the Del Mar Fire Department for 25 years. O'Neil started his career at the La Mesa Fire Department after receiving a fire science degree from Miramar College. "I've enjoyed helping people and our community," O'Neil said. "The job was the best job ever."

The fire crews trained 3,669 hours in 2017.

The department has one fire station located on the southeast corner of the Del Mar Fairgrounds at 2200 Jimmy Durante Boulevard. Three captains, three engineers, and three firefighter/paramedics staff the station. Eighty percent of the fire department's calls are medical aids. The ISO (Insurance Service Office) rating was upgraded to a 2 in 2016 from a 4 in 2012.

The department had one fire engine in 1959. In 1960, it bought a pumper at a cost of $18,600. In 2012, it purchased a Pierce PUC engine. Currently it operates one front-line fire engine, one rescue unit, and one reserve engine.

The department uses an integrated 800 MHz radio system and contracts with the Rancho Santa Fe Regional Dispatch Agency for 24-hour dispatch services.

Year after year, the department illustrates dedication in protecting the lives and property of residents.

CALLS RECALLED:

*1889: The hotel Case del Mar burned to the ground.

*1973: Captain Tom Wolf responded on his first call to a train wreck. The train was transporting fertilizer.

*1974: A 9,000-gallon gasoline tanker overturned on Via de la Valle in front of Flower Hill Mall. There was no fire.

*1982: In 1982/1983, El Nino flooded the San Dieguito River and the heavy rain destroyed the road by Torrey Pine beach. The northern third of Del Mar lies less than 20 feet above sea level and within the potential flood zone. Now homeowners within the FEMA flood risk area are required to have flood insurance if they have a federally-backed mortgage.

*1986: A seven-alarm brush fire burned east of Del Mar in September 1986. The fire, started by heated exhaust from a truck, spread quickly to homes on the hills. More than 200 firefighters and 50 pieces of fire equipment from San Diego, Cal Fire, and departments throughout the county fought the fire. Two air tankers also dropped fire-retardant chemicals on the fire. No one was hurt and no homes were lost in the fire.

*1997: The Del Mar fire crew rescued three people from a fire in 1997.

*2002: The firefighters saved a family's home after they left for a concert with a pot of soup boiling on the stove.

*2007: During the Witch Creek Fire in October 2007, Chief David Ott set up emergency operation centers in Del Mar and Solana Beach.

*2008: In December 2008, a home was damaged in a fire in a two-story Tudor-style residence in the 1800 block of Ocean Front.

*2009: On August 1, 2009, a fire burned for 90 minutes at the six-unit condominium Del Mar Woods complex overlooking Torrey Pines State Beach, injuring one person and causing an estimated $3.5 million damage.

*2011: On August 9, 2011, a fire damaged an apartment complex near the Del Mar Racetrack. Flames spread through the three-story building. It took crews about 25 minutes to extinguish the blaze.

*2011: On October 11, 2011, a fire caused damage to PrepKitchen in the 1200 block of Camino Del Mar.

*2012: On June 15, 2012, Garrett McMillian Hughes, 35, was riding a Harley Davidson Sportster motorcycle south on Interstate 5, near Del Mar Heights Road, when he was killed as he tried to use the freeway shoulder to pass traffic as he raced another vehicle through traffic on Interstate 5 and rammed a car.

*2012: In July 2012, three people suffered second and third degree burns after a stereo-style lantern dropped on them.

*2012: On August 16, 2012, a freight train struck and killed 42-year-old Denise Oberlercher of San Francisco who was sitting on the tracks at Coast Boulevard and 15th Street shortly after midnight.

*2014: On March 4, 2014, firefighters from Del Mar, San Diego, Solana Beach,and the Rancho Santa Fe Fire Protection District responded to the report of a structure fire in the 3000 block of Via De La Valle. The fire at the Sublime Tavern had been extinguished by one sprinkler head. The sprinkler head gave the occupants time to evacuate and kept the fire from spreading. The damage was $50,000.

*2014: On March 28, 2014, a drunk driver killed 27-year-old Rachel Anne Morrison. He ran a stop sign and struck her at a high rate of speed at the intersection of Camino Del Mar and Coast Boulevard.

*2014: On June 5, 2014, a seven-year-old boy was critically injured when he fell about 30 feet out of a third-story window at the Clarion Del Mar Inn. Paramedics airlifted him to Rady Children's Hospital to treat a broken femur and major head trauma.

*2014: On August 6, 2014, a travel trailer caught fire near the Del Mar Fairgrounds. The firefighters had it knocked down in 17 minutes.

*2015: On January 9, 2015, a Carmel Valley man suffered fatal burns when flames spread through his condominium located in the 3500 block of Caminito El Rincon.

*2015: On March 12, 2015, a woman was killed as she lay across the tracks on the outskirts of Seagrove Park. The woman remained on the tracks as the southbound Coaster locomotive bore down on her.

*2015: On June 24, 2015, June Takekawa Hsu died after her 1995 Nissan Sentra stalled in the northbound lane of Interstate 5 near Via de la Valle and was rear-ended by a 2008 Honda Accord. After the initial crash, a 2006 Chevrolet Silverado and a 2015 Honda Accord crashed into the other two vehicles.

*2016: On February 25, 2016, a Burlington Northern Santa Fe freight train struck an abandoned car on the railroad track near the intersection of Coast Boulevard and 15th Street. No one was injured.

*2016: On March 11, 2016, a train struck a pedestrian on a stretch of rail off the 100 block of 12th Street.

*2016: On May 13, 2016, nine children and an adult were injured when a car jumped a curb and struck them in front of Del Mar Heights Elementary School. Medics took six of the injured youngsters to hospitals, three with major trauma injuries.

*2016: In September 2016, a a 19-year-old man was killed after being struck by a train just north of 13th Street.

*2016: On November 29, 2016, a 71-year-old man was killed when he was struck by an Amtrak train off the 1400 block of Ocean Avenue.

*2017: On January 16, 2017, a driver was injured when backing out of a steep driveway in Del Mar Heights when his car rolled over and came to rest upside-down.

*2017: On February 4, 2017, a southbound Coaster commuter train hit an SUV in the 1600 block of Coast Boulevard. The driver was taken to Scripps Memorial Hospital to be treated for serious injuries.

*2017: On July 7, 2017, a man wearing headphones was killed after being hit by a Coaster train. The collision occurred on the bluffs near 13th Street and Stratford Court.

*2017: An elderly man and his caregiver who were trapped on the second floor of a home on Camino Del Mar were rescued by fire crews. The man was taken to the hospital for treatment of minor injuries. It took the firefighters 20 minutes to extinguish the fire.

*2017: In November 2017, a woman and her dog were killed by a Coaster train when they tried to walk across the tracks near 11th Street.

*2017: In December 2017, the Del Mar racetrack sheltered 850 horses evacuated from wildfires that broke out across Southern California.

*2017: During the Lilac Fire, Martine Bellocq risked her life to save thoroughbred horses from the San Luis Rey Training Center. She suffered burns over 60% of her body and was in an induced coma for months. In August 2018 she was awarded the Laffit Pincay Jr. Award at the Del Mar Fairgrounds for her heroics.

*2017: On December 13, 2017, a 58-year-old motorcyclist was killed after running into the back of a Toyota Camry on south Interstate 5.

*2017: The Del Mar Fire Department had three strike team deployments on three different fires in 2017.

*2017: Del Mar crews responded to 1,454 emergency calls in 2017, including calls for fires (65), EMS/rescues (878), hazardous conditions (22), service calls (77), good intentions (264), false calls (143), severe weather (2), and other (3). The average response time was 5 min. 7 sec. The value of structures saved was $8,132,540. The structures value lost was $1,215,640.

*2018: On April 8, 2018, a woman was hit and killed by an Amtrak train in Del Mar. The Amtrak train was traveling north around 48 mph when the woman walked past the intersection's signal guards and was hit.

*2019: In February 2019, a two-story home on 27th Street was damaged in a two-alarm fire. An elderly couple were evacuated. Firefighters broke through the roof to access flames in the home's attic. The Del Mar crew was assisted by firefighters from Encinitas and Rancho Santa Fe. The damage cost was $200,000.

*2019: In August 2019, a blaze broke out at the Taste of Thai restaurant off San Andres Drive north of Via de la Valle. The fire began in the kitchen and quickly spread to the restaurant's roof and attic area.

*2019: On October 6, 2019, just 20 minutes from their home in Del Mar, Kozy and Thomas Royden's Honda CRV was hit by a 49-year-old tow truck driver who ran a red light at the intersection of El Camino Real and Carmel Valley Road. Thomas Royden was killed in the crash. His dog was riding in the CRV and was also killed. Kozy Amemiya, his wife, sustained minor injuries in the crash. Under the auspices of the United Nations, Thomas worked in Kitete in Tanzania and helped poor farmers in Ecuador and Bolivia. In his later years he owned a large avocado grove in Ramona.

*2019: On October 28, 2019, Paul Palmer, a 76-year-old man, was killed in a traffic collision. While driving a Honda CRV northbound on Camino Del Mar, he crossed into the southbound lanes and sideswiped a Honda RAV4 driven by a 39-year-old woman, then slammed head-on into a Toyota van. The two men in the Toyota van, a 28-year-old driver and his 27-year-old passenger, suffered major injuries and were taken to Scripps Memorial Hospital.

*2020: In February 2020, the Del Mar Fire Department and the U.S. Coast Guard rescued 13 people and searched for three missing persons from a smuggling boat off the coast of Del Mar.

*2020: In April 2020, a father died and his teenage children were injured when his BMW sedan slammed into a tree in Carmel Valley. The driver's 17-year-old son had major head injuries and was taken to a hospital with life-threatening injuries. His 15-year-old daughter sustained minor injuries.

*2020: On July 4, 2020, a 28-year-old motorcyclist was killed in a three-vehicle accident on the northbound Interstate 5 near Via de la Valle.

*2020: In July 2020, a pedestrian was struck by an Amtrak near 8th Street and Stratford Court and seriously injured.

DULZURA-BARRETT VOLUNTEER FIRE DEPARTMENT

Dulzura and Barrett Junction are located seven miles north of the Mexican border, west of Potrero and Tecate, east of Jamul, and southeast of Deerhorn Valley in the unincorporated region of San Diego County. Together they cover nearly 75 square miles with a population of 1,100. State Highway 94 (Campo Road) is the only major road through the communities.

Dulzura has a post office, a grocery store, and a community center. Barrett Junction has a cafe and some small businesses. There are old ranches and stage stops in the area, some are over 100 years old. There are also Native American cultural sites.

John S. Harbison established apiaries at Engineer Springs in 1873. His partner was Daniel Dowling who bought 160 acres and built a ranch to produce honey from Harbison's bees. The Dowling ranch produced honey until it was sold to Garret and Fannie Eaton in 1894 and they turned it into a dude ranch called the Honey Springs Ranch.

Before Barrett Lake became a reservoir, it was a valley where George Barrett homesteaded in the 1870s.

Between 1908 and 1914, Dulzura was the home of a candied fruit known as "Clark's Pickelized Figs" that was sold across the United States. The figs were produced at Clark Ranch by Frank and Lila Clark. World War I resulted in a sugar shortage and ended the business.

The property at the Barrett Junction Cafe & Mercantile was a homestead in the 1800s, turned commercial in 1915, and became a well-known Friday night fish fry house after World War II. The Barrett Cafe was purchased by Bill and Viola Avril in 1946. They added a saloon in 1947 and a Quonset hut in 1950 to accommodate the large crowds attending the free dances. The field across the street from the cafe was used for rodeos. The current owner, Leon Herzog, purchased Barrett Junction Cafe & Mercantile in 2000 and has continued with the famous fish fry.

The Barrett Mobile Home Park was previously known as Waddell's Barrett Lake Trailer Park. It was started by Robert and Elva Waddell in 1948. Elva Waddell was active in the Dulzura-Barrett Volunteer Fire Department.

Dulzura and Barrett Junction have steep slopes, rocky terrain, deep canyons, and high hills. The area includes Mother Grundy Peak, Otay Mountain, and Barrett Lake, which is located just south of the Cleveland National Forest.

For many years the only fire protection for the area came from the California Department of Forestry (CDF) in La Mesa. Luther Gordon, who became the county fire warden in 1924, would dispatch men and trucks if a fire was reported anywhere in the East County. In 1942 a CDF station was built on J Street near the Hilltop Circle defense housing project in Chula Vista. In 1956 the Forestry personnel from J Street were relocated to Dulzura, housed in a tent cabin and equipped with one old truck, a 1949 REO. In 1970, this station moved to Campbell Ranch Road.

The Dulzura-Barrett Volunteer Fire Department was organized across the highway from the CDF tent cabin about 1970. It had 35 men and a truck that was housed in the barn of Chief Dale Fuller. In 1992 the volunteers moved to a new building on the hill behind the Dulzura Community Center.

The Dulzura-Barrett Volunteer Fire Department had 10 members in 1995 but is now inactive. Cal Fire along with the San Diego County Fire provides fire and emergency medical services.

The fire station on Highway 94 at Campbell Ranch Road was originally a county road maintenance station until 1970 when it became Cal Fire Station 30. The station at 17304 Highway 94 is staffed full time. It houses Brush 35 (2004 International 7400).

In 2018, the Community Wildfire Protection Plan was developed by the Dulzura-Barrett Fire Safe Council, Fire Safe Council of San Diego County, Cal Fire, Bureau of Land Management, and San Diego County Fire Authority.

Dulzura and Barrett are considered wildland urban interface areas. They have seen greater than average fire return intervals, making them high risk areas.

When a fire alarm is received at a station, whether it be for a structure, vehicle, or wildland, the number one priority will always be rescue, the saving of human life. It is therefore critical that the fire service maintain the public trust by maintaining the integrity of a rapid operational response at all times. If not, people may die!

Cal Fire is the primary wildland fire protection in San Diego County. The firefighters are wildland experts who use specialized firefighting equipment on the ground and in the air. The public trusts fire officials with the hope that they will exercise sound judgment and always act in good faith to protect our families and communities.

It is only a matter of time before we are faced with another catastrophic event from any number of natural and human threats.

CALLS RECALLED:

*1980: On January 31, 1980, a flood ruined the Barrett Mobile Home Park. The flood also destroyed all the buildings of the Barrett Feed and Livestock Store.

*1995: Five hundred firefighters fought the 5,970-acre El Monte Fire in August 1995 which burned on the east and west sides of the El Capitan Reservoir. The fire was caused by strong winds, low humidity, and high temperatures. The cost of the fire was $3.95 million.

*2007: The Harris Fire started on October 27, 2007, at 9:23 a.m. and was contained on November 5, 2007, at 9:45 p.m. It started on State Highway 94 and Harris Ranch Road near Potrero. Both Dulzura and Barrett burned in the fire. The fire destroyed 100 of the 130 homes in the Barrett Mobile Home and RV Park. The Harris Fire killed five people, destroyed 253 homes, 2 commercial properties, 293 outbuildings, and burned 90,440 acres. There were 756 firefighters on the fire, 36 engines, 15 fire crews, 3 helicopters, and 6 water tenders. The cost of the fire was $21 million.

*2010: In May 2010, two people were injured in a vehicle and a motorcycle collision at Barrett Lake. One passenger in the car had a partial leg amputation.

*2011: In August 2011, the Barrett Fire, east of Barrett Lake, burned 95 acres.

*2016: In June 2016, a wildfire between Dulzura and Barrett Junction burned 7,500 acres.

*2016: In July 2016, a brush fire started when a motorcycle's hot underside ignited brush after it left the paved roadway on State Highway 94 east of Dulzura. The fire burned six acres. About 70 firefighters and four aircraft extinguished the blaze.

*2016: In December 2016, one person was killed in a two-car crash. A 28-year-old driver of a 2003 Ford Explorer was heading eastbound on State Highway 94 west of Barrett School Road. A 44-year-old woman of El Cajon was driving a 2011 Ford Fusion westbound on State Highway 94 with a 20-year-old passenger seated in the front right passenger seat. The driver of the Explorer's car crossed the double yellow lines and struck the Fusion head-on.

*2018: In July 2018, a blaze started off State Route 94, near Community Building Road. The fire broke out during a heat wave, burning 10 acres and destroying one home.

*2019: In May 2019, three brush fires erupted east of Otay Open Space Preserve in the Dulzura area. About 100 firefighters fought the fires by ground and aboard water- and chemical retardant-dropping aircraft. The largest of the three fires was 15 acres.

*2020: In July 2020, a hiker was bitten by a rattlesnake on a trail off State Highway 94 west of Dulzura. A Cal Fire crew aboard a sheriff's helicopter airlifted the injured hiker to a hospital, where the patient was admitted in critical condition.

*2020: In September 2020, residents of Dulzura and Barrett Junction were impacted by the Valley Fire. The fire began on September 5 off Spirit Trail and Carveacre Road and spread rapidly through dry vegetation. The resources dedicated to battling the fire included 48 engines, 4 water-dropping helicopters, 2 bulldozers, 15 water tenders, 13 hand crews, and 609 personnel, San Diego Gas & Electric's Sky Maverick assisted with the air response. One air drop of the Sky Maverick is equivalent to 2,650 gallons of water. The Orange County Fire Authority dispatched a strike team of five engines and two battalion chiefs to assist with the fire. The fire was contained on September 24. The fire burned 16,390 acres and destroyed 30 homes and 31 outbuildings.

EL CAJON FIRE DEPARTMENT

Fifteen miles northeast of San Diego is the city of El Cajon (sometimes called "The Box"). The city was given its name by the Spanish settlers because the floor of the valley is surrounded by hills. In 1912 it had a population of 200; now it has a population of about 104,000 in a 14.7 square-mile area.

The Mission San Diego de Alcala acquired 57,000 acres in the valley in the 1920s. In the 1830s Governor Pio Pico granted 48,799 acres of the land to Maria Estudidillo de Pedrorena, wife of Don Miguel. It was known as the El Cajon Rancho. Isaac Lankershim bought most of the land in 1869 from the heirs of Don Miguel de Pedrorena. Early settlers such as Levi Chase, Jesse Julian Ames, John Rea, T. T. Miller, and Arthur Ballantyne and his four sons discovered the rich land of El Cajon Valley. Amaziah Lord Knox settled in El Cajon in 1869. He built a seven-room hotel and a livery stable in 1876 at a cost of $1,000, located at the present southwest corner of Main and Magnolia Streets. He rented rooms for one dollar per night, which included feed for the animals. Amaziah Lord Knox, who became the first postmaster in 1878, sold the hotel in 1908.

Every November the Mother Goose Parade draws thousands of people to EL Cajon. The nonprofit event, founded by Tom Rigton in 1947, has floats from the chapters in Mother Goose. Today it is one of the largest parades in California.

El Cajon was officially incorporated on November 12, 1912, by a majority of residents. Of the 158 votes, the citizens decided by 3 and one half to 1 in favor of cityhood, a 1 and 1/4 square mile area near Main and Magnolia Streets. A board of trustees met and assigned committees to get the administration functioning, including the appointment of a fire chief. On April 10, 1916, the council approved the purchase of 250 feet of hose at 60 cents per foot including the couplings and a nozzle.

During the early pre-World War I years, the history of the El Cajon Fire Department is somewhat vague. What is known is that general alarms for fires and other emergencies did exist. The alarm bell was a broken steam locomotive wheel that was suspended on a crossbar in front of the El Cajon Drugstore. When the wheel was struck with an iron rod, the townspeople ran outside to find out what the emergency was.

The El Cajon Valley Volunteer Fire Department was officially formed in 1923. In the same year Reyford "Rex" Hall was named fire chief. Chief Hall was the son of Wilson Hall, who opened a lumber business in El Cajon in 1897. He graduated from the University of California at Berkeley in 1917. After serving in World War I, he worked for W. D. Hall Lumber Company and lived on the property where the firefighters kept the hose cart. In 1953, Chief Hall was named Citizen of the Year, and in 1956 he was considered "Son of El Cajon."

The firefighters in 1923 were Andrew (Andy) Ballantyne, Bill Meredith, Warren Hawley, Fred Jones, Harry Apelman, Arthur Rossberg, Ed Mueller, Harry Hill, and Skill Hall.

Andrew Ballantyne was appointed assistant fire chief in 1924. The tax rate that year was $1.60 for each $100 in assessed evaluation. Of this amount, $1.25 cents went to the volunteer fire department.

Charlie Burns, a truck driver for W. D. Hall Company, was a volunteer firefighter from 1925 to the late 1940s. He was appointed the designated driver because he was the first person to get to the fire equipment. On one Halloween Charlie's son and some other teenagers, without the knowledge of the firefighters, pulled the hose cart down Main Street.

In the midst of the Great Depression and after the resignation of Chief Hall in 1933, El Cajon appointed a new volunteer fire chief, L. J. McCosky. Raymond "Hal" Halgren took over the volunteer fire chief's job in 1937. Rex Huffman, who became a volunteer in 1938, later became El Cajon's first police chief. Two of the firefighters who made the transition from volunteer to paid were Al Petree, who served from 1940 to 1975, and Felix Landis, who was with the department from 1947 to 1960.

By 1940, the population was 1,471. In 1948 the city council appointed the first two full-time paid firefighters, Fire Chief Raymond Halgren and firefighter Herbert "Herb" Teeples. The two men received no sick leave or vacation. Halgren was paid $225 a month. Herb Teepes served the department from 1948 to 1975. In 1948 the department had 10 volunteers. A year later Tom Owen was hired as a firefighter.

By 1950 there were five paid firefighters. During the early 1950s the population increased to 8,000 people and there were more fire losses. The firefighters responded to two to three calls per week. The city continued to hire more full-time firefighters to lessen the need for volunteers. Between 1953 and 1956 eighteen new firefighters were hired. By 1960 the incorporated area increased to 9.8 square miles and the population had increased to 37,618. During the next decade El Cajon bought additional firefighting equipment which improved insurance ratings. The fire department expanded its fire prevention and medical aid programs, adding ambulance service in 1970.

Fire Chief Raymond Halgren ended his long and highly distinguished 35-year career of service and dedication to his community in 1970. Thomas Owen, one of the first full-time firefighters for El Cajon, was appointed the new fire chief. In 1949, at the age of 21, Owen had been hired as a firefighter at a salary of $175 a month plus free board at the fire station. He was promoted to engineer in 1955, captain in 1957, assistant fire chief in 1962, and fire chief in 1970.

Owen recalled one of the Wednesday night drills in those early days—the crew was driving back to the station on Chase Avenue when they almost crashed into a herd of cows that were crossing the street. In those days the crew only put out fires. However, as fires became more expensive, fire prevention became an added responsibility of the firefighters. Chief Owen died in 1992. His son Steve became a firefighter with El Cajon's department in 1979.

When Chief Owen retired in May 1980, Roger Dean House became the fire chief. House became a volunteer at the age of 21 for the Santee Fire Department. He was hired as an El Cajon firefighter in 1959 and promoted to battalion chief in 1971. He was an instructor at the Heartland Fire Academy in El Cajon.

In the same year, the department upgraded its emergency medical services (EMS) to provide paramedic level care for the citizens of El Cajon. The paramedics responded to any emergency in the district within two to five minutes. The service was financed by a benefit fee charged to each dwelling. In September 1981 a two division shift schedule was changed to a three division schedule and the work week for the firefighters was reduced from 60 hours to 56 hours. An automatic aid agreement was implemented on July 1, 1984, with Grossmont-Mt. Helix, La Mesa, Lakeside, Lemon Grove, San Diego, Santee, and Spring Valley fire departments.

Harry Kraft, an El Cajon firefighter for 30 years, retired in 1987. When he first became a firefighter, there were a lot of grass fires, but with growth of the population, there were fewer as the grass was replaced with houses. One call he always remembered was the response to a baby who was blue and breathless after drowning. On the way to the hospital the baby began to cry and resume breathing.

When Chief House retired at the age of 53 on May 13, 1988, Robert Hitchens, 50, took over as chief. He had been a division chief for the Orange County Fire Department for the previous eight years. Hitchens' career as a firefighter began at the Chula Vista Fire Department in 1964.

A fire prevention bureau was added to the department in 1989 under the leadership of Fire Marshall John Traylor. The bureau oversees fire safety, fire investigations, and fire inspections.

Richard Hardy was appointed chief in February 1993. His first firefighting position was with El Centro Fire Department in 1965. He had previously been in construction for six years. Hardy was hired as a firefighter by Chief Halgren in 1967, then promoted to engineer in 1973, captain in 1975, battalion chief in 1984, and operations chief in 1990. The department had 87 firefighters who responded to about 8,000 calls a year. There were four engine companies, one truck company, one rescue unit, and two paramedic units. The budget increased from $20,000 in 1950 to $350,000 in 1965 to over $4 million in 1993.

Richard "Rich" Henry was selected to be chief in 1995. He retired as chief in 2002 after 30 years of fire service. Henry rose through the ranks of the department, holding the ranks of firefighter, paramedic, engineer, captain, fire marshal, battalion chief, and chief. Chief Henry served as the chair of the Heartland Fire Chiefs and the Heartland Communications Board of Chiefs, coordinator of the Heartland Zone, and training manager of the Heartland Fire Training Facility.

El Cajon joined La Mesa and Lemon Grove Fire Departments on January 1, 2010, to form a combined agency to manage fire and medical services called Heartland Fire & Rescue. The three cities share the expenses of the staff of a fire chief, four division chiefs, five battalion chiefs, a fire marshal, a deputy fire marshal, an emergency preparedness coordinator, and four administrative support staff.

Mike Scott was appointed the Heartland Fire & Rescue chief in October 2009. He had been the chief of El Cajon since 2005. Chief Scott began his career with the department in 1984 as a firefighter/paramedic. During his 28 years with El Cajon, he was one of the original California Task Force-8 Urban Search and Rescue team members in California. He started as a technical rescue specialist and deployed to the Northridge Earthquake in 1994 and to the Atlanta Olympics bombing in 1996. Scott transferred to the Canine Division where he was partnered with a devoted black Labrador, Billy, in November 1998. Chief Scott and Billy became the second canine search team in the county to be certified by FEMA. They served several local missions before being deployed to Ground Zero shortly after the 9/11 terrorist attacks in New York. Chief Scott retired on July 29, 2012.

Rick Sitta, who earned a commendation for bravery in the 2003 Cedar Fire, was selected as chief for Heartland Fire & Rescue in August 2012. Between 2003 and 2010, he had been a fire division chief in El Cajon and Coronado. In January 2010, he was appointed deputy fire chief of Heartland Fire & Rescue. He had command staff positions on Cal Fire Type I incident management teams for major wildland responses throughout California. Chief Sitta retired on August 12, 2016.

Colin Stowell became chief of Heartland Fire & Rescue in December 2016. He had worked for San Diego Fire-Rescue Department for 28 years. He was appointed chief of the department by Mayor Kevin Faulconer on August 13, 2018. He joined the San Diego Fire-Rescue Department in 1988, promoted to captain in 2002, battalion chief in 2007, deputy chief in 2012, and assistant chief in 2015. He earned an Associate of Fire Science from Miramar College, a Bachelor of Science in Public Administration from San Diego State University, and completed the Executive Fire Officer Program at the National Fire Academy.

Chief Stowell was responsible for four operating budgets as well as capital improvement projects for Heartland Fire & Rescue. He handled contract negotiations and oversight and was accountable to three city managers and city councils.

On October 20, 2018, Steve Swaney was appointed to lead the Heartland Fire & Rescue. He had been a division chief for Heartland Fire & Rescue since 2013. Chief Swaney began working with the El Cajon Fire Department in 1985. He also served as the fire chief for the Julian Cuyamaca Fire Protection District. He obtained an Associate of Fire Science from Miramar College and participated in paramedic training at the University of California San Diego. He is a 2016 graduate of the Leadership East County. Swaney has a Bachelor of Science in Management from California Coast University.

Besides serving Heartland Fire & Rescue, Chief Swaney is a certified Federal Emergency Management Agency canine evaluator and is a lead instructor for the FEMA Canine Search Specialist School. He started working with a chocolate Labrador named Sherman in 1997. Chief Swaney and his dog, Sherman, were in New York within 24 hours of the Twin Towers collapse to aid in rescue efforts. They were also deployed to Hurricane Katrina in New Orleans and Hurricane Rita in southeast Texas in 2005, Hurricane Ernesto off the Atlantic Coast in 2006, and the Torrey Pines Bluff collapse in 2004. After Sherman retired in 2006, Swaney continued rescue work in San Diego with two other rescue dogs, Icon and Tank.

In summary, here is a list of the fire chiefs: Rexford "Rex" Hall (1923-1933), L. J. McCoskey (1933-1937), Raymond Halgren (1937-1970), Thomas Owen (1970-1980), Roger House ((1980-1988), Robert Hitchens (1988-1993), Richard Hardy (1993-1995), Richard Henry (1995-2002), Ed Jarrell (2002-2005), Mike Scott (2005-2012), Rick Sitta (2012-2016), Colin Stowell (2016-2018), and Steve Swaney (2018-).

The first fire station was a building that was formerly the office of the W. D. Hall Company located near the intersection of Julian and East Main Streets—now the open area in front of the El Cajon City Hall. A room was added to the office building to house the fire truck.

In 1943 a new firehouse was built for $3,800. Half the money was raised through donations and the other half provided by the city. The department made a house-to-house canvas soliciting money to pay for the new station located at 115 S. Orange Avenue between W. Main Street and Douglas Avenue. In 1947 the El Cajon Police Department, which had five policemen, moved into the same building as the fire department.

The 1950s were a period of great change and growth for the El Cajon Fire Department. In 1952 the firehouse was becoming too small to meet the growing needs of the department. A new station was built at a cost of $75,000 at 210 Highland Avenue to house both the police and fire departments. A second fire station was built at Third Street and Peach Street in 1958.

During the 1960s the growth continued. A third fire station was built in Fletcher Hills at Tyrone Street and Fletcher Parkway. In May 1975, El Cajon completed a fourth fire station in the industrialized area on North Marshall Street. This was also a training facility, one of the best in the county, with props, a smoke room, flammable liquid pits, and a tower.

El Cajon, Santee, and Lakeside installed a central dispatch system that is stationed at the El Cajon headquarters. This became the main dispatch center for all the Heartland agencies as well as all the unincorporated areas of the county.

In 1923, the city had a two-wheeled chemical hose cart. This apparatus was officially named the Big Wheel by the volunteer firefighters. The Big Wheel had to be hand pushed to the scene of the fire by the volunteers, then when the tank ran dry the firefighters turned to the old standby—the bucket brigade.

On January 19, 1924, El Cajon received its first real fire engine, a Diamond Rio Speed Wagon equipped by Hirsch & Hirsch of Los Angeles. It cost $5,350, of which $3,300 was raised by the public, $1,000 from the San Diego Board of Supervisors, and $1,000 from the City of El Cajon.

In 1938 the fire department purchased a Chevrolet pumper with 350-gpm capabilities. A new American La France 1,000-gpm pumper was purchased in 1950 and stationed at the Orange Avenue firehouse. Between 1953 and 1956 another new pumper was purchased, two-way radios were installed in the emergency vehicles, and three new engines and an 85-foot aerial truck were purchased from American La France in Elmira, New York.

A 1,250-gpm pumper was purchased in March 1960 at a cost of $26,995, The increased number of medical aid calls in the late 1960s led the fire department to purchase an ambulance to transport patients.

El Cajon Fire Department bought a 1,250-gpm pumper in the summer of 1970 for $45,000. In 1976 the department once again upgraded its apparatus with the purchase of three new 1,500-gpm American La France pumpers. A Pierce Rescue R-9 was acquired in 1986 for $81,921 and two Pierce engines were bought in 1987 for $302,000. A Pierce Arrow aerial ladder truckle weighing 30 tons was purchased in 1988 at a cost of $410,000.

The combined resources of El Cajon, La Mesa, and Lemon Grove are eight fire stations, nine engine companies, two truck companies, three paramedic transport units, and one BLS transport unit (Peak Hour Unit) to serve 180,000 residents.

The stations in El Cajon are:

Station 6, located at 100 East Lexington Avenue, El Cajon, was built in September 1986. The 20,000-square-foot station was built at a cost of $2.2 million. Most of the funding for the facility was from a Federal Community Development block grant. The building houses administration, firefighters, paramedics, and equipment. It is also the central dispatch center for the Heartland agencies. It houses Engine 8, a 2013 Pierce Arrow XT, Truck 6, a 2005 Pierce Lance 2000, and Squad 6. Squad 6 is a custom-built 2017 Ford F-250 that is used to respond to low-acuity medical emergencies, freeing up the department's Engine 6 and Truck 6 to respond to more significant emergencies. The truck cost about $82,000.

Station 7 is located at 695 Tyrone Avenue, El Cajon.

Station 8, located at 1470 Madison Avenue, El Cajon, houses Engine 8, a 2019 Pierce Arrow XT. The pumper has a Detroit Diesel DD13, 505 hp, TAK-4 Independent front suspension, a spring rear suspension, Command Zone electrical system, Husky 3 foam system 1,500 gpm, foam and water tank, and 500-gallon tank size.

Station 9, located at 1301 North Marshal Street, El Cajon, houses Engine 9, a 2008 Pierce Velocity.

On October 18, 2019, firefighters welcomed 8-month-old Yara, a black Labrador Retriever puppy, from the East Coast. She has her own spot in a front office at Station 6 with a big dog bed. She is part of a Fire Station Dog Pilot Program, an El Cajon wellness initiative. Considered a therapy dog and not a service dog, Yara offers support to firefighters following a critical incident. She lives at the station 24 hours a day, seven days a week to provide companionship. The city budgeted $8,000 in early 2019 for the dog and her training.

The dedicated fire personnel provide superior service to the residents of El Cajon and neighboring communities.

CALLS RECALLED:

*1923:   Chief Hall responded with the chemical cart to a fire on March 3, 1923, at 4:30 a.m. Aubrey Sears backed his roadster up to the cart and Chief Hall took the handle of the cart and climbed onto the car. Thus, they hurried to the fire where other firefighters joined them. They were able to save one-third of a building. The cause of the fire was unknown.

*1923:   At 2:30 p.m. in March 1923 a barn one block north of Main Street on Magnolia Street owned by Amaziah Knox was destroyed by fire. By the time the firefighters reached the scene, it was too smoky for them to use the chemicals cart. La Mesa firefighters responded with their fire truck.

*1923:   Two boys throwing fire crackers at a wild cat in a cage at the grammar school caused a fire. The school located two blocks north of Main Street on Magnolia Street was a total loss.

*1923:   On July 9, 1923, a fire caused by paraffin on a stove resulted in the loss of a home on Pepper Drive.

*1924:   At 7:30 p.m. on January 19, 1974, the El Cajon firefighters responded in their new Aero fire truck to a fire in Lakeside. By the time they arrived, a chicken house was totally on fire. The source of the fire was unknown.

*1924:   The El Cajon volunteers helped extinguish a brush fire in Alpine that was close to the hospital. They pumped water from a well to use on the fire.

*1925:   A shed and two cabins behind a restaurant were destroyed in a 2:00 a.m. fire on January 5, 1925.

*1925:   On November 25, the Reynolds barn caught fire. The fire crew arrived too late to save the barn, hay, and bulk. However, they kept the fire from speeding to adjacent buildings.

*1945:   There was a $50,000 fire at the El Cajon Theater. In the 1940s fires were often out of control before the firefighters could get there.

*1946:   There was a very large oil and gasoline fire at the Langley Oil Products Company on East Main Street and Claydelle Avenue. The explosion caused by the flammable liquid emptying from the tanks was powerful enough to threaten all of downtown El Cajon. The blaze caused $50,000 worth of damage.

*1955:   Buy and Save Market suffered fire damages totaling $75,000.

*1959:   The firefighters fought a blaze at Del Falco's Market that caused $55,000 damage.

*1965:   David Market had a big fire that resulted in $85,000 damage.

*1970:   Firefighters from El Cajon and the entire East County were confronted with a major conflagration in September 1970—the Laguna Fire. This fire, fed by strong Santa Ana winds, burned for six days and consumed 175,425 acres. Five people died in the fire and 382 structures were destroyed. El Cajon was the command center during the long six-day battle to extinguish the fire.

           The Laguna Fire brought many changes, not only in the El Cajon Fire Department and surrounding fire agencies, but in the fire service itself. A standard communications language was established, called Clear Text, and the Incident Command System (ICS) was developed through a cooperative local, state, and federal effort.

*1977:   On May 3, 1977, 40 firefighters tried unsuccessfully to save a commercial building that had been at the corner of Magnolia Avenue and Main Street since 1913. The fire started in the first-floor ceiling at 2:30 a.m.

*1983:   Thirty-three percent of the calls in 1983 were fire incidents; 60% of the fires were in dwellings and apartments; 16.67% of the fires occurred on Saturdays. The largest number of structure fires occurred between 5:00 a.m. and 6:00 p.m.

*1984:   Firefighters Wayne Anders and Robert Zaqrick were commended by the California Highway Patrol for their efforts to save a 42-year-old teacher at a traffic accident near Ocotillo Wells on January 22, 1984. They helped her for 90 minutes—until the Life Flight helicopter arrived. She died at University Hospital on February 17.

*1988:   Forty-five firefighters from El Cajon, Bostonia, La Mesa, Santee, Spring Valley, and Grossmont-Mount Helix responded to a three-alarm fire in a Jack in the Box at Broadway and Graves Avenue in El Cajon. There were no injuries but the fire resulted in $415,000 damages.

*1988:   In September 1988, the Cowles Mountain Fire burned 600 acres in Santee and San Carlos and damaged 21 homes.

*1988:   An F-14 Navy jet crashed into a building at Gillespie Field, causing four passengers to die and destroying two hangers.

*2017:   El Cajon responded to 13,951 calls.

*2019:   In February 2019, a FedEx trailer at Precision Metal Products south of Gillespie Field caught fire. The fire involved magnesium, an element that can't be extinguished with water. Water makes the magnesium burn hotter rather than extinguishing it. A hazardous materials team from the San Diego Fire-Rescue Department helped fire crews handle the situation.

*2020:   In August 2020, a house was destroyed by a fire at the Lynwood Mobile Estates on East Washington Avenue.

*2020:   In September 2020, a two-alarm fire on Hacienda Drive destroyed a home. Two of the eight adults who lived in the home were taken to a hospital. The first crew arrived at the home within eight minutes.

ELFIN FOREST/HARMONY GROVE FIRE DEPARTMENT

The 12-square-mile fire district is bordered on the east by Escondido, on the north by San Marcos, on the west by Encinitas, and on the south by Rancho Santa Fe. The community is close to the Santa Rosa Mountains. The area has a population of about 2,100. According to a neighborhood census in 2018, there are 500 horses in the community.

Elfin Forest has one of the largest areas of coastal chaparrel in Southern California. Harmony Grove is bordered by the Elfin Forest Recreational Reserve and Del Dios Highlands Preserve. Ancestors of the Dieguerno Indians are believed to have lived in Harmony Grove 9,000 years ago. It was the peace grounds for various tribes.

Pierre Renand acquired 160 acres in Harmony Grove in 1843. Mr. Spook homesteaded in Elfin Forest in the 1880s. Harmony Grove was incorporated in 1896. The area is renown for the 640-acre Questhaven Retreat; the church and 29 residences of the Harmony Grove Spiritualist Association; and the 97-acre Elfin Forest Vacation Ranch.

The area's first fire brigade was formed in 1972 at the Elfin Forest Vacation Ranch. Its equipment consisted of a flatbed truck with a water barrel and a hand pump. The hose was donated by CDF (California Department of Forestry). The truck was parked under an oak tree until 1978 when a riding stable was converted into a fire station and a garage was built by volunteers from the community.

From 1975 to 1982 the Elfin Forest/Harmony Grove Volunteer Fire Department was part of the San Diego County's fire protection program. Elfin Forest received fire vehicles and equipment from the County. In May 1982, eighty-nine percent of the voters in the Elfin Forest and Harmony Grove communities approved a county service area (CSA 107) with a benefit tax to support the fire department. The voter turnout of 92% is the highest turnout in San Diego County's history. New boundaries were formed, Harmony Grove was absorbed into the district, and the fire department was incorporated into a private nonprofit public corporation named the Elfin

Forest/Harmony Grove Fire Department. In 1988, the corporation contracted with San Diego County to provide fire protection within CSA 107. In 1989, a local law was implemented requiring new structures to have sprinkler systems. The annual fire budget increased from $23,318 in 1982 to $194,000 in 1988.

Four directors of the Fire Advisory Board were elected from the community at large. The fifth director was a firefighter who represented the fire department. Past chairpersons of the Fire Advisory Board were Jeff Chandler, Byron MacFarlane, Jim McKim, Herb Sanford, and Tom Clarke.

The department's paid fire chief was nominated annually by the firefighters. Their vote had to be accepted by the Fire Advisory Board; only under special circumstances could the board override the vote of the firefighters. The board always confirmed the chief picked by the firefighters. The fire chief had a contract with the board which specifically defined the position's administrative and operational duties.

Jim Cunningham served as fire chief from 1972 to 1976 and Ron Urban from 1976 to 1978.

William "Bill" Lee Barker was elected chief in 1978. His experience as a businessman helped him in running the department. He served for five years as a volunteer county fire inspector, belonged to the California and San Diego Fire Chiefs Association and was president of the San Diego County Volunteer Fire Chiefs Association for two years. He was nominated for County Volunteer of the Year and presented a Proclamation for Outstanding Service upon his retirement from the fire department by the San Diego County Board of Supervisors.

Chief Barker joined the Elfin Forest volunteer fire brigade in 1977 when the garage of his newly built house caught fire and he discovered the fire brigade only had one old truck that was parked under an oak tree. He took the fire training the County of San Diego offered and arranged training for the entire brigade. He moved the department into a renovated stable with parking for two trucks then to a renovated manufacturing building with garage space for their six trucks and a crew of 40. In 1981, his wife, Abby, joined the fire department. In 1998 he and his wife Abby moved to Borrego Springs. He died of respiratory failure on January 26, 2019.

Frank Twohy, who joined the Elfin Forest/Harmony Grove Fire Department in 1985, became chief in 1993. In August 2002, he was picked as Firefighter of the Year by his colleagues. He worked with birds at Sea World for 18 years.

The department's charter allowed 40 firefighters. Only five of the firefighters could live outside the district and the others had to be able to reach the station within 15 minutes. New members of the department were on probation for six months. All members had to complete courses in advanced first aid and attend training classes. The average length of service for the firefighters was seven years, the average age was 36. The volunteers trained each month on the first and third Tuesday evenings for three hours and on the fourth Saturday for six hours.

The department had almost 30 firefighters, four of whom were women. Nona Barker, who joined the fire department in 1990, retired as a captain in June 2016. She also served as a fire board member. Her husband, Steve, was also a volunteer captain with the department. Nona and Steve Barker are founders of Eagle Creek Outfitters. Steve Barker volunteers with The Escondido Creek Conservancy, which he co-founded, and the Elfin Forest Town Council. In November 2007, Vanity Fair Corp. (VFC) recognized Steve Barker with the VF100 award for his volunteer efforts in the community. One hundred people were honored, out of nearly 43,000 employees worldwide.

John David Hershfield, a longtime member of the Elfin Forest/Harmony Grove Fire Department, died on February 10, 2011. A celebration of life was held at the fire station. He was in the Marine Corps in the late 1960s in Vietnam and received the Purple Heart. Hershfield was an avid outdoorsman with interests ranging from scuba diving, sailing, fly fishing, hiking, camping, and riding dirt bikes.

Ryan Kennedy joined the department in February 2014. He was an EMT with Americare Ambulance from March to August 2013 and an EMT with the Pala Fire Department from February to July 2015. He has an Associate of Fire Technology from Palomar College and attended California State University, Long Beach, from 2008 to 2012.

In May 2014, there were seven fires burning in the county. Firefighters Mark Martinez, Brian Serocke, and Ken Gardner were assigned to the Bernardo Fire and later to the Cocos Fire.

Three of the volunteer firefighters worked as paid firefighters for other fire departments and one worked as a paramedic with the Oceanside Fire Department.

In 1990, an 8,600-square-foot warehouse on two acres at 20223 Elfin Forest Road was purchased by the department. People from the community transformed the warehouse into a fire station. Behind the fire station, a Life Flight helipad was built.

The station housed a 1992 1500-gpm Central pumper with a seven-person cab; a 1984 1,000-gpm FMC Roughhouse pumper with a 750-gallon water tank; a 1987 680-gpm medium-rescue truck with a 600-gallon water tank; a 1978 380-gpm Pierce quick-attack rig with a 250-gallon water tank and class A foam for extinguishing ordinary combustible material; a 1976 2,200-gallon Ford diesel water tender that could carry potable water during emergency situations; and a utility Ram Charger. On December 19, 2006, the department received a HME Ahrens-Fox rescue pumper with a 1,500 pump rate and an 800-gallon tank. In 2015, the station also housed a 1990 GMC 7000/FireBann 500/500-20A.

A non-suppression auxiliary formed in 1988 assisted in administration, fundraising, and support activities. It served as the "food and drink brigade" at emergencies, making sure that the firefighters were well fed at times when they were on emergencies for a long period of time. Some of the members of the auxiliary were: Nona Barker, Ray and Bettie Boettger, Nils and Friedel Lunnerdal, Nancy Magistro, Linda McKim, Gervais Pimentel, Gretchen Sergeant, Mary Lou Selig, Darlene Stapp, and Regina Zielinski.

The volunteer firefighters contributed not only their time to firefighting but also their talents as electricians, cabinetmakers, mechanics, etc. Beginning in 1978 the fire department held a yearly 4th of July picnic to raise money for emergency funds, equipment, and uniforms. This annual event was held at the fire station on the Saturday closest to the holiday. Chief Barker's wife, Abby, chaired the picnic for 10 years. The picnic committee consisted of over 90 residents. Beginning in 1980, the Elfin Forest Town Council organized a parade to precede and promote the fire department's picnic. There were only a few bystanders because most of the people in the community were in the parade! After the parades, the people socialized and enjoyed a potluck and bake sale, live music, and games at the picnics. On July 4, 1991, a ceremony was held to dedicate the flagpole in front of the fire station which was purchased with money donated by the community. Only a few people attended the first picnic in 1978 but the department made a profit of $300. Almost eight hundred people attended the picnic in 1992 and the department made a profit of over $8,000.

Chief Barker credited the whole community with fire safety awareness, noting that the total structural fire loss over 15 years was only $30,000.

On June 30, 2016, the Elfin Forest/Harmony Grove Fire Department became part of the Rancho Santa Fe Fire Protection District. The engines got new logos and the crews new uniform patches. The community got the services of a larger fire department.

There are two stations in the area:

Station 5 at 2604 Overlook Point Road is in the Harmony Grove Village in Escondido. Construction began on a station in August 2019 and opened on October 8, 2020. The Rancho Santa Fe Fire Protection District personnel had been using two single-wide trailers as the station for over four and half years. The 9,000-square-foot station includes five dorm rooms, gym, kitchen and dining room, recreation room, training room, and a three-wide apparatus bay. The station cost was $7 million.

Station 5 houses one paramedic engine company and one paramedic ambulance. The 2020 personnel are: A shift, Mertz, Duncan, and Cloyd; B shift, Krueger, Schmid, and Pane; C shift, Bennett, Wood, and Canfield.

Station 6 is at 20223 Elfin Forest Road, Elfin Forest. The Rancho Santa Fe Fire District Foundation donated a new septic system and living quarters to the station in 2019. It houses one paramedic engine company and one paramedic ambulance. In 2020, the personnel are: A shift, Roman and Carranza; B shift, Worley and Trottier; C shift, McVey and Scheiber.

Rated a Very High Fire Hazard Severity Zone by Cal Fire, since 1980 there have been 19 wildfires within three miles of Harmony Grove and Elfin Forest. Santa Ana winds often begin east of Harmony Grove and travel through Harmony Grove to threaten Elfin Forest and other communities. The two main roads in Harmony Grove are Harmony Grove Road and Country Club Drive, both two-lane roads that make it difficult to get residents out and fire engines in during a wildfire. In 2018, the Elfin Forest Harmony Grove Town Council filed a lawsuit against the San Diego County Board of Supervisors for amending the General Plan to approve more housing without safe evacuation plans. The community maintains a strict requirement on the minimum lot size of two acres and does not allow subdividing.

The people who reside in Elfin Forest and Harmony Grove come from diverse economic backgrounds, yet they have a close-knit community that is very involved with local issues such as fire and medical. Fire Captain Nona Barker said, ""Here everybody knows everybody else, and everybody looks out for each other. We have a very strong community."

CALLS RECALLED:

*1940: A fire burned part of the Questhaven Retreat. The retreat's founders, Flower and Lawrence Newhouse, invited the director of the Santa Barbara Botanical Gardens to help plan the replanting. He described the dwarf trees and shrubs in the area as "elfin forest."

*1943: In 1943, a blaze burned 40,428 acres, including the chaparral and coastal sage in Harmony Grove and Elfin Forest.

*1977: The corner of Bill and Abby Barker's house caught on fire shortly after the couple moved to Elfin Forest. By the time firefighters arrived in a 1942 Seagrave Bill Barker had extinguished the fire.

*1987: The volunteers responded to 78 calls during the year, including 45 medical services, 2 vehicle fires, 2 refuse fires, 4 structural fires, 19 miscellaneous calls, 2 public service calls, and 4 mutual aid calls outside the district.

*1991: The Elfin Forest Town Council awarded the "Citizens of the Year" award to the community firefighters for their part in keeping the 1990 3,000-acre Del Dios Fire from entering the district.

*1992: In 1992, the department responded to 130 calls.

*1996: On October 21, 1996, the Harmony Grove Fire started at the intersection of Harmony Grove Road and Elfin Forest Road and crossed over the Cerra de las Posas ridgeline to the north and across Rancho Santa Fe Road to the southeast. "There was a wall of fire coming down that ridge, moving as fast as I could sprint," said Bill Browning, whose home was lost. "Everybody was running and screaming. It was the scariest thing I ever saw." It destroyed 120 homes, burned 8,600 acres in 24 hours, and killed David Hammond who was trapped in his car.

*1997: In 1997, an arsonist started the Del Dios Fire which threatened Harmony Grove and Elfin Forest and burned 3,000 acres.

*2014: In May 2014, there were 14 wildfires in the county as the result of drought conditions, high temperatures, and early Santa Ana winds. These fires claimed 46 homes, 26,000 acres, and caused two deaths.

*2014: On June 22, 2014, the Rocky Fire started in the area of Elfin Oaks Road and Rocky Road. It burned 3.5 acres before being contained by the Elfin Forest/Harmony Grove Fire Department, Cal Fire, and San Marcos Fire Department.

*2014: In 2014, the Cocos Fire destroyed 11 homes and 25 structures in Harmony Grove and burned 1,995 acres. It was difficult to evacuate because the traffic came to a halt. Some residents were unable to make multiple trips back to rescue all of their animals after mandatory evacuations began.

*2017: On December 14, 2017, 32-year-old Cory Iverson died in the line of duty while working with Cal Fire's Monte Vista Unit at the Thomas Fire in Ventura County. He was overrun by fast moving flames and died of smoke inhalation and burn injuries. Engineer Iverson volunteered at the Elfin Forest/Harmony Grove Fire Department between 2008 and 2015. He received the Firefighter of the Year award in 2010 by his colleagues. In 2009, he accepted a position with the Riverside unit of Cal Fire's Riverside Unit. His assignments included time spent on a helicopter out of the Hemet-Ryan Air Attack Base and a season with the Bear Divide Hotshot Crew. He is survived by his wife, Ashley, and two daughters, one born in 2015 and another in 2017.

*2017: In August, two SUVs collided at the intersection of Elfin Forest Road and Harmony Grove Road. Seven teenagers, one mother, and two children were transported to the hospital.

ENCINITAS FIRE DEPARTMENT

Encinitas is located about 25 miles north of San Diego along about six miles of the Pacific Ocean coast. Covering 19.6 square miles with a population of 61,928, the city has five areas: Historic Encinitas, New Encinitas, Olivenhain, Leucadia, and Cardiff-by-the-Sea.

The city is home to the 37-acre San Diego Botanic Garden, named as one of the top ten North American gardens by the American Gardens Association. Encinitas was also named as one of the 20 best places to surf in the world by National Geographic.

It wasn't until Lake Hodges Dam was built that Encinitas had a continuous flow of water.

In 1927, petitions were circulated in Encinitas and letters were sent to the San Diego County Board of Supervisors to establish fire protection in the city. A petition wasn't approved. However, the residents didn't want to pay additional taxes for the service. Instead, the California State Division of Forestry did when they could to provide fire protection for the next 18 years.

It wasn't until October 1945 that residents filed a petition with the San Diego County Board of Supervisors requesting the formation of a fire district. The fire department was established by the board on December 3, 1945. At that time, the population was about 8,500. The district remained inactive for six years until the fire department began out of a garage that was at 2nd and C Streets. It housed a 1941 International crash truck that was war surplus. The volunteer wage was $3 a call and raised to $6 in 1974. In October 1952 the district purchased a Mack that pumped 500 gpm and had a hose carrier and ladders. It also had a Willys pickup with a surplus fruit spraying rig that was used for grass fires and a 1953 GMC pumper provided by the Office of Civil Defense.

In 1957, the fire department headquarters was opened at 415 Second Street.

The district's name was changed to Encinitas Local Fire District and remained so until the early 1960s when it was renamed the Encinitas Fire Protection District.

The volunteer department had 20 men and three paid men who responded to emergencies when a siren on top of the station was sounded. One man was on duty at all times with a call man "sleeper" at night. Regulations for firemen were a height of 5 feet, 8 inches with a proportional weight and not be older than 31. By 1974, there were no longer volunteer firemen.

Bob Dohrer, 70, served as a volunteer from 1964 to 1974. He kept his plectron in his General Electric repairman's truck. He said, "I'd get two to three calls a week to

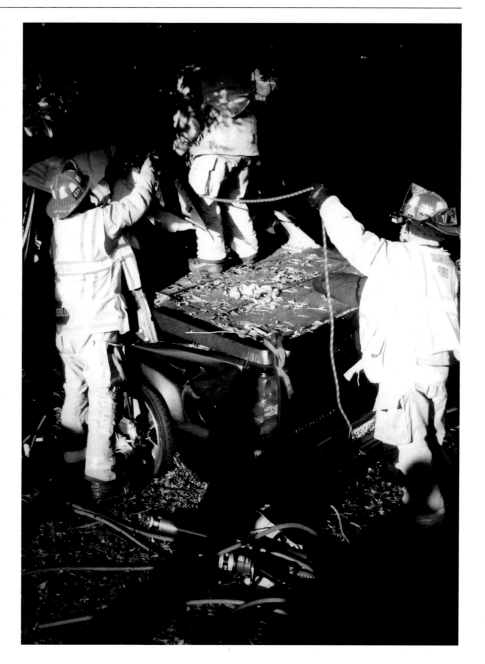

go to auto accidents, house fires, or brush fires. There were a couple of big fires. One started at Village Park where the city dump was. I drove my GE truck out there and it sat there for a couple of days. Once I was gone for three days on a brush fire. My company considered it a civic duty."

Steven Marvin, who served the district for 26 years, said, "We never thought about the smoke. The biggest indoctrination for a fireman was to get him smoked, get his eyes watering at a fire. We liked to think of the fire service as 100 years of tradition unaffected by progress."

In 1981, the district purchased an American La France 75-foot aerial ladder truck to supplement the four pumpers, mini-pumper, and EMT ambulance it had.

The district served about 15 square miles within the city and one square mile outside the city limits in 1985. To consolidate the responsibility of emergency and fire protection, a reorganization of the Encinitas Fire Protection District took place on January 1, 1988. The reorganization expanded the fire district's area to cover 23 square miles and serve about 57,000 residents. The expansion included New Encinitas and Olivenhain.

In 1985, the district's administrative offices and the fire prevention bureau moved from Station 1 at 415 Second Street to leased offices at 527 Encinitas Boulevard. On October 1, 1986, the city of Encinitas was incorporated. The Encinitas Fire Protection District became a subsidiary of the city with the five elected city council members serving as the board of directions for the fire district.

On July 1, 1995, the Encinitas Fire Protection District was dissolved and the organization became a department of the city of Encinitas.

The Encinitas Fire Department received a $701,629 grant from the Federal Emergency Management Agency in September 2003 to buy and implement a video conferencing system to be used by 11 North County fire departments. The televised system allows firefighters to train in their own stations instead of traveling to classes.

In October 2009, Encinitas, Del Mar, and Solana Beach entered into a Cooperative Fire Management Services Agreement for a two-year period, along with the Rancho Santa Fe Fire Protection District. The Rancho Santa Fe Fire Protection District withdrew from the agreement in 2013. After approval of the second amendment to the Cooperative Fire Management Services Agreement, a Joint Strategic Work Agreement was created for the Encinitas, Solana Beach, and Del Mar fire departments. Through this agreement, Encinitas and Solana Beach fire staff provide operational oversight for the three departments. By consolidating expenses such as fire chiefs and equipment, the cities save more than $250,000 a year.

Encinitas, Solana Beach, and Del Mar cover 24.8 square miles with a population of 79,696. They have eight stations.

The Encinitas Fire Department's surf team won gold at the California Firefighter Olympics in Santa Cruz in 2014. It was the 10th time that Encinitas won the championship.

The fire chiefs include: Curtis Havens (1945-1955); Vernon Stafford (1955-1970); Richard Shand (1970-1980); John J. Sueppel (1981-1984); John Brooks (1984-1985); Robert LaMarsh (1985-1992); Donald Heiser (1992-2006); Mark Muir (2006-2011); Scott Henry (2011-2013); Mike Daigle (2013-2015); and Mike Stein (2016-).

Curtis D. Havens was selected as fire commissioner with Jack Van Buskirk and Bruce Land in June 1951. On October 16, 1951, Havens was appointed chief. His volunteer staff included Assistant Chief Fred E. Jones; Captains Vern Stafford, Virgil Stallings, and Victory Sanford; and Firemen Boyce Brownlee, Bill Elliott, Arnold Hewitt, Frans Van Els, Gordon Whiting, W. V. Young, Lyle Burton, Jr., Robert Burton, Tom Brannin, W. Z. Cook, James Weller, Leon Hershman, and Doyle Stamps.

Richard Shand, who became chief in 1970, joined the fire district in 1958.

Donald Heiser was appointed chief in 1992. He modernized the department, developed a master plan for the department, and used regional video conferences to teach firefighting. He began his career as a volunteer firefighter at the Alpine Fire Protection District in 1970 and worked for the California State Department of Forestry before returning to Alpine. In 1986, he joined the Encinitas Fire Department as a battalion chief and, in 1992, was promoted to chief. Chief Heiser retired on July 1, 2006, at the age of 53 after 36 years in the fire service. He continues to teach wildfire fighting for the California Fire Chiefs Association and, as a certified chef, spend time at his catering business and teaching cooking.

Mark Muir became chief of Del Mar, Encinitas, and Solana Beach in 2009. Chief Muir, who served in the fire service for 35 years and the Encinitas City Council for seven years, was chief of the Encinitas Fire Department from 2006 to 2011. He joined the Lemon Grove Fire Department when he was 18 years old, then became a firefighter in Encinitas for most of his career.

Scott Henry was chosen to lead the Del Mar, Encinitas, and Solana Beach Fire Departments in December 2011 after serving as deputy chief. He joined the Encinitas Fire Department in 1980, promoting to captain in 1987. He was active in the Burn Institute, Make-a-Wish Foundation, UCSD Medical Center, and Tri-City Hospital Foundation. He retired in October 2013.

Jon Canavan served as chief from October 14, 2013, to December 5, 2013. He decided not to keep the job because of the time and energy commitment needed in the position. He had joined the Poway Fire Department in 2003, promoting to division chief, after spending 13 years with the San Marcos Fire Department.

On December 19, 2013, Deputy Chief Mike Daigle was promoted to chief. He replaced Jon Canavan, who resigned after holding the position for only two months and returned to Poway as fire marshal. Chief Daigle, who was in the fire service fo over 30 years, retired in late 2015.

After serving as acting chief for eight months, Mike Stein was promoted to chief of Del Mar, Solana Beach, and Encinitas in 2016. Chief Stein was hired by Encinitas in September 2013 and has been battalion chief, deputy chief, and acting chief. During his 30-year career in the fire service, he has moved up the ranks from reserve firefighter to chief. Previously he worked for the San Miguel Fire District for 23 years.

In 2009 as a battalion chief, Stein was assigned to San Diego's Office of Homeland Security where he managed a regional training program for both fire and law enforcement personnel from around the entire county. In 2013, he was given the Major's Award from the U.S. Army Sergeant of the California Emergency Management Agency for his work in Homeland Security.

Chief Stein holds a Bachelor of Science in Business Administration from San Diego State University and a Master of Public Administration from Cal State Dominguez Hills. He is a third generation firefighter with his grandfather serving with the Los Angeles Fire Department and his father serving with the Santa Monica Fire Department for 31 years.

The department has 70 personnel and five divisions: Fire Operations and Support Services, Fire Administration, Fire Prevention, Emergency Preparedness, and Marine Safety Services.

The Administrative Division is comprised of seven employees: fire chief, deputy fire chief, senior management analyst, management analyst, administrative support coordinator, program assistant, and administrative assistant (funded and located in Solana Beach). This division provides management, direction, and administrative support for all three departments. In 2016, Corina Jimenez-O'Donnell was promoted to senior management analyst and Ashlee Stratakis to management analyst. In 2017, Sarah Duffy was hired as the administrative support coordinator. In 2018, Jed Glober was hired as a program assistant and Lois Yum as a management analyst.

The Fire Operations Division is overseen by Deputy Chief Robbie Ford. It includes 51 fire suppression personnel in Encinitas. There are three shifts of firefighter/paramedics assigned to each station in order to provide 24-hour service. On each shift, the firefighter and engineer check out the equipment. The captain on duty consults with the battalion chief. The crew does business inspections and hydrant maintenance in between training and calls.

In 2016, Brian Crain was hired as a firefighter/paramedic in Del Mar. James Hancock was hired as a firefighter/paramedic in Solana Beach. Kyle Menzies, Mike Rigali, Jonathan Lim, and Ray Tellechea were hired as firefighter/paramedics in Encinitas. Adam Heer was promoted to captain in Encinitas. Eric Phillips and J.J. Siberell were promoted to captains in Solana Beach. Chris Cincotta and Bill Frisch were promoted to engineers in Encinitas. Ryan Pester, Billy Styers, and Zack Toth were promoted to engineers in Solana Beach.

In 2017, Don Butz, Matthew Colley, and Dan Phin were hired as firefighter/paramedics in Encinitas. Nick Cortez was hired as a firefighter/paramedic in Del Mar. Joe Masnica and Charles Mead were hired as firefighter/paramedics in Solana Beach. David Dumain, David Evans, and Peter Fink were promoted to captains in Encinitas. Josh Gordon was promoted to captain in Encinitas. Jim Mickelson was promoted to battalion chief in Encinitas.

In 2018, Jeremy Armstrong, Damian Guilliani, and Kyle Menzies were promoted to engineers. Chad Delude, Toby Lehman, Jesse Nelson, and Jon Peterson were promoted to captains. Terry Chiros was promoted to battalion chief.

The crews in Encinitas trained 18,014 hours in 2019. They train at least two hours a day. On one of the wildland training exercises in Indian Head Canyon in 2017, the crew from Station 3 practiced strategic hose placement, water pumping, radio communication, and being overrun by flames and having to deploy a fire shelter.

The Fire Prevention Division oversees the business inspection and weed abatement programs and enforces hazardous materials laws. It manages all facilities improvements and planning. The department consists of one fire marshal, two senior deputy fire marshals, one deputy fire marshal, and one program assistant.

The Emergency Preparedness Division is headed by Battalion Chief Jim Mickelson. The division manages the implementation of the Emergency Operations Center (EOC), which is activated during a local emergency or natural disaster, and coordinates EOC training for all city staff.

The Marine Safety Division provides lifeguard services for the 3.5 miles of state beaches managed by the city. The lifeguards provide safety information to the public, water rescues, and mitigation of safety hazards on the beach. There are about 20 lifeguards certified in swift water rescues in teams that deploy countywide. Larry Giles is the marine safety captain. The division has one lieutenant and four sergeants. A new Encinitas Marine Safety Center opened in 2018.

County Service Area 17 (CSA-17) provides ambulance service in Encinitas and nearby communities. CSA-17 contracts with American Medical Response for ambulance service. The personnel on each ambulance provide advance life support (ALS) at an emergency. When a call for a medical aid is dispatched, both an engine company and ambulance respond. Property owners pay a benefit fee of $26.13 per year to cover the cost of emergency services. Residents requiring transportation in an ambulance are assessed a fee of $400 plus $20 per mile.

In 2012, the Department of Homeland Security awarded the Encinitas Fire Department the Assistance to Firefighters Grant in the amount of $126,709 to purchase 44 portable, mobile, and base station radios. It allowed the department to upgrade current communications equipment to meet the standards of Project 25 network.

In 2019, the thermal imaging units were replaced in all six stations. These units help locate downed citizens or firefighters. Also, in 2019, the department developed and hosted an active shooter drill at the Del Mar Fairgrounds which included 238 firefighters, 27 EMS personnel, 118 law enforcement officers, 88 law enforcement volunteers, and over 100 volunteers used as role players.

The department has an ISO Rating of 2.

The Encinitas Fire Department has six strategically located stations. In 2008, Encinitas approved spending an estimated $13.5 million to reconstruct older fire facilities throughout the coastal community.

Station 1, located at 415 Second Street near Moonlight Beach, oversees the downtown area in Encinitas. The original station opened in 1957. The station was remodeled in 2020. It houses Engine 231 (2013 Pierce Arrow XT).

Station 2, located at 628 Birmingham Drive west of Interstate 5, is in Cardiff-by-the-Sea. The original Station 2 was opened on November 7, 1960, with only one firefighter. As the district grew, another firefighter was assigned to the station.

A single-story 6,330-square-foot Station 2 that was designed by Domus Studio in 2012 and constructed by Balfour Beatty opened in January 2013. The sloping sawtooth roof lines and clerestory windows are intended to emulate Encinitas's history of flower fields and greenhouses. The poinsettia flower is represented graphically on the masonry wall. The station has a free-standing hose drying tower that is cylindrical in plan and covered with perforated metal panels to enclose the hose drying lift. It houses Engine 232 (2012 Pierce Arrow XT) and Medic 232.

Station 3, located at 801 Orpheus Avenue in Leucadia, serves northwest Encinitas. The original station opened in a converted home on December 8, 1964. In February 1978, the home was torn down and replaced with a station completed on August 8, 1978. In 1982, a repair and maintenance facility was added to the rear portion of the property.

A 7,256-square-foot three-bay station designed by Domus Studio and built by HAR Construction was opened in 2009. A temporary trailer was put on site for the firefighters to use during construction. The curving metal roofs, exposed bead blasted cinder blocks, lap siding, and expansive glazing to the west allowed the new Station 3 to fit within its residential neighborhood setting and still retain the uniqueness of Leucadia. Station 3 houses Engine 233 (2020 Pierce Arrow XT, Detroit Diesel DD13, 1,500-gpm pump, foam and water tank, and 500-gallon tank).

Station 4, located at 2011 Village Park Way, is in Encinitas. Station 4 was originally opened in a small house on Seeman Drive on May 11, 1981, to serve the eastern part of the district. Some residents strongly opposed having a fire station in their neighborhood. This station was closed on July 16,1983, and then reopened two months later with a temporary use permit. It remained open until August 12, 1985, when a station was opened in a temporary building at 135 El Camino Real, protecting the growing commercial shopping centers and housing in the east portion of the fire district. Later it was moved to the current location.

Station 4 houses Engine 234 (2017 Pierce Arrow XT) and Brush Rig 234 (2010 International 7400 4 x 4 / Pierce Type III wildland). The brush rig has a Navistar/International chassis, 330 horsepower, Husky 3 foam system, Darley Midship pump, a Maxx Force engine, 500-gpm pump, foam and water tank, and a 500-gallon tank.

Station 5 located at 540 Balour Drive west of Oakcrest Community Park in Encinitas was designed by Domus Studio and built by KRPS Construction Company. It was dedicated on December 20, 2001 and opened in February 2002. The $1.5 million facility occupies one acre. It houses Truck 235 (2011 Pierce Arrow XT 100' tractor-drawn aerial).

The 6,948-square-foot Station 5 consists of living quarters, fire training and maintenance, an apparatus bay for the fire trucks, and an equipment tower. The construction consists of concrete block, steel, and wood framing. The circular driveway is designed so that engines will not be forced to back up.

The tile roof is on top of a hose tower that extends 29.4 feet from ground level. To conform with the height level codes in Encinitas, a pit was dug at the base of the tower to allow hoses to be suspended their full length to dry out.

Interior night-vision lightning comes on automatically during emergency calls. A backup generator is used for emergency needs.

On the second floor of Station 5 is a 32- x 12-foot gymnasium where firefighters can work out. A 25-foot brass pole runs through the center of the building.

Station 6, located at 770 Rancho Santa Fe Road, is in Olivenhain. Construction began on this station in 2012 and opened in 2013. It has an engineer and a firefighter/paramedic. A Type 3 brush engine is stationed here that can respond to medical aid calls and fires. It houses Patrol 236 (2017).

A mini-fire station was opened at a parking lot on North Coast Highway in the north Leucadia and Saxony Canyon areas in August 2019 to reduce response time to the area. A captain and a firefighter/paramedic staffed the station 12 hours a day, 7 days a week, at peak hours. The station responded to 359 calls in 2019. In June 2020, council members decided to close the station.

In November 2014, Firefighter/paramedic Josh Gordon said, "I realize that memorable moments are made every day in the Encinitas Fire Department. They don't always make the news. In fact they rarely do, but every day there's a firefighter assisting, helping, and improving the lives of others. Every day memorable moments are made; they are just rarely shared. That is what makes the job of a firefighter so rewarding."

The dedicated personnel work tirelessly to handle emergencies in the communities and promote fire safety.

CALLS RECALLED:

*1882: In 1882, a brush fire spread to a school in a farm building in Leucadia's Seaside Gardens in J. N. Young's farm, causing the evacuation of the children and teacher from the small school.

*1893: In 1893, when the Noonan home was destroyed in a blaze, Ida Noonan Truax with her doll escaped through a window and was followed by her brother, mother, and father. The site is now home to the Self-Realization Encinitas Temple.

*1967: In 1967, a tanker fire burned 23 vehicles.

*1969: In 1969, a building was lost in the Electrolab fire.

*1996: The Harmony Grove Fire in 1996 took four days to extinguish. It destroyed 122 homes in Encinitas, Carlsbad, San Marcos, and unincorporated areas of the county and burned more than 8,600 acres.

*2014: In 2014, Encinitas, Solana Beach, and Del Mar responded to 9,011 incidents.

*2015: A two-alarm fire at a house on Rancho Encinitas Drive occurred in July 2015. A 23-year-old woman and a mastiff dog died in the fire. Crews had the fire out in 45 minutes. The damage loss was almost $1.5 million.

*2015: In 2015, Encinitas, Solana Beach, and Del Mar responded to 9,571 incidents.

*2016: In April 2016, a two-acre brush fire threatened several homes on Scott Road.

*2016: An arsonist set fire to St. Andrew's Episcopal Church and Oak Crest Middle School in 2016. He was arrested in his home in July 2017. He was sentenced to 10 years in federal prison in September 2018.

*2016: In 2016, Encinitas, Solana Beach, and Del Mar responded to 9,803 incidents.

*2017: The fire personnel from Encinitas, Solana Beach, and Del Mar responded to 48 requests for assistance from departments fighting wildfires in California. Encinitas firefighters had 32 strike team deployments in 2017 on 24 fires, including the Thomas Fire in Santa Barbara and Ventura counties, which killed two people, destroyed 1,063 structures, and burned 281,893 acres.

*2017: The crews from Encinitas, Solana Beach, and Del Mar responded to a total of 10,181 incidents in 2017, including fires, traffic collisions, heart attacks, suspicious odors, smoke, and more.

*2017: The Encinitas Fire Department responded to 6,868 calls in 2017, including fires (135), explosions (5), EMS/rescues (4,474), hazardous conditions (108), service calls (546), good intentions (1,239), false calls (338), severe weather (12), and other (11). The average response time to calls was 4 min. 49 sec. The structure value loss was $5,663,228. The structure value saved was $47,323,678.

*2018: Units responded to a house fire in Sandlewood Court in 2018. A man and his dog were evacuated. The fire was extinguished in half an hour.

*2018: Two homes were damaged in a fire in September 2018. Coals disposed of in a can might have ignited the fire.

*2018: In 2018, Encinitas, Solana Beach, and Del Mar responded to 9,628 incidents.

*2018: In 2018, the Encinitas, Solana Beach, and Del Mar departments assisted federal, state, and local fire agencies with 61 personnel for 185 days to 25 wildland fires, as well as hurricane relief efforts in Hawaii. The agencies received over $979,000 in reimbursements for the services performed on these incidents.

*2019:   On January 3, 2019, a man was killed in a fire at 470 Arroyo Drive. A deputy of the San Diego's County Sheriff's Department went into the home to try to save the man but was unable to get to the second floor. The deputy was taken to UCSD hospital for treatment of smoke inhalation.

*2019:   In September 2019, a building was destroyed by fire in Leucadia that housed Mozy Cafe, Peace Pies, Shatto & Sons T-Shirts, and the Cali Life Art Gallery. The fire broke out around midnight and took hours to contain.

*2019:   In December 2019, a three-alarm fire burned for more than two hours. A home was severely damaged in the 1400 block of Neptune Avenue and a 40- by 60-foot long bluff collapsed.

*2019:   The Encinitas Fire Department responded to 6,847 calls in 2019: fires, 130; rupture/explosions, 4; EMS/rescues, 4,536; hazardous conditions, 92; service calls, 390; good intention, 1,222; false calls, 458; severe weather, 7; other, 8. The average response time was 5 minutes, 38 seconds. The structure value loss was $7,714,310. The structure value saved was $18,284,000. Encinitas, Solana Beach, and Del Mar responded to 10,231 incidents in 2019.

*2020:   In August 2020, crews fought a fire that ignited about 2 a.m. west of Highway 101, south of Swami's Beach, in brush along steep cliffs.

ESCONDIDO FIRE DEPARTMENT

Escondido is 30 miles northeast of San Diego and about 18 miles inland from the coast, covering 37.5 square miles, with a population of 151,969.

The land was granted to Juan Batista Alvarado in 1843. His heirs sold the property to Oliver Witherby in the 1850s. In 1868 Witherby sold the land to the Wolfskill brothers for $8,000 who started a sheep ranch on the land. A group of grape growers in Escondido formed the Escondido Company in 1883 to buy the land. The area was known as Rincon del Diablo until it was incorporated on October 8, 1888. For years it was an agricultural community, initially growing muscat grapes, then citrus. In 1900 the city had a population of about 1,200. In the 1920s and 1930s lemons were the largest crop. In 1950, Highway 395 connected Escondido to San Diego.

In the center of the city is Grape Day Park which was established in 1908 to celebrate the grape harvest. There are historical buildings in the park, including a turn-of-the-century barn, train depot, and blacksmith shop. Escondido's first library was established in 1895. Andrew Carnegie funded a larger library in 1910 that was moved from Kalmia Street to Grape Day Park in 1971. Mina Ward, the city's first librarian, assisted those using the library, swept the floor, cleaned the oil lamp, and paid the bills for the oil.

In the 1890s, volunteers used a hand-drawn cart and a garden hose to put out fires. When the fire marshal saw smoke on Grand Avenue, he would ring a hand bell to alert the volunteers. The hose cart, made up of two buggy wheels joined by a drum, was at the City Hall on Valley Boulevard on a platform with a six-foot ramp. In 1892, a 30-inch, 300-pound bell was purchased for $54.47 and hung in the City Hall belfry.

In 1905, a volunteer company was formed and C. L. Charles was named fire marshal; Charles Shultz, assistant fire marshal; and John Markle, secretary.

In 1914, Escondido purchased a Federal Chemical fire truck for $3,965. It was parked in the Central Garage at the southwest corner of Ohio and Broadway Avenues. K. D. Franklin, who worked at the garage, was the driver.

In 1924, the volunteers established a fire department. They were paid 25 cents a month until 1930 when the city council allocated $225 a month for the fire department which included $175 for equipment. The chief received $10, his two assistants received $3 each, and the 17 volunteers were paid $2 each.

In 1926, the department purchased an American La France engine with a 500-gallon water tank. It became known as the "Old Betsy"

Courtesy of Escondido History Center

and was retired in 1958. The Escondido Firefighters Historical Society was formed in 1980 to restore the engine, which they displayed in a small museum outside of the station. The American La France "Old Betsy" is now housed in Station 1 at 310 N. Quince Street.

The firefighters wore leather helmets and canvas turnout coats. The alarm bell was replaced with a whistle that signaled which section of the city was in danger by the number of short blasts.

On November 21, 1939, a groundbreaking ceremony was held at 150 Valley Boulevard for the department's first fire station. The adobe firehouse was finished in 1940.

Two Mack fire engines were purchased in 1949 and 1951. The department was expanded to 18 full-time firefighters and a fire prevention bureau. In 1961, voters approved a $595,000 bond that allowed the building of a fire station on Midway Drive, a headquarters station on Quince Street, and purchasing two Crown fire engines.

In the 1960s, the department grew to four stations and employed 67 fire suppression personnel. In 1967, a municipal alarm system was installed, using alarm boxes but the system was dismantled in 1979. Paramedics were added in late 1977, responding to 763 calls in the first six months.

In 1984, the Rincon del Diablo Fire District, which served much of the unincorporated area around Escondido, merged with the Escondido Fire Department.

The fire chiefs of the department include: Karl Petersen (1924-1958); Ward Ensley (1958-1962); Louis Whyte (1963-1982); Bob Watts (1982-1992); Miles Juliun (1992-1996); Victor Reed (1997-2008); Mike Lowry (2008-2016); Russ Knowles (2016-2017); and Rick Vogt (2017-).

In 1997, Victor Reed was chosen to lead the department. Chief Reed rose through the ranks from paramedic firefighter to division chief. In 2000, he initiated a Standards of Response Study to analyze fire station locations and response times. The study identified the need for two additional stations and the relocation of Station 3.

Chief Reed retired December 1, 2008.

Michael "Mike" Lowry, who served the Escondido Fire Department for 33 years and 10 months, was appointed chief in November 2008. The Alpine Fire Department hired Lowry in 1979 as a paid call firefighter, and he also worked for the U.S. Forest Service and Rancho Santa Fe before being hired as a cadet for the Escondido Fire Department on September 20, 1982. He became a paramedic in 1984. Chief Lowry was a firefighter/paramedic, engineer, and captain until November 2001 and then a division chief for seven years. He has many stories about his years in the fire service. When he was doing a ride along as a cadet, the fire crew responded to an incident involving a vehicle and a pedestrian. His supervisor said that the oxygen that Lowry was carrying wouldn't be needed as the victim had died, being almost cut in half in

Courtesy of Escondido History Center

the accident. During his seven years as a paramedic he delivered seven infants. Chief Lowry led the department through the fiscal crisis that started in 2008 and resulted in a reduction of personnel. He has a Bachelor of Science in Vocational Education from California State University, Long Beach, and an Associate of Fire Technology from Miramar College. He retired on December 31, 2016, but continued to work as interim chief until June 30, 2016.

On June 5, 2016, Russ Knowles was appointed fire chief. Knowles joined the Escondido Fire Department as a firefighter/paramedic in 1991. He served as a captain from 2001 to 2007, battalion chief from January 2007 to December 2009, division chief from December 2009 to August 2013, and deputy chief from September 2013 to June 2016. He has a Bachelor of Science in Fire Service Administration from Cogswell Polytechnical College and an Associate of Fire Technology from Santa Ana College. Chief Knowles served as the chair of the North Zone Operations Chiefs and the North Zone liaison to the San Diego County Operations committee. He also served as president for the Escondido Firefighters Association.

Rick Vogt succeeded Russ Knowles as chief in April 2017. He has worked in the fire service for over 30 years, beginning as a volunteer for Palm Desert Fire Department. Chief Vogt served as a firefighter II for Cal Fire in Temecula; engineer in Desert Hot Springs, Sky Valley, and North Palm Springs; and station captain for Cal Fire throughout Riverside County. He was the administrative and field battalion

chief for the San Marcos Fire Department from August 2005 to March 2015 before joining the Escondido Fire Department as the division chief for training and EMS in March 2015 and being promoted to deputy chief of operations in June 2016. He has a Bachelor of Arts in Speech Communications and Philosophy from Point Loma Nazarene College and a Masters of Public Administration from California State University, San Bernardino. In July 2020, Chief Vogt was elected as the 2020-2021 president of the San Diego County Chiefs Association.

The staff of the Operation Division includes: John Tenger, division chief; Jeff Sargis, battalion chief; Andre Paredes, battalion chief; and Britt Mathews, battalion chief.

The staff of the Support Services Division includes: Art Holcomb, division chief, and Jeanne McFarland, EMS program coordinator.

The staff of the Administration Division includes: Laura Costello, administrative manager; Jennifer Vasquez, administrative coordinator; Andrea Watkins, administrative assistant; and Jean Wold, department aide.

The staff of the Fire Prevention Division includes: LaVona Koretke, deputy fire marshal; and Robyn Taylor, Gabe Young, Andrew Modglin, Mike Roppo, and Chris Vaccaro, fire prevention specialists.

Jeff Murdock is the manager of the Emergency and Disaster Preparedness Division.

On November 2, 2004, Escondido voters approved Proposition P, which provided $82.6 million for the construction of a joint police and fire facility, as well as the construction of three new fire stations and a replacement Fire Station 1.

The Escondido Fire Department Administration offices are located at the combined police and fire facility at 1163 North Centre City Parkway. The fire department includes administrative and training spaces, fire prevention services, paramedic services management, and community education areas.

Station 1 opened on November 14, 2009, at 310 North Quince Street. The station was built with the intention to be used for 50 years. This structure replaced the original station which was constructed in the 1960s. The new station was designed by JKA Architecture and constructed by Jaynes Corporation. The 28,340-square-foot facility, one of the largest in southern California, cost $14.5 million, which included design, construction, parking, furnishings, six-story training tower, and classroom. Message boards located throughout the station notify the firefighters about emergency calls, including call type and units dispatched for the fastest possible response.

There are 19 people on each shift. It houses a 2014 Sutphen 100-foot aerial ladder mid-mount that costs about $1.2 million, a Pierce Type 1 engine, a 1998 Sutphen ladder, two ambulances, and a Ford F-250 battalion chief's vehicle.

The history museum is located near the building entrance at Station 1. It has on display the Escondido Fire Department's first engine, "Old Betsy" along with a mural depicting events in the history of the department.

Firefighters train every day on each shift. The training room at Station 1 also serves as a meeting space. It has an exterior public entry that allows access while maintaining security of the station when the crew is on an emergency call. The room is equipped with the best audio and video technology available. There are separate rooms for emergency medical services training and support.

The offices on the first floor of the station are divided by operational areas. The front offices are for the on-duty company officers and battalion chief. The open office is for on-shift personnel. The rear offices are for training and EMS support.

The apparatus bay consists of three drive-through bays and three back-in bays to house a fire engine, ladder truck, brush engine, medic ambulance, and battalion chief's vehicle. It is equipped with a vehicle exhaust removal system for firefighter health and safety.

There is a shop area next to the apparatus bay for storage of emergency medical supplies and tools to maintain equipment.

Since firefighters need to stay in good physical condition, the fitness conditioning room has state-of-the-art equipment and ample space.

The day room has television and recliners for personnel to use after hours. The officers quarters on the first floor has four bedrooms with individual quarters.

Firefighting crews work 24-hour shifts and cook their meals in the station. To accommodate their cooking needs, there are three refrigerators and three pantries to serve the station's three different crews. The firefighters fix their own breakfasts and lunches but two firefighters prepare the dinners. Each member of the crew chips in $6 for dinner. Everyone helps with the clean up.

Large ventilated lockers are installed for each firefighter in the turnout room. These lockers allow storage of safety gear and supply bags.

On the second floor of Station 1 there are individual sleeping quarters to serve a firefighting crew of up to 19 personnel each day. Each dorm room is programmable to the station's alerting system.

The five-story training tower located at the rear of the facility includes two burn rooms, one room is equipped with a kitchen prop and the other is equipped with a bedroom prop. The tower is equipped with a smoke machine to simulate smoky conditions throughout the structure. From the roof level firefighters can repel down to the ground or practice lowering equipment or patients.

A reserve building has four bays to store reserve apparatus and four upstairs rooms for supplies and equipment for the Explorer Post (a program to help young people learn about the fire service), Community Emergency Response Team (CERT) program, and protective equipment.

Firefighting in burning structures requires large amounts of compressed breathing air to supply the air packs. To ensure an adequate and safe supply of breathing air, an air compressor and storage system is installed to allow firefighters to safely fill cylinders and monitor air purity. There is a hose lift to dry wet fire hose and a room to store fire hose. Since it is a two-story fire station, it has a brass pole!

An extractor washing machine is installed in the station as protective gear needs to be decontaminated after calls. After a fire, car accident, or similar event, turnout gear can be laden with life-threatening chemicals, blood, body fluids, or particulate matter.

Station 2, located at 420 Midway Drive, houses one fire engine, one brush engine, and one ambulance (2020 Medix). It also houses Escondido's police and fire command vehicle.

A dedication ceremony was held on August 2, 2008, to celebrate the opening of Station 3 located at 1808 Nutmeg Street. The station cost $6 million which included $4.5 million awarded to Murray Builders for its construction. The station has one fire engine and one brush engine. It replaced the station at 2165 Village Road which was built in 1977 at a cost of $120,000.

Station 3 is located at 1808 Nutmeg Street and houses 1 paramedic fire engine and 1 wildland brush engine (Brush 1363, 2012 International 7400 SFA 4 x 4).

Station 4, located adjacent to Kit Carson Park at 3301 Bear Valley Parkway, houses one fire engine and one brush engine. The station was closed in 2010 because mold was discovered throughout the facility. The station was rebuilt by Erickson-Hall Construction Company at a cost of $2.4 million. It was reopened in 2012.

Station 5, located southwest of I-15 at 2319 Felicita Road, houses one fire engine, one ambulance (2018 Medix), and one Type 6 brush patrol.

Both Station 6 and Station 7 opened in November 2008. Exhaust hoses hook up to vehicles, pumping diesel outside. The two stations are equipped with 500-gallon diesel storage tanks and emergency generators. Durable concrete blocks are used in the apparatus bays instead of drywall. The kitchens and bathrooms have long-lasting terrazzo walls and marble countertops.

Station 6, located at 1735 Del Dios Road, houses three firefighters and one fire engine although it has room for four firefighters and two more vehicles. An OES Type 2 engine is housed at this station.

Station 7, located at 1220 N. Ash Street, houses one fire engine and one ambulance (2020 Medix). The original station was built in 1978.

The personnel are dedicated to protecting the lives and property of Escondido's residents.

"Old Betsy"

ESCONDIDO FIRE DEPARTMENT

CALLS RECALLED:

*1955: The firefighters responded in the 1926 American La France engine for the last time in 1955 to a fire at Ting's Pharmacy at the corner of Grand and Broadway. The engine was retired in 1958 and deteriorated in the city yard until 1980 when the Escondido Historical Firefighters Association was formed and restored the American La France engine, which they then placed on display in a small museum built by the firefighters outside of Station 1 on Quince Street.

*1980: Firefighter/paramedic John Gregory Tormey died April 1980 when his car hit the center divider on Interstate 5 north of Del Mar Heights Road. He had worked for the Escondido Fire Department since 1977.

*1992: In 1992, Captain Mike Lowry and his crew responded to a head-on collision on East Valley Parkway. A mother and her two twin little girls had been headed into town to buy things for the twin's upcoming birthday party when an impaired driver crossed into their lane. The mother died at the scene, but the girls were saved and taken by helicopter to Rady's Children's Hospital.

*2007: The Witch Creek Fire that started October 21, 2007, merged with the Guejito Fire. Escondido lost 36 homes. A 58-year-old mortgage broker and his 55-year-old wife, a teacher, were found in the ruins of their Escondido home. Countywide, two people died, 1,265 homes were destroyed, and 247,800 acres burned. Over 500,000 people were evacuated and 600 firefighters fought the fires.

*2014: The Cocos Fire began in San Marcos on March 14, 2014, and spread into western Escondido. Residents living west of Valley Parkway, including the community south of Citracado Parkway and west of Del Dios Highway, as well as areas north of Via Rancho Parkway and west of Felicita Road, were evacuated. The fire was fought by 514 firefighters, 21 engines, 13 fire crews, and 2 water tenders. Forty structures in the county were destroyed and 1,995 acres burned.

*2014: In May 2014, there were 14 wildfires in the County. They burned 26,000 acres and destroyed 65 homes, including some in Escondido.

*2014: On October 15, 2014, Escondido and San Diego crews worked together in responding to a three-car crash. One patient needed to be extricated from a car and was hoisted and transported by helicopter to Palomar Medical Center. Two patients were transported by ambulance.

*2016: In December 2016, a fire in a mobile home at Greencrest Mobilehome Park killed a 5-year-old girl, left an 11-year-old boy in critical condition, and injured seven other family members.

*2017: A crew from Escondido fought wildfires in Riverside, San Luis Obispo, Santa Barbara, Mariposa, and Modoc National Forest. On some incidents, the firefighters stayed two weeks before being replaced.

*2017: Cory Iverson, 32, from Escondido, was killed while fighting the Thomas Fire in Ventura County. His death was caused by thermal injuries and smoke inhalation. He had been a firefighter with Cal Fire since 2009.

*2018: On August 14, 2018, a home at 3900 Foxley Drive sustained extreme damage from a fire that started in the garage. The Escondido Fire Department was assisted by firefighters from San Marcos. The Red Cross helped with immediate aid and the California Fire Foundation gave a gift card to the family.

*2018: On September 29, 2018, fire crews responded to a garage fire in the 1600 block of Cambria Place. The garage and two vehicles were heavily damaged. A gift card from California Fire Foundation was given for immediate emergency aid to the family.

*2018:   On October 24, 2018, a single-family residence in the 1200 block of Joshua Street caught fire. Four engines, one truck company, one ambulance, and two battalion chiefs responded to the incident. The fire was contained in about 20 minutes. Four dogs and three pet birds died in the fire due to smoke inhalation.

*2018:   On December 28, 2018, at 8:45 a.m. the Escondido Communication Center received a call of a fire at Escondido Resource Recovery on W. Washington Avenue. The two-alarm fire was controlled in about 45 minutes. Nine fire engines, three truck companies, two rescue ambulances, and two battalion chiefs responded to the call.

*2020:   On October 1, 2020, a small vegetation fire at Bear Valley Parkway and Royal Crest Drive burned close to structures.

*2020:   In October, 2020, E137 contained a 120-gallon fuel spill when a pick up truck collided with a semi truck. E137 was assisted by Escondido Police Department as well as San Diego Fire Hazmat and San Diego County Hazmat.

*2020:   On October 16, 2020, crews responded to a structure fire in the area of Via Rancho Pkwy and Bernardo Lane. Firefighters contained and controlled the fire in approximately one hour. The garage and contents were a complete loss. The dwelling area of the home sustained major damage near the garage.

*2020:   In October 2020, BR132 was assigned to the wildfires in northern California for two weeks.

*2020:   On October 27, 2020, 8632 was deployed to the Blue Ridge Fire in the Yorba Linda and Chino Hills area in Orange and San Bernardino Counties. The fire burned 13,964 acres, destroyed 1 structure, and damaged 10 structures.

FERNBROOK VOLUNTEER FIRE COMPANY

Fernbrook is situated in a lovely valley four miles southwest of Ramona. The valley begins at Highway 67, runs alongside Mussey Grade Road, and ends at San Vicente Reservoir. It encompasses 14 square miles and has a population of about 1,000. Fire poses a special danger to this community because there is only one road leading in and out of it.

The first settler was a man from Vermont with the last name of Mussey who built an adobe house in a grove of live oaks at the south end of the dirt road in the late 1870s. Teamsters traveling the road would park their wagons under Mr. Mussey's trees and spend the night.

The road was used for over 50 years to reach Ramona, Santa Ysabel, Julian, and Warner Hot Springs. Freight was transferred from the San Diego Eastern and Cuyamaca Railroad to wagons at the Foster depot south of what is now San Vicente Reservoir, then hauled north, traveling at the rate of a mile an hour. There was a spring on the side of the hill where drivers could quench their thirst. Mussey Grade Road had turnouts where two wagons could pass.

George DeClyver Curtis homesteaded 160 acres near Mr. Mussey in 1910. Curtis's father was the Army physician who attended Abraham Lincoln when he was shot and removed the bullet from his brain. Prior to coming to California, Curtis studied

at Harvard University, Columbia University, and Ecole Julien and Academie Colarossi in Paris, then took a position cataloging rare books for the New York Public Library. In "The Lone Homestead" he described a fire in Fernbrook in September 1913:

"Suddenly on an afternoon of fierce heat, I saw thick smoke surge up behind the ridge to the east. It looked dangerous even to inexperienced eyes, and I felt relieved, after some watching, to see how the wind carried it along parallel to the ridge, not crossing over toward me.

"The next day the thermometer on my porch showed 100, and I thought I would do no hard work. As it turned out, I was just kidding myself.

"At two o'clock in the afternoon a fierce, gusty wind sprang up from the east and the smoke that had passed me by the day before reared up again, thick and high, casting a murk over all the sky. The sun's face through it was angry red. I fell to work at once, raking out dead grass and leaves, clearing firebreaks, and carrying away everything inflammable from around the house. Nothing looked so good to me as the small patches of bare earth where I had cultivated the ground. I dragged out my trunk, bedding, tools, books, easy chair, and gun and put them on that bare dirt; then I filled water pails and set them handy.

Pearl Ellis

"The day after that there was still a distant but ominous smoke to the northeast. The fire, as I learned later, had swung toward the town ten miles up the road. In those days, there was no organization and no such equipment as we have now, only the primitive tools—shovel, axe and rake, and wet sacks. The fire warden had power to impress any man as a firefighter, and the usual source of supply was the billiard or poolroom in the nearest small town; the theory being that any man who had nothing more important to do than chalk a cue or look on at a game might as well be on the fire line."

In 1976 the San Diego County Board of Supervisors decided not to renew the contract with CDF (California Division of Forestry) for protection of homes in the unincorporated areas. Without adequate protection the residents of Fernbrook faced increased or unavailable fire insurance for their homes. Fernbrook

didn't have the tax base to support a paid department, or even a partially paid department, so a group of volunteers was needed who could be on call 24 hours a day.

On April 3, 1976, a meeting was held at Dos Picos Park to form a volunteer fire company for the 14 square miles in the immediate area and for 100 square miles in the nearby areas. Seven people were elected by the community to serve on the board of directors. Twenty people signed up to become firefighters. We were basically formed to take care of structure fires in the Fernbrook area. Brush fires were handled by the California Department of Forestry. We, of course, would assist but our first responsibility was to the buildings in our area. Ira W. Walter III was elected fire chief. When he quit after several months to run his construction business, I was selected as the fire chief and served from 1976 to 1982.

Some of the crew were: Pearl Ellis, chief; Tom Lynch, assistant chief; Mike O'Betz and Roy Law, captains; Ron Rowe and Glenn Maadsen, engineers; Alice Lynch, fire marshal; and Ira Walters, Mike Langdon, Gerry Carlson, Walt Nikuls, Bob Perkins, Pat Perkins, Ron Rudolph, Art Bale, Fern Stovall, and Dale Stovall, firefighters. We had a core group of 14 people and at times we had as many as 25 in the volunteer department. Board members included: Carol Levin, Glenn Madsen, Bob Perkins, Sandy Rudolph, and Franklin Ingham.

We trained several hours every Wednesday night, went to training sessions offered by San Diego's Office of Fire Services, attended classes at Miramar College, and became EMTs. We had some turnover when prospective volunteers found out it was more than just a truck ride to a fire. It took us about two minutes to respond to a call in our area.

In addition to training over 300 hours from July 1, 1976, to June 30, 1977, the volunteer firefighters helped the residents of the community raise $3,674.65. Fundraising continued in the following years of the fire company with potlucks, donations by merchants and residents, aluminum can collections, dances, picnics, and the sale of shirts and sweatshirts with the logo "Buzzard Gulch" on them, a nickname inspired by the local vultures in the eucalyptus trees. The number one goal of the community was to build a fire station as our engine was parked in an open one-acre lot donated by Newt Homer, across from my home. Some of the men said they were going to install a pulley from my house down to the engine so I could get there faster. At least, I think they were joking. I never had any problem being the female chief of the department. It was all team work; we weren't there as individuals. All our lives depended on the other persons we were trusting.

The San Marcos Fire Department donated a 1940 Van Pelt engine to the Fernbrook Volunteer Fire Company. In August 1976, a 1956 Coast fire engine was purchased by the county from the Stockton Fire Department for the Fernbrook volunteers. The County later replaced it with a 1963 International fire engine and gave the fire company a rescue van.

Besides serving as volunteers in our local community, the County's Office of Fire Services would send the Fernbrook Volunteer Fire Company on many alarms throughout the County, whether it be fire or rescue. We answered the alarms as first responders.

After the Ramona Municipal Water District and the Ramona Fire Protection District merged in 1982, the Fernbrook Volunteer Fire Company was dissolved and the area it covered became part of the water district. The apparatus of the fire company was given to the Ramona Fire Department. The 1940 Van Pelt was purchased and restored by William Carroll of San Marcos. For a brief time, some of the Fernbrook firefighters became reserves with the Ramona Fire Department.

The Ramona Municipal Water District signed a contract with CDF (California Department of Forestry) in July 1993 to provide firefighters to staff Ramona Fire Department's fire apparatus.

Art Bale

So, daily, including weekends and often late into the nights, Fernbrook volunteers forsook work, leisure pursuits, or sleep to answer emergency calls along the winding backcountry roads.

Residents of the area still recall the days of the Fernbrook Volunteer Fire Company. People were proud of their firefighters, grateful for the emergency services, and enjoyed the fundraisers. The firefighters appreciated the financial and moral support provided by the community. The board of directors contributed administrative skills to its success. It was a complete circle that suited the community.

Pearl Ellis and Art Bale

CALLS RECALLED:

*1976: The Fernbrook volunteers were pleased at how quickly they extinguished a fire that was burning in a pasture on Highland Valley Road. When they saw a fire in another section of the field, they extinguished it too. Then they saw a rancher on the back of his truck lighting fires; he had a controlled burn permit. The firefighters were putting out his fires as fast as he was lighting them!

*1976: We responded to a medical aid at Wildcat Canyon Road on a Sunday night. The firefighters drove for a long time and looked and looked with no success for the person who needed help. Much later we learned that a passing motorist had taken an injured boy with a broken arm to Ramona. A week later a van overturned on the same road with a man trapped in it. We received a letter from the hospital where he was taken commending us for saving his life.

*1977: In January 1977, the crew responded to a three-car collision on State Highway 67. A man tried to pass a pickup truck on a blind curve. He had pulled into the southbound lane to pass when he saw a station wagon headed toward him. When he tried to pull back into the northbound lane, he hit the truck, bounced back into the southbound lane and hit the station wagon head-on before plunging down a 40-foot embankment. We were able to free the man by cutting off the top of the car.

*1977: David Walter, the brother of Ira Walter, was killed in a one-car accident on Mussey Grade Road.

*1979: Firefighters responded to a call on Old Julian Highway for a downed power line in a field. A fierce Santa Ana wind condition had developed, fence posts were on fire, and the fire was headed towards Ramona.

*1980: We have a vivid memory of a fire on Dye Road that had flames 300 feet in the air.

*1981: Many of the calls to which the firefighters responded were on State Highway 67, a curvy road with one or two lanes in each direction. There were heartbreaking incidents involving people the firefighters knew. When friends and relatives needed help, the work was particularly difficult.

*1986: In 1986, Thomas Lynch, who served as our assistant chief, was killed when his experimental plane crashed on his property in Fernbrook.

*2003: In the Cedar Fire, 106 homes were destroyed on Mussey Grade Road. On this road no fire trucks went past Dos Picos Park Road. Many of the residents in the area felt that the firefighters should have tried to help them. Art Bale and I lost the beloved home and the guest log cabin we had built. Also destroyed was the Honduran mahogany bed in the cabin belonging to George Curtis's father, the doctor who took the bullet out of Abraham Lincoln when he was assassinated. Art had a heart attack four months after the fire from dealing with the stress. No one who has not lost his or her home in a fire can really understand how devastating it is. It's something one never gets over. The fire caused some people to divorce, some were underinsured, and others found it too difficult to rebuild and moved away. Chi Varnardo, a lifelong resident, wrote a book titled "A Canyon Trilogy: life before, during and after the Cedar Fire" about her experiences during the fire.

*2007: Fernbrook was evacuated during the huge Witch Creek Fire as a precautionary measure. There was a very long line of cars on Highway 67 as residents tried to evacuate.

While I was at Amelia Island in Florida, the fire was spreading on October 21, 2007, in San Diego County, from Santa Ysabel, 30 miles north of Ramona, to soon cover thousands of acres. This fire, the Witch Creek Fire, was caused by downed power lines. The same day, the Harris Fire was started by Santa Ana winds. On October 22 the Guejito Fire in San Pasqual Valley merged with the Witch Creek Fire.

By the time I arrived in San Diego County on October 22, all residents of Ramona had been evacuated. In the midst of the evacuation, the paramedics had taken Art Bale to the hospital. Art was very sick, our three Bouvier des Flandres dogs were anxious to go home, the motels were full, our neighbors were nervous, our friends were worried, and I was in a daze, reliving the Cedar Fire that had taken everything from us four years earlier.

There were parallels between the Witch Creek Fire of 2007 and the Cedar Fire of 2003. The Witch Creek Fire started almost on the anniversary of the Cedar Fire. Both times the fires occurred on a weekend, with fire resources spread thin because of flare-ups in other parts of California (2007, Malibu; 2003, Los Angeles). Lives were lost (2007, 2; 2003,15). Structures destroyed (2007, 1,700; 2003, 2,820). Art was very sick (2007, heart palpitations; 2003, heart attack). Two fires both times (2007, Witch Creek Fire and Harris Fire; 2003, Cedar Fire and Guejito Fire).

Some of us were at the evacuation center in Poway, where the volunteers were wonderful, the food was plentiful, and the cots were uncomfortable. A stranger helped me in a surprising way! While I was sitting in my car, a young woman named Yoko invited me to her home. She sat me down and brought me food and drinks. Friends and strangers, all there in time of need. My friend, Martine Spina, who lives in Nice, France, wrote, "I am admirative of the Americans' sense of commitment and solidarity."

The fires were menacing, merciless, devastating, and deadly. I'm struck with the chilling certainty that we will be in the path of a fierce and potentially deadly inferno again.

*2019: Sadly, on August 24, 2019, Captain Michael Dean O'Betz received his last alarm at the age of 70. And true to his dedication, Mike answered "Reporting for duty." Mike was an enthusiastic member of the Fernbrook Volunteer Fire Company in the late 1970s and early 1980s.

HARBISON CANYON VOLUNTEER FIRE DEPARTMENT

Harbison Canyon is 23 miles northeast of San Diego, located in a canyon between Crest and Alpine. There is a population of 4,223 (2018) in a 10-square-mile area.

John Stewart Harbison settled in the canyon in 1874. He imported bees into California and invented new methods of rearing bees. Within seven years' time, he was the largest producer of honey in the world, operating 2,000 to 3,000 hives.

The Harbison Canyon Volunteer Fire Department was supported entirely by donations and projects in the 1950s and 1960s. The Ladies Auxiliary held an annual rummage and bake sale in the Fire Hall at 127 Francis Drive to benefit the department. In December 1958, five teenage boys damaged equipment at the volunteer fire department. They removed fuses to the station's siren, cut wires to the sirens of the vehicles, and cut the flagpole rope.

In 1976 the San Diego County Board of Supervisors decided not to renew the contract with CDF (California Division of Forestry) for protection of homes and buildings in the unincorporated areas. Some of the areas were able to join other nearby fire districts. If not, the county provided apparatus and gear to unincorporated areas in the county. It arranged for professional firefighters from area fire departments to train the volunteers. Harbison Canyon was one of the volunteer fire departments operating in the unincorporated areas.

In October 2007, the local planning commission voted 15 to 0 to build a new fire station. In 2008, Harbison Canyon came under the jurisdiction of the San Diego County Fire Authority which contracts with Cal Fire for fire services in unincorporated areas.

A new fire station, Station 24, at 551 Harbison Canyon Road near St. George Drive opened in February 2009. The station is built of prefabricated steel with a slate roof. It was funded by the Sycuan Indian Reservation and the San Diego County Fire Authority. The station houses Patrol 7224, a 2015 Ford F-550, and an engine. The original wood station burned down in the Cedar Fire as well as two of the three fire trucks used by the department. The one remaining was a 1987 engine that was parked at the captain's house after 2003.

Ed Humerickhouse, known as "Uncle Ed," was the unofficial mayor at the time of the Cedar Fire. He would drive out of the burn area after the fire, just to look at something green. He was a firefighter for 33 years for Cal Fire and also worked for the San Miguel Fire Protection District.

The Harbison Canyon Lions Club was formed after the 2003 Cedar Fire. Besides being a source of fiscal aid to fire families, the Harbison Canyon Lions teamed up with Local Carpenters Union 495 to assist in rebuilding 25 under insured homes.

There have been 1,300 California firefighters who have died in the line of duty since 1850. The number brings home the risks taken by volunteer and career firefighters while serving their communities.

Harbison Canyon 1936 fire truck

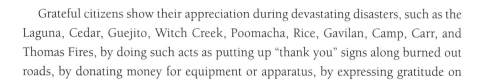
Harbison Canyon, 1993

Harbison Canyon

Residents
DO NOT
need to boil
tap water.

Grateful citizens show their appreciation during devastating disasters, such as the Laguna, Cedar, Guejito, Witch Creek, Poomacha, Rice, Gavilan, Camp, Carr, and Thomas Fires, by doing such acts as putting up "thank you" signs along burned out roads, by donating money for equipment or apparatus, by expressing gratitude on social media, by delivering food to fire stations, or by identifying them as heroes. The firefighters in Harbison Canyon not only lost their homes in the Cedar Fire but also their fire station. Like firefighters everywhere, they put their own lives at risk to help their communities.

CALLS RECALLED:

*1946:   On Labor Day weekend in September 1946, a devastating fire burned in Harbison Canyon.

*1959:   In September 1959, the Harbison Canyon Volunteer Fire Department was first on the scene of a brush fire in the Harbison Canyon area south of Chocolate Drop Mountain that burned 12 acres.

*1970:   During the Laguna Fire in 1970, Harbison Canyon lost 117 homes. The fire started from a downed power line in the Laguna Mountains, moving rapidly towards Crest and Harbison Canyon. The fire killed eight people, burned 175,425 acres, and destroyed 382 homes and 1,000 structures. The damage cost $5.6 million.

*1979:   In September 1979, while a woman was smoking her bee hives in Harbison Canyon, a fire was ignited and started burning nearby brush. More than 80 firefighters from 15 stations fought the blaze.

*2003:   On October 27, 2003, Harbison Canyon lost 287 homes out of 388 homes in the community during the Cedar Fire. The Emmanuel Christian Church in Harbison Canyon was destroyed in the fire. One-third of the church's 90 members lost homes in the fire. A welding shop, a trailer dealership, and a tavern were also lost in the fire. President George W. Bush and Governor Arnold Schwarzenegger visited Harbison Canyon 10 days later on November 4. Insurance companies called it a clean burn because the fire was so hot that even the soot was consumed. After the fire, a pickup truck arrived from the Home Depot loaded with wheelbarrows and sifters and buckets.

More than half the residents didn't rebuild. Eutha and Bill Scholl's home, a converted 1927 fishing cabin, survived the fire, but her mother's house, nearby, was destroyed. "People run away from grief," Eutha Scholl said. "They didn't stay and deal with their feelings of loss or abandonment, and there was a feeling that God had abandoned them."

The community received help in rebuilding from many organizations, most notably from the New York Says Thank You Foundation which was created in response to the support given to New Yorkers from people all over the United States after the terrorist attacks of 9/11/2001.

The Cedar Fire was started by a lost hunter setting a fire to signal for help. The fire was reported at 5:37 p.m. on October 25. There was not an initial aircraft attack because it was too late to dispatch aircraft due to impending nightfall, in accordance with federal and state aviation policies. The Santa Ana winds blew the fire southwest at speeds of over 15 miles an hour. Fifteen lives were lost, 2,820 structures (2,232 homes) destroyed, and 273,246 acres burned in the fire. The cost was $27 million.

*2007:   Harbison Canyon was once again in danger in October 2007 when the Witch Creek Fire burned in Blossom Valley and the Harris Fire burned in Jamul.

*2013:   On February 20, 2013, the Harbison Canyon firefighters responded to a vehicle rollover with two injured passengers.

*2017:   An automobile exhaust started the Jennings Fire along Interstate 8 and Old Highway 80, burning 400 acres.

*2019:   In February 2019, a $2 million house was destroyed by fire in Harbison Canyon.

HEARTLAND FIRE & RESCUE

On January 1, 2010, El Cajon, La Mesa and Lemon Grove entered into a joint exercise of powers agreement for organizational management of fire protection, fire prevention services, emergency medical services, and community emergency preparedness. The expected savings was $560,000 among the three cities without a loss of service to the public.

Mike Scott was appointed the Heartland Fire & Rescue chief in October 2009. He had been the chief of El Cajon since 2005. Chief Scott began his career with the department in 1984 as a firefighter/paramedic. During his 28 years with El Cajon, he was one of the original California Task Force-8 Urban Search and Rescue team members in California. He started as a technical rescue specialist and deployed to the Northridge Earthquake in 1994 and to the Atlanta Olympics bombing in 1996. Scott transferred to the Canine Division where he was partnered with a devoted black Labrador, Billy, in November 1998. Chief Scott and Billy became the second canine search team in the county to be certified by FEMA. They served several local missions before being deployed to Ground Zero shortly after the 9/11 terrorist attacks in New York. Chief Scott retired on July 29, 2012.

Rick Sitta, who earned a commendation for bravery in the 2003 Cedar Fire, was selected as chief for Heartland Fire & Rescue in August 2012. In January 2010, he had been appointed deputy chief of Heartland Fire & Rescue. Chief Sitta led the transition of three East County fire departments into one. He had command staff positions on Cal Fire Type I incident management teams for major wildland responses throughout California. He was a division chief in El Cajon for nine years. Before then, the Mount Helix resident was a firefighter, engineer, captain, and division chief in Coronado for 14 years. A graduate of Point Loma High, he was a commercial fisherman for 13 years before beginning his firefighting career at age 34. Chief Sitta retired on August 12, 2016, at the age of 56, with a salary of $178,000.

Colin Stowell became chief of Heartland Fire & Rescue in December 2016 and served in the position until August 2018. Chief Stowell was responsible for four operating budgets as well as capital improvement projects for Heartland Fire & Rescue. He handled contract negotiations and oversight and was accountable to three city managers and city councils.

Chief Stowell had worked for the San Diego Fire-Rescue Department for 28 years and was appointed chief of the department by Mayor Kevin Faulconer on August 13, 2018. He joined the San Diego Fire-Rescue Department in 1988, promoted to captain in 2002, battalion chief in 2007, deputy chief in 2012, and assistant chief in 2015. He earned an Associate of Fire Science from Miramar College, a Bachelor of Science

in Public Administration from San Diego State University, and completed the Executive Fire Officer Program at the National Fire Academy.

On October 20, 2018, Steve Swaney was appointed to lead the Heartland Fire & Rescue. He had been a division chief for Heartland Fire & Rescue since 2013. Chief Swaney began working with the El Cajon Fire Department in 1985. He also served as the fire chief for the Julian Cuyamaca Fire Protection District. He obtained an Associate of Fire Science from Miramar College and participated in paramedic training at the University of California San Diego. He is a 2016 graduate of the Leadership East County. Swaney has a Bachelor of Science in Management from California Coast University.

Besides serving Heartland Fire & Rescue, Chief Swaney is a certified Federal Emergency Management Agency canine evaluator and is a lead instructor for the FEMA Canine Search Specialist School. He started working with a chocolate Labrador named Sherman in 1997. Chief Swaney and his dog, Sherman, were in New York within 24 hours of the Twin Towers collapse to aid in rescue efforts. They were also deployed to Hurricane Katrina in New

Courtesy Heartland Fire & Rescue

Orleans and Hurricane Rita in southeast Texas in 2005, Hurricane Ernesto off the Atlantic Coast in 2006, and the Torrey Pines Bluff collapse in 2004. After Sherman retired in 2006, Swaney continued rescue work in San Diego with two other rescue dogs, Icon and Tank.

The chief officers of Heartland Fire & Rescue are: Steve Swaney, chief; Brent Koch, operations division chief; Jay Wojnowski, administration/emergency medical division chief; and Brian Manns, logistics/support services division chief.

The staff includes: Andy McKellar, emergency preparedness coordinator and CERT manager; Shaun Richardson, fire marshal; Frankie Rodriquez, El Cajon fire inspector II; Sonny Saghera, public information officer and Rachel Clark and Angela Pele-Toalepai, La Mesa fire inspectors I.

Heartland Fire & Rescue received a class 1 rating from the Insurance Services Office (ISO) in 2015! Of the 58,000 fire departments across the United States rated by ISO, only 98 have a class 1 rating, including only eight fire districts in California. The ISO surveys fire departments on fire suppression service, examining water availability, equipment, deployment, training, personnel, and risk reduction. Districts are ranked 1 through 10, with a class 1 rating presented only to those districts that score 90 or higher out of a possible 100 points.

In October 2012, the Viejas Band of Kumeyaay Indians and Heartland Fire Training Authority entered into a Joint Powers Agreement (JPA). Viejas Chief Don Butz said, "This JPA finally allows Viejas to have a seat at the table and have a full and meaningful partnership with other fire agencies that we've worked with for years in a very productive way. Ultimately, this benefits the entire region, since wildfires and other natural disasters do not recognize geographic, political or other borders. We are all stronger and better protected when we work and train together."

In January 2019, the Heartland personnel mourned the death of its rescue dog, Stella. Eleven-year-old Stella passed away after a battle with cancer. Stella was with the department for nearly a decade. She had worked alongside Captain Matt Kirk since 2009. They were paired together through the National Disaster Search Dog Foundation, which trains K-9s to find people during disasters. Stella had been on several deployments, including Hurricane Irma and the mudslides in Montecito, California. She was also part of Urban Search & Rescue Task Force 8 as a FEMA type 1 canine search dog.

The combined resources of El Cajon, La Mesa, and Lemon Grove are eight fire stations, nine engine companies, two truck companies, three paramedic transport units, and one BLS transport unit (Peak Hour Unit) to serve 180,000 residents.

Station 6 is located at 100 East Lexington Avenue, El Cajon. The administrative office is at this station. It houses Engine 8 (2013 Pierce Arrow XT); Truck 6 (2005 Pierce Lance

2000); and Squad 6. Squad 6 is a custom-built 2017 Ford F-250 that is used to respond to low-acuity medical emergencies, freeing up the department's Engine 6 and Truck 6 to respond to more significant emergencies. The truck cost about $82,000.

Station 7 is located at 695 Tyrone Avenue, El Cajon.

Station 8, located at 1470 Madison Avenue, El Cajon, houses Engine 8, a 2019 Pierce Arrow XT. The pumper has a Detroit Diesel DD13, 505 hp, TAK-4 Independent front suspension, a spring rear suspension, Command Zone electrical system, Husky 3 foam system 1,500 gpm, foam and water tank, ad 500-gallon tank size.

Station 9, located at 1301 North Marshal Street, El Cajon, houses Engine 9, a 2008 Pierce Velocity.

Station 10, located at 7853 Central Avenue, Lemon Grove, houses Engine 10, a 2014 Pierce arrow XT.

Station 11, located at 8054 Allison Avenue, La Mesa, houses Engine 2016 a Pierce Arrow XT.

Station 12, located at 8844 Dallas Street, La Mesa, houses Rescue Engine 12, a 2013 Pierce Quantum.

Station 13 is located at 9110 Grossmont Boulevard, La Mesa.

The mission of the department is: "We will selflessly strive to serve the needs of our communities through collaboration, innovation, and personal accountability while embracing change and planning for the future."

CALLS RECALLED:

*2011:   In June 2011, a nine-year-old boy was struck by a vehicle at Madison Avenue and East Main Street while riding his bike to school. Firefighters used airbags and cribbing to safely lift the vehicle off the child. They attribute a bicycle helmet to saving the boy's life.

*2017:   The Heartland crews responded to nearly 26,000 emergency calls in 2017.

*2019:   In June 2019, six ducklings trapped in a storm drain in the 200 block of Fletcher Parkway were rescued by Heartland firefighters and animal rescue personnel. "Firefighters were able to remove the grates and called for the assistance of animal control. While playing duck sounds on their phone to lure them out, firefighters and animal control were able to use a net to rescue each duckling one by one," said Captain and Public Information Officer Sonny Saghera. The ducklings were turned over to Project Wildlife to release into the wild.

*2019:   In August 2019, firefighters used oxygen to revive a cat found unconscious in the front yard of a home on fire. The cat ran off after it was resuscitated.

*2020:   In April 2020, crews responded to a two-story home in the 1300 block of Helix View Drive in El Cajon, where they battled to extinguish flames up to 50 feet high. Two firefighters were taken to the hospital.

*2020:   A 78-year-old woman was transported to a hospital after suffering injuries when a trolley struck her red Toyota car near the trolley station at the intersection of Spring Street and La Mesa Boulevard. Firefighters used the Jaws of Life to rescue the woman.

HEARTLAND FIRE TRAINING FACILITY

Fernbrook Volunteer Fire Company at Hearthland Fire Training Facility, 1976

Fernbrook volunteers at Hearthland Fire Training Facility, 1976

On December 1, 1973, an agreement was entered into by El Cajon, La Mesa, and the fire protection districts of Santee, Lakeside, and Spring Valley to form a Joint Powers Authority for training. The agreement was later amended to change the name of Spring Valley to San Miguel.

The facility was dedicated in 1975. It is funded and operated by a Joint Powers Authority, which consists of El Cajon, La Mesa, Lemon Grove, and Santee; the fire protection districts of Alpine, Bonita-Sunnyside, Lakeside, and San Miguel; the Viejas and Barona Reservation Fire Departments; and the San Diego County Fire Authority with its cooperative agencies. These fire agencies from the Central Zone often train together which improves coordination on all emergency incidents. This cooperative approach provides a benefit to the taxpayer through the sharing of resources such as training, apparatus, dispatch, communication, and purchasing. It also reduces unnecessary duplication and bureaucracy while decreasing response times and increasing efficiency.

These East County agencies represented Zone 4 of the San Diego County Mutual Aid Agreement and adopted the name of Heartland, becoming the Heartland Fire Training Facility. The name was later changed to the Thomas H. Owen Heartland Fire Training Facility after it was dedicated to one of its founders, former El Cajon Fire Chief Tom Owen.

The Authority is governed by a commission which is comprised of elected officials from each member jurisdiction, along with a Board of Fire Chiefs which includes each respective fire chief. Contract agencies are non-voting members. Zone training officers oversee the training components and set curriculum. The annual budget is derived from fees paid by participating agencies which are based on a formula using the number of on-duty personnel from each agency. Funds are also generated from contract agencies, the rental of the facility to other public safety agencies, and from the delivery of college fire science classes. Contract agencies have the ability to utilize all of the available resources but are not voting members.

The Heartland Fire Training Facility occupies close to 4 acres of land at 1301 N. Marshal Avenue owned by El Cajon next to Fire Station 9. The facility consists of a 5-story drill tower, an environmental building capable of performing hot fires, a pump test area, two classrooms, a computer based simulator used for command testing and training, and all of the props required by the State Fire Marshal Office to hold a variety of heavy rescue classes. An accredited fire academy is provided each year along with community college fire science classes in addition to in-service training.

One example of how in-service training is accomplished is the Color Group method of scheduling. More than 40 engines, trucks, and paramedic ambulances use the facility at least twice a month on regularly scheduled drill days. The schedule also has a combination of day drills, night drills, and multi company-multiagency drills all of which are recommended by the National Fire Protection Association (NFPA) and the ISO evaluation service.

With the Color Group training, a yearly schedule provides each company access to the facility while maintaining coverage in the zone and minimizing overcrowding at the facility. This time is primarily used for single company skill maintenance and training.

Group B training is generally scheduled four to five times a year and is designed to have companies from different agencies work together. Group B training also focuses on specific topics like officer command training, annual wildland refresher training, and annual hazardous materials training.

Every year from January to April a 486 hour accredited Firefighter 1 Academy is run for firefighters from participating agencies as well as open enrollees.

Any company from a participating agency may use the facility when needed as long as there is not a scheduling conflict.

A new additional site in Casa de Oro is scheduled to start in the near future that will provide a greater variety of training props and drill ground space to accommodate the addition of more fire companies, public utility teams, and law enforcement.

On April 26, 2010, the 20th Heartland Firefighter 1 Academy graduation was held at the Ronald Reagan Community Center, 195 East Douglas Avenue in El Cajon. Twenty-four graduates successfully completed 14-weeks (488 hours) of firefighter training at the Heartland Training Facility in conjunction with San Diego Miramar College. The San Diego Firefighters Emerald Society Bagpipe & Drum Band led the graduates in as the ceremony began. The graduates took positions with the El Cajon, La Mesa, Coronado, and Mt. Laguna Fire Departments, and the San Miguel Fire Protection District as firefighters, reserve, and volunteer firefighters. Four of the graduates were open enrollment students from Miramar College. The firefighter academy consisted of classroom instruction and manipulative practice. Academy classes were held every Monday, Wednesday, Friday, and Saturday for 14 weeks, approximately ten hours per day. Some of the graduates were auxiliary reserve firefighters.

Thomas "Tom" Owen, one of the first full-time firefighters for El Cajon, was appointed the El Cajon's fire chief in 1970. In 1949, at the age of 21, Owen had been hired as a firefighter at a salary of $175 a month plus free board at the fire station. He was promoted to engineer in 1955, captain in 1957, assistant fire chief in 1962, and fire chief in 1970.

Owen recalled one of the Wednesday night drills in those early days—the crew was driving back to the station on Chase Avenue when they almost crashed into a herd of cows that were crossing the street. In those days the crew only put out fires. He retired in May 1980. Chief Owen died in 1992. His son Steve became a firefighter with the El Cajon Fire Department in 1979.

The Heartland Fire Training Facility is dedicated to Chief Owen, co-founder of the facility, by being named the Thomas H. Owen Sr. Heartland Fire Training Facility.

Pearl Ellis at Hearthland Fire Training Facility, 1976.

IMPERIAL BEACH FIRE-RESCUE DEPARTMENT

Imperial Beach was founded in June 1887 and became a city on July 18, 1956. It is the southernmost city in California, 14.1 miles south of San Diego and five miles northwest of downtown Tijuana. The city has a population of 27,428 and covers an area of 4.5 square miles with four miles of beaches.

The U.S. Open Sandcastle Contest brings 400,000 people to Imperial Beach each August. The surfing history in Imperial Beach began in an area called the Tijuana Sloughs, first surfed by Dempsey Holder in 1937. Imperial Beach's big waves had an impact on the surfing pioneers from 1937 to the 1950s. The outdoor Surf Museum commemorates the city's surfing heritage. The 1,330-foot wooden pier is also popular with its scenic ocean views, fishing, and seafood restaurants.

The Imperial Beach Civic Group was formed in 1945. A volunteer fire department and auxiliary were established in 1946. Civic leader Paul Smith became the chief of the department.

In March 1949, there were only five men in the community who were trained to use the fire equipment. Chief Mike Poindexter told the Imperial Beach Civic Group: "You can't have a fire department without trained men, and you can't train men if they don't come out to drills. What benefit is there in the lowering of insurance rates at Imperial Beach by the formation of a district if we don't build an adequate fighting force?" However, by June there were 30 volunteers who trained eight hours a week. Chief Mike Poindexter asked community members to treat his firemen with respect and courtesy as all their services were voluntary.

In 1949, a fire station was built on Palm Avenue. Since district funds were available only for actual firefighting equipment, a series of social events were held to raise money for the fire department.

In 2008, the department received a $142,000 Community Development Grant from the Department of Housing and Urban Development (HUD). The money was used to purchase 12 sets of turnout gear, two Lifepak 12 defibrillator/monitors, and replace the floors, cabinets, and lighting in the station.

Chiefs include: Paul Smith (1946-1949), Mike Poindexter (1949-1950), Johnnie Allen (1950-1951), Mike Poindexter (1951-1952), Miles Bowler (1952-1958), Al Hague (1958-1961), Clarence Gish (1961-1975), M. Earle Humphrey (1975-1980), David Engleman (1980-1981), John Holsenback (1981-1996), Ron Johnston (1996-2000), David Ott (2000-2003), Frank Sotelo (2003-2010), Thomas "Tom" Clark (2010-2015), and John French (2015-).

Frank Sotelo joined the department on September 15, 2003 and retired on June 30, 2010. He was in the fire service for 25 years, starting his career in Compton, California, as a firefighter and promoting through the ranks to captain, then serving

as acting chief and director of public services. As public service director in Imperial Beach, Chief Sotelo was responsible for more than 50 city employees, 22 contract workers, city lifeguards, animal control, special events, and movie shoots. He was also the city's fire marshal. He has a Bachelor of Arts in Public Administration from California State University, Long Beach and a Master of Business and Public Administration from Keller University.

Thomas "Tom" Clark became head of the department on July 10, 2010. Chief Clark's career spanned 42 years, including time spent as an engineer, captain, battalion chief, and deputy chief for the San Diego Fire-Rescue Department. He has an Associate of Fire Science from San Diego City College as well as a Bachelor of Arts in Public Administration from San Diego State University. He retired June 17, 2015.

John A. French, who was born and raised in Imperial Beach, was promoted to fire chief and director of emergency services in June 2015. He has been with the Imperial Beach Fire-Rescue Department for over 35 years, working his way up the ranks from firefighter to captain to chief.

While Bradley French, the chief's son, was in high school in 2008, he raised funds to send a young burn survivor to the Burn Institute's Camp Beyond the Scars. Bradley and the Imperial Beach Fire-Rescue Department teamed up to raffle off a dinner for four at the fire station. Dinner was prepared and served by the firefighters on duty.

Chief John French oversees a staff of one assistant fire marshal, one administrative assistant, three captain/paramedics, three engineer/paramedics, and six firefighter/paramedics. The suppression staff work a 48-96 schedule consisting of three platoons (A, B, C).

The staff includes Tom Santos, assistant fire marshal; Jason Bell, Craig Weaver, and Ehren Kahkle, captains; and Paulina Mamahua, administrative assistant. Tom Santos was the Burn Institute's Volunteer of the Year in 2017 for his work in raising funds for the fire and burn prevention education and burn survivor programs.

In December 2014, the Imperial Beach and Sycuan firefighters worked together on a Habitat for Humanity six-unit home complex at 776 10th Street. Some of them had the days off, others switched shifts to volunteer.

The department participates in an annual Public Safety Cook-Off at the Imperial Beach Library featuring homemade food from Imperial Beach lifeguards, sheriffs, and firefighters. Originally, local fire departments participated in the cook-off, then it became a competition among Imperial Beach public safety departments. In 2019, Firefighter Jorge Martinez won the "People's Choice" with a spicy chili with Spam.

The Imperial Beach Firefighter IAFF Local 4692 hosts an open house each October which includes ways to prepare for an emergency and demonstrates auto extrication and a vehicle fire. In 1922, the National Fire Protection Association (NFPA) named the second week of October Fire Prevention Week in commemoration of the Great Chicago Fire in 1871.

The Imperial Beach Fire Prevention Bureau provides property inspection, public safety education, fire and life safety plan review, and applicable code enforcement for Imperial Beach and its residents.

Station 39, located at 865 Imperial Beach Boulevard, was built in 1979.

Apparatus includes a 2014 Pierce Arrow XT 1,500-gpm triple combination pumper, with a Series 60 Detroit Diesel engine, 500-gallon water tank, 30-gallon class A foam tank, full ALS EMS compartment, full complement of hydraulic rescue tools, chain saw, rotary saw, and smoke ejector. The department also uses a 2004 Pierce Arrow XT 1,500-gpm triple combination pumper, with a Series 60 Detroit Diesel engine, 500 gallon water tank, 25 gallon class A form tank, 25 gallon class B tank, hydraulic ladder lift, full ALS EMS compartment, full complement of hydraulic rescue tools, chain saw, rotary saw, and smoke ejector. This engine is also used as the wildland engine which has been fully modified for an in-county or out-of-county strike team response.

In 2016, the department received a F-350 squad car, a smaller fire apparatus that is equipped with EMS equipment. Two firefighter/paramedics are assigned to the squad car to go on calls with or without the engine. The squad car costs less to run and is easier to maneuver. The Imperial Beach Fire-Rescue Department has mutual aid with other departments, but the squad car is only used in the city.

The city contracts with a private ambulance company for transport of patients to hospitals. The department quickly responds to many types of emergencies and has an ISO class 3 rating.

The department keeps a training schedule which includes fire suppression activities, live fire training, hazardous materials, confined space rescue, rescue systems, vehicle extrication, ventilation techniques, forcible entry techniques, rapid intervention control training, and updates for emergency medical services

On April 20, 2019, the Imperial Beach Fire-Rescue Department and the San Diego Small Business Forum held its 3rd Annual Derby Daze at the Pier Plaza. The event features egg hunting, local businesses, and a silent auction. It helps the fire department raise funds for the Burn Institute. The department enters a vehicle in the Burn Institute's Demolition Derby that takes place during the San Diego County Fair each year. However, in 2020 it was cancelled because of the COVID-19 virus.

(paramedic). The fire department spends at least two hours each shift on training exercises as well as eight hours a month at in-service training. All firefighters obtain firefighter 1 and 2 certifications as well as attending department paid classes for additional training and certifications.

In 2008, Imperial Beach and Coronado Fire Departments combined their CERT (Community Emergency Response Team) training to offer residents in both coastal communities joint classes in disaster preparedness.

To become a firefighter with the Imperial Beach Fire Department, the minimum qualifications are to be 18 years of age or older; be a high school graduate or possess a G.E.D.; possess a California class "C" driver's license; obtain firefighter 1 certification; possess current certification as an emergency medical technician paramedic (EMT-P); pass a written test, a physical ability test, and an oral interview; and pass a background investigation, polygraph test, and a psychological assessment.

Measure I, a sale tax measure on the November 2020 ballot was approved, helping first responder services and updating emergency communications! A yes vote supported authorizing an additional sales tax of 1% generating an estimated $1,300,000 per year until ended by voters, thereby increasing the total sales tax rate in Imperial Beach from 7.75% to 8.75%. The yes vote received 70.16%.

The department proudly provides fire suppression, emergency medical services, fire prevention, and community service to the residents and visitors of Imperial Beach and surrounding communities.

CALLS RECALLED:

*1931:   Fire crews from Imperial and Coronado Volunteer Fire Departments responded to a man drowning in the surf. The victim, J. A. Ford, could not be resuscitated.

*1950:   In January 1950, a fire destroyed a garage used as a storeroom behind the Elm Avenue residence of V. De Joungue. Damage was estimated at $1,400.

*1987:   The rescue rig and ambulance responded to an automobile accident involving three vehicles on July 11, 1987, at 3:10 a.m. Two people were transported to Coronado Hospital.

*1987:   On July 12, 1987, at 9:47 a.m., fire personnel assisted a woman who was having severe back pain. She was transported to Coronado Hospital.

*2004:   In 2004, the department responded to 2,100 emergency calls.

*2006:   In 2006, the personnel responded to 63 fires, 40 hazardous conditions, and service calls.

*2006:   On January 5, 2006, there was a water vehicle fire. The fire was caused by flammable liquid used to start a fire. The damage cost was $6,000.

*2012:   In March 2012, a house in the 1200 block of 7th Street was destroyed by fire. The three-bedroom house and the garage were stacked high with belongings. There were no fire hydrants near the house. Firefighters had to lay hoses 1,500 feet to reach the nearest hydrants.

*2015:   Fire personnel responded to 2,528 calls in 2015. They also helped to distribute more than 10,000 sand bags to the public and even delivered sand bags to the homes of seniors and disabled residents who needed assistance.

*2016:   On March 2016, a crew responded to a house fire on Donax Avenue. Firefighter C. J. Marin located an unconscious man and locked his arms around him and carried him out of the house. The man, who had respiratory burns, was taken by ambulance to UC San Diego Medical Center. Marin said:"Everything went smoothly. It's the result of all the training we do. When you train, you don't know if you'll ever use the training. But because of that, someone is alive."

*2017:   In January 2017, very strong winds caused power outages and damaged trees. The fire department made up 3,000 sand bags and had another 10,000 pounds of sand for residents.

*2018:   In November 2018, a two-alarm fire occurred at a six-unit apartment complex in the 1200 block of Iris Avenue. Thirty adults and 10 children were evacuated. Firefighters from Imperial Beach Fire-Rescue Department, San Diego Fire-Rescue Department, Chula Vista Fire Department, National City Fire Department, and Coronado Fire Department put out the blaze.

*2019:   In October 2019, Ehren Kahle, Cory Cooper, and Nick Morales were deployed as part of a strike team of five Type I engines from the San Diego area to the Kincade Fire. "It was almost a 24 hour deal the first night," said Captain Kahle. "The winds were horrific and we spent the night in the fire line—everything was burning." After five days at the fire, the three Imperial Beach firefighters were assigned to a a a fire in Ventura. The Kincade Fire in Sonoma County burned 77,758 acres, destroyed 374 structures, damaged 60 structures, and caused $77.1 million in damages.

*2019:   The personnel responded to about 2,800 calls in 2019.

*2020:   In September and October 2020, Imperial Beach fire personnel Craig Weaver, Ehren Kahle, Jorge Martinez, Dan Holian, Nick "Popeye" Morales, Henry "Yoda" Yorba, Jeff Blatnik, and James "Coop" Cooper were assigned to the Valley Fire (southeast of Alpine), the Creek Fire (Maderia and Fresno Counties), and the Glass Fire (Napa and Sonoma Counties). In the two months, the firefighters were deployed to wildfires for 32 days.

INTERMOUNTAIN FIRE-RESCUE DEPARTMENT

The department was co-founded by Glen Larson and John Cain to protect the property owners in an area of 125 square miles including Sutherland Dam, Mesa Grande, Old Julian Highway, and parts of Highways 78 and 79. It includes Santa Ysabel, which is 52 miles northeast of San Diego and 7 miles northwest of Julian at 2,983 feet at the base of Volcan Mountain.

The Mission Santa Ysabel was founded on September 20, 1818, and a chapel was added by the Mesa Grande Indians in 1898. The original chapel was destroyed In a fire; however, two bronze bells that hung on a post near the chapel were saved. One of the bells was made in Loreto, Italy, in 1723; the other was made in San Pedro, Mexico, in 1767. The bell from the Loreto Mission in Baja, California, was the oldest bell in California.

The bells were used to notify people in the valley of events and emergencies such as fire. Henry Lactuse rang the bells from the age of eight until he was an elderly man. His father had been a bell ringer before him. A new chapel was built in 1924; two years later the bells mysteriously disappeared, then in 1959 the clappers of the bells were left on the steps of the mission.

Jose Joaquin Ortega and his son-in-law, Edward Stokes, were granted 17,719 acres in Santa Ysabel in 1872. In the 1880s the land was sold to Brackett and Company. The Santa Ysabel Indian Reservation was established in 1893. There is an Indian burial ground at the mission.

At the intersection of Highway 78 and 79 can be found two well-known landmarks—Dudley's Bakery and the Olde Santa Ysabel Store. The land was sold by a building contractor to Dudley and Mary Pratt in 1963. When Dudley Pratt died in 1975, Mel Ashley and Marilee Strech bought the bakery. It is now owned by Laurie and Barry Brunye. The Olde Santa Ysabel Store, which dates back to 1870, has two-foot-thick adobe walls and was once a Butterfield stage stop.

The Santa Ysabel Art Gallery is housed in a two-story home built by John Hellyer in 1930. Don Blackburn, who was the owner in 1992, organized a festival then that raised $540 for the volunteer fire department. Annie Rowley is now the owner of the gallery.

The Intermountain Fire-Rescue Department was incorporated in 1988 to protect the 529 property owners who lived in the area. The department now serves 4,000 residents. Glen Larson served as the first fire chief and John Cain as the deputy chief and medical officer. The original 14 volunteers learned advanced first aid and basic fire fighting technique from the two officers. In October 1990 the Poway Fire Department gave a 1961 American La France to the organization and it also had a 1959 International brush rig that was purchased from the San Pasqual Volunteer Fire Department for $1,500. A 1990 4-wheel drive vehicle was donated anonymously. Julian Volunteer Fire Department donated $10,000 of used equipment to the volunteers. Other equipment was donated by Aguanga, Borrego, Cuyamaca, and Ramona Fire Departments.

The San Diego Regional Fire and Emergency Services Foundation gave the department $3,500 in 1990 to buy communication equipment, tires for the American La France, and medical supplies. The foundation is a non-profit organization founded in July 1989 to raise funds for local fire protection agencies. Other cash grants were made by the California Rural Community Fire Protection Program and the California Department of Forestry.

The department had a ribbon-cutting ceremony for a new station in June 2005. Major funding for the project was made by the Viejas, Barona, and Sycuan Indian Reservations.

In October 2008, twenty-three volunteers graduated from the Intermountain Fire-Rescue Department's academy. Fire Etc. provided a large supply of training equipment. Cal Fire helped train engine crews. The San Diego County provided a training budget as part of its consolidation program.

In 2009, the San Diego County Board of Supervisors awarded $30,000 to the department for an emergency generator.

In 2008, the department, under the leadership of Chief Cary "Dusty" Coleman, joined the San Diego County Fire Authority. The Fire Authority began lending the fire department vehicles and paying the expenses on them. In 2015, Chief Jeremy Christofferson and the board of directors received a paramedic fire engine funded by the county and staffed by Cal Fire. Also the station was updated. A fire captain, two engineers, and three firefighter paramedics were added to the staff.

On June 26, 2010, the auxiliary, the "Hot Spots," raised $25,000 at a "Fly Me to the Moon" fundraiser held at the Ramona Airport to support the operating costs of the department. In November 2012, the Hot Spots raised $10,000 for the department at a fundraiser with a Bavarian theme held at the Ramona Outdoor Community Center Pavilion. The board members in 2010 were Charles Teichert, Russ Meskell, Maurice Waters, Ron Peterka, Jeff Uran, Kimberly Kelly, and Scott Toothacre.

For 18 years, the department had an ISO rating of 10. In May 2010, the Insurance Service Office changed it to a 4 rating for those living with 5 miles of the station and the rest of the district would have a 9 rating.

Firefighters Jorge Hernandez, Jesus Carbaja, Austin Mann, Drew Loftis, Adan Topete, and Eric Jimenez responded to a request from firefighters in Baja to help with training in June 2012. "When we got there, we expected a crowd. But there were between 30 and 50 departments that showed up. They invited all the rural firefighting departments in Baja to this training. One guy drove three days to receive two days worth of training—that's how important this was to them, " said Carbaja.

In 2012, Ron Peterka was honored by the Intermountain Fire-Rescue Department for 21 years of service. In 1991, Peterka joined the board of directors of the department. At that time, the department had one chief and one fireman. The only equipment was a 1955 engine.

The Intermountain Fire-Rescue Department Board President Maurice Waters and Chief Jeremy Christofferson received word on April 1, 2015, that the station would have a 24/7 paramedic engine and staff of Cal Fire.

The department is a member of the Fire Safe Council of San Diego County. The council helps residents protect their homes and families from wildfire.

 Station 85, located at 25858 A CA-78, houses Engine 7815 (2013 Ferrara Inferno), Rescue 7885 (1994 International), Brush 7867, and Water Tender 7855 (2014 Ferrara Igniter).

Chief Cary Coleman said, "I believe a firefighter's first act of bravery is to decide that it is a duty and obligation to act for those who cannot. It is a position of public faith and trust. Technical skills of being a firefighter can be taught. These values you have to bring with you."

Since Highways 78 and 79 are major arteries to the mountains and deserts, weekend traffic is particularly heavy, resulting in accidents to which the firefighters respond.

CALLS RECALLED:

*1990: The firefighters responded to a head-on traffic accident on Highway 78 and Witch Creek Road on August 11,1990. Three women were transported to Palomar Medical Center.

*1991: Douglas Jenson, 44, of Temecula, California, and Scott Brewer, 21, of Edmonton, Canada, were killed when Brewer's car crashed into Jenson's motorhome on Highway 78 west of Santa Ysabel.

It was an hour before the firefighters could extinguish the fire enough to reach the drivers.

*1991: Carl Adams, 41, died when his motorcycle was struck by a pickup truck on Highway 78.

*2003: The firefighters were first responders during the devastating 2003 Cedar Fire.

*2007: On October 21, 2007, the department's station was threatened in the Witch Creek Fire. During the effort to save Station 85, the building housed 10 civilians who evacuated their homes and could not get up or down the road. A crew of four—one from Station 85, one from Shelter Valley, and two trainees from Julian-Cuyamaca Fire cut a line around the station. Later, about 35 firefighters arrived to help save the station. An American Red Cross and Federal Emergency Management Agency (FEMA) station was set up at the site, providing hot meals, supplies, equipment, and help for two to three weeks after the fire.

*2012: The department had about 300 calls in 2012.

*2013: The fire personnel at the department showed support for the 19 firefighters who died in Arizona by placing a black band across their fire badges. The 19 killed were part of the Granite Mountain Interagency Hotshot Crew, an elite wildland unit sponsored by the Prescott Fire Department in Arizona. All but one of the crew was overrun by a massive wildfire near Yarnell, Arizona. Flags at all stations in the county were lowered to half-staff.

*2020: On November 1, 2020, two people on a motorcycle were killed when their motorcycle collided with an off-road side-by-side utility task vehicle on Littlepage Lane..

JACUMBA VOLUNTEER FIRE DEPARTMENT

Jacumba is located 74 miles east of San Diego, south of Interstate 8 near the Mexican border along the original Highway 80 at an elevation of 2,822 feet. It covers 6.1 square miles and has a population of 561.

The Kumeyaay frequented the area for thousands of years. The name Jacumba means magic springs in their language. Ranchers occupied the area in the 19th century and were often in conflict with the Native Americans. Many of the Kumeyaay Indians were slain by ranchers for cattle rustling in the 1870 Jacumba Massacre.

In 1919, rail service connected Jacumba to San Diego. In 1925, Bert Vaughan opened the Jacumba Hotel. The 180-room hotel was a popular place in the 1920s and 1930s for celebrities to visit and to enjoy the natural hot springs. After Interstate 8 bypassed Jacumba by two miles, the community went into economic decline. The Jacumba Hotel was destroyed by an arson fire in 1983.

David Landman bought the Jacumba Hot Springs & Resort and 80% of the town in 2012 for $1.5 million. In August 2020 a San Diego event design group bought the property for $3.9 million.

The Jacumba Airport was acquired from the federal government in 1953. The airport is unattended and unlighted. It is used mainly as an operation area for gliders, especially on weekends. The Jacumba Mountains Wilderness contains a total of 31,357 acres and is managed by the Bureau of Land Management.

The Jacumba school closed in 2017 after being opened in the 1930s. The elementary school children are bused to Boulevard and middle school children are bused to Campo.

The Jacumba Volunteer Fire Department was formed in 1937. In 1949, A. R. Lewis led a crew of 30 firemen. In 1972, John Ketchum was the department's captain and soon was promoted to chief, serving the department until 1984 when he moved to Washington. His assistant chief joined the El Centro Fire Department. At that time, the fire department had a 1944 Ford engine and a 1957 Ford engine.

Pat Fauble, 93, served as fire chief from 1984 to 1999. The 16 volunteers had a fire engine and a water tender but no station. During this time the department became part of the San Diego Rural Fire Protection District. From 1999 to 2014, Jacumba

The Jacumba Volunteer Fire Department's fire building in 1955.

Chief Pat Fauble with her crew in front of the current Jacumba fire station in 1984.

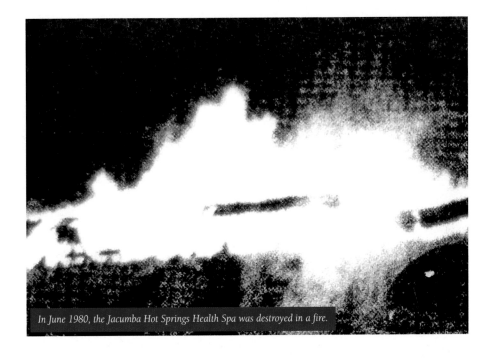
In June 1980, the Jacumba Hot Springs Health Spa was destroyed in a fire.

In 1983, the 1925 Jacumba Hot Springs Hotel burned.

had no fire department, relying on the Boulevard Volunteer Fire Department to respond to calls in the area.

In October 2015 Jacumba became a San Diego County Fire Authority service area. The county provides a paramedic fire engine and firefighting equipment and contracts with Cal Fire for staffing.

On December 7, 2020, San Diego County Fire Authority was renamed the San Diego County Fire Protection District. It is a dependent special district under the Board of Supervisors.

The San Diego Fire Rescue Foundation donated $131,600 and the San Diego Regional Fire Foundation donated $32,900 to the county to install mobile data computers in vehicles in rural communities such as Jacumba in May 2018. The computers are used for communications with dispatch and navigation and include potential hazards by area for reference in the field.

The Jacumba fire station (San Diego County Station 43) is located at 1255 Jacumba Road, close to the Jacumba Post Office. It is manned 24 hours a day, seven days a week, 365 days a year. A Cal Fire captain and one paramedic/firefighter cover the station, three days on duty and four days off.

The hot springs, desert environment, and wonderful climate attract visitors to the area.

CALLS RECALLED:

*1937:   On August 9, 1937, the Los Angeles Times reported that "An army of C.C.C. enrollees, State and Federal forestry employees, tonight battled flames that roared for two miles through a ravine 10 miles west of Jacumba, near the San Diego-El Centro highway. "Head of fire checked," was the terse bulletin from the fire front to State forestry division headquarters. One report from the Live Oak Springs store, about a mile and a half from the fire's starting point, said that the fire started from a cigarette.

*1983:   The Jacumba Hotel caught fire in 1983. Chief Joe O'Brien's firefighters extinguished the blaze with assistance of departments from Jamul, Potrero, Campo, Dearborn, Lake Morena, Descanso, Pine Valley, Ocotillo, and Santee.

*2011: In June 2011, the Border 9 Fire that began near In-Ko-Pah Park Road burned 380 acres (40 in the United States and 340 in Mexico). Four air tankers and five fire engines fought the blaze.

*2011: In June 2011, the Buffalo Fire burned 26 acres. There were 211 firefighters at the fire, and the fire suppression cost was $200,000.

*2013: Navy pilot Richard Noble, 63, and Coast Guard veteran Martin Rothwell, 54, were both killed when their Perkoz SZD-54 glider crashed soon after taking off from the Jacumba Airport.

*2014: At 4:36 p.m. on May 5, 2014, the Jacumba Fire was reported off Interstate 8, east of McCain Valley Road. The fire burned 29 acres.

*2018: Gonzalo Martinez, a 22-year-old man from Hemet, died and another person was injured when a black SUV crashed into a metal guardrail along Interstate 8 in Jacumba.

*2020: In July 2020, a vehicle veered out of control, overturned and caught fire on the eastbound side of Interstate 8 near Old Highway 80 in Jacumba. Two of the occupants died at the scene of the accident.

*2020: In October 2020, a man was killed when he lost control of his blue 2008 Toyota Camry on westbound Interstate 8, west of Carrizo Gorge Road in the Jacumba area. The car plunged down a rocky embankment, overturned, and caught fire, causing a small brush fire..

Jamul Fire Department

Jamul is located in rural East County, covering an area of 16.57 square miles.

More than 12,000 years ago the Kumeyaay Indians lived in the Jamul Valley. El Rancho de Jamul was established in an 8,296 parcel grant gifted to the last Mexican governor of California, Pio Pico, in 1829. In 1837, the normally peaceful Diegueno Indians attacked the rancho because of a land dispute, killing four defenders and carrying off two young women who were never heard from again. In 1852 a number of squatters were driven off the ranch and several were lynched on a nearby tree. The ranch was eventually purchased and converted by George Daley and his nephew into a farm and ranch.

Nowadays, Jamul is a thriving community with a casino on the 6-acre reservation of the Jamul Indian Village. Prior to the tribal casino opening in 2016, many tribal members lived below the federal poverty line. In 2018, the name was changed from Hollywood Casino to Jamul Casino. The Pio Pico RV Resort and Campground and the Casi Cielo Winery also brings visitors to the area.

In November 2012, Chris Zombro, 19, accepted a Volunteer Firefighter of the Year award from the San Diego Regional Fire Foundation for his work with the Jamul fire station. He started out in the Firefighter Explorer program when he was only 15; he graduated from the San Diego County Fire Authority academy in 2012. Zombro, whose father is Kelly Zombro, a Cal Fire San Diego deputy chief, said he has found his calling with the fire service. "In my senior year in high school, I took an EMT course and worked one shift a week to meet the minimum (requirements)," Zombro said. "I worked at the station for three years. The crew I work with, we've seen a lot and we work really well together."

Beginning in March 2015, paramedics were assigned to every engine in Jamul to provide advanced life support. Previously emergency medical technicians were on the apparatus.

In 2017, the Jamul Indian Village tribal members presented $2,677,500 to the San Diego Fire Authority at the Jamul Fire Station. The tribal council has donated over $5 million towards the Fire and Life Safety Services Agreement with San Diego County that was approved in 2016. The tribe's contributions will increase 5% per year and will result in an additional $85 million over the next 20 years for equipment, personnel, training, and operating expenses for emergency services in the region.

San Miguel Chief Augie Ghio said, ""As an old retired fire chief, I can't tell you how wonderful this is to have such a collaborative, cooperative and successful partnership between the Jamul Indian Village and Cal Fire and the County. It's agreements like this that provide service to our communities that really improve their life safety and the protection of their property." Jamul Indian Village Chairwoman Erica M. Pinto, whose mother was a fire dispatcher and the first female graduate of the Heartland Fire Academy, said, "We are here today to honor our brave men and women who put their lives on the line day in and day out to protect our community. Thank you to each and every one of you who answers the call to serve. We know the sacrifices you and your families make, and we are proud to do our part to support that work."

The San Diego County Fire Authority was formed in 2008 to bring fire and medical emergency services to the unincorporated areas of the county. The San Diego County Board of Supervisors has invested over $500 million to improve fire and emergency services. The county retains ownership of the apparatus it purchases and maintains the apparatus through the County Department of General Services Fleet Management for the life of the apparatus. The county contracts with Cal Fire for fire protection services.

Over $7 million in funds from the County General Fund, Tobacco Trust Funds, Community Development Block Grant Funds, and Indian Gaming Trust Funds has been used for purchasing apparatus. The County has purchased 56 apparatus including 28 structural engines, 4 wildlland engines, 12 Type VI patrols, 2 trucks, 4 rescue apparatus, 14 water tenders, and 7 specialty apparatus.

Station 36 is located at 14145 Highway 94 in Jamul. It houses Truck 36 (2016 KME Predator), Engine 36 (2016 Spartan ERV), Patrol 36 (2015 Ford F-550), and Rescue 7386 (2012 Ferrara Igniter).

In 2016, Truck 36 was provided by the Jamul Indian Village at a cost of $1 million. It is staffed by four firefighter/paramedics. Truck 36, manufactured by KME, is known as a quint combination apparatus named for the components the unit provides which include a rated fire pump that is capable of delivering 1,500 gallons of water a minute, 500-gallon water tank, 500 feet of large diameter fire hose, 105-foot aerial ladder, and ground ladders. The truck also carries a full complement of Holmatro hydraulic rescue tools (Jaws of Life) that are used to extricate occupants that are trapped in a vehicle after a collision, rescue equipment and ropes for performing high and low angle rescues, and medical equipment including a defibrillator and medications used in delivering advanced life support by paramedics.

The casino also donated $500,000 in 2016 to purchase Engine 36, a 2016 Spartan ERV.

The Kumeyaay Indians in Jamul have made a significant impact on the high-quality fire and emergency services provided in the region.

CALLS RECALLED:

*1970:   In September 1970, the Laguna Fire burned 185,000 acres and destroyed 380 homes and 1,000 other structures. In Jamul, on the southwest edge of the fire, 40 homes were lost.

*2007:   In October 2007, the Harris Fire destroyed 253 homes, killed 2 civilians, and burned 90,000 acres. It began on October 21 in Potrero and by October 23 more than 500,000 people were evacuated, including everyone in Jamul. It was extinguished on November 5. Over 1,200 firefighters fought the fire.

*2010:   In August 2010, fire crews responded to a house fire off of State Route 94 and Vista San Diego. The fire caused about $150,000 in damages.

*2011:   On December 29, 2011, a home at Skyline Truck Trail and Lawson Valley Road was severely damaged by fire. Firefighters were able to enter the home and save some personal belongings and photos.

*2012:   In June 2012, a wildfire burned 30 acres in Jamul. Four air tankers, 4 helicopters, 15 engines, 5 water tenders, 5 hand crews, and 80 firefighters were used to fight the fire.

*2012:   In July 2012, the Proctor Fire burned 20 acres in Jamul. There were 15 engines, 5 fire crews, 1 bulldozer, 2 water tenders, 3 helicopters, and 4 air tankers at the fire.

*2013:   On November 17, a Navy man was killed when his motorcycle hit a stopped motorhome on Otay Lakes Road.

*2015:   On September 1, 2015, a construction worker who was working at the casino at the Jamul Indian Village died when he fell off an elevator lift.

*2015:   On December 26, Jae Han Chung, 25, of Chula Vista, missed a curve on Otay Lakes Road and struck a Prius. Chung went under the car. Paramedics initiated CPR but could not revive him.

*2016:   In September 2016, a brush fire on Skyline Truck Trail in the Lyons Valley area burned 30 acres.

*2017:   In May 2017, the Gate Fire burned 2,056 acres southeast of Jamul along Highway 94. Six fire engines, one helicopter, two air tankers, two water tenders, four hand crews and an airtactical aircraft from Cal Fire were initially assigned to fight the fire. U.S. Forest Service personnel also responded, along with firefighters from Lakeside, Santee, and Viejas.

*2017:   On August 6, 2017, a 51-year-old man from San Diego was killed after driving his 2008 Acura MDX off of Skyline Truck Trail and striking an embankment.

*2017:   In December 2017, a lost hiker set off a flare that started a half-acre fire in Lyon Valley.

*2019:   In June 2019, the driver and a passenger in a 1997 GMC Sonoma were killed following a head-on collision with a Jeep on Lyons Valley Road.

*2019:   In August 2019, a head-on collision on State Route 94 killed one driver and started a brush fire.

*2019:   On December 31, 2019, Yannis Alekos Floros, 21, was driving eastward on State Route 94 near Lyons Valley Road when he lost control of his car and collided with a westbound SUV. Flores and his passenger, Tabia Watson, 20, were killed in the accident.

*2020:   In January 2020, Tiffany Rose King, 22, was killed while attempting to cross State Route 94 on Peaceful Valley Ranch Road. She was struck by a Chevrolet Astro van driven by a 67-year-old man.

*2020:   In May 2020, a vegetation fire burned an acre near Presilla Drive.

*2020:   In June 2020, the Skyline Fire burned about 100 acres near Jamul. It started off of the 17000 block of Skyline Truck Trail in Lawson Valley.

*2020:   In June 2020, a bonfire burned out of control on Old Campo Road. Nearly 12 fire rigs responded to the incident. The homeowner would not allow the fire crews to enter his property.

*2020:   On July 19, 2020, Joseph James Wingen, 47, of San Diego died after skydiving. Paramedics removed his parachute equipment and initiated CPR, but to no avail.

*2020:   In August 2020, the Hillside Fire burned two acres in the area off of State Route 94 and Honey Springs Road.

*2020:   On September 5, 2020, the Valley Fire started at Japatul Road and Carveacre Road in the Japatul Valley, southeast of Alpine, at 2:15 p.m. The fire burned 17,665 acres, destroyed 30 homes and 31 other structures, and damaged 11 structures.

Barb Huber, who lost outbuildings and a tractor in the fire, said the fire was devastating but she and her husband are grateful to still have their home; their three cows and six pigs were spared. They had extensive smoke damage in their home. Anabel and Dewey Bratcher lost not only their home on Montiel Truck Trail but also their five cats and their son's urn who had recently passed away.

Hyslop Horse Haven, a sanctuary for neglected and abused horses, lost eight sheds that contained medication, horse feed, and equipment in the Valley Fire. When owner Patty Hyslop returned to the property after the fire, all 20 horses were alive and well.

Kimberlee Jones escaped the fire with her two children, ages 5 and 3. Her home of five years was destroyed. A rescuer found her 11 horses in their paddocks, alive, about 50 feet away from the house and not far from some burned fences.

JULIAN VOLUNTEER FIRE DEPARTMENT

Julian is located fifty miles northeast of San Diego at the intersection of Highways 78 and 79 in the Cuyamaca Mountains. It covers 7.8 square miles at an elevation of 4,222 feet and has a population of about 1,500. The town was named by Drue Bailey after his cousin Mike Julian, who later was elected San Diego County Assessor.

Gold was discovered in the community in 1869. It was the only gold rush in San Diego County. Unlike most mining camps which became ghost towns, Julian survived after the end of the gold rush period in 1876. Julian produced about $2 million worth of gold. In June, Julian celebrates the Julian Gold Rush Days with gold panning, gold mine tours, and historic reenactments.

James T. Madison brought the first apple trees to Julian in the early 1870s. The first apple day festival was in 1909. Thousands of people go to the community year round to enjoy the four seasons and especially for the Julian Apple Days Festival in September.

After the 1970 Laguna Fire, the Julian Volunteer Fire and Rescue was established with Larry Tuttle as chief. In 1981, Larry Hutchinson became chief and he and Chief Al Sprague of Cuyamaca created the Julian Cuyamaca Fire Protection District (JCFPD). It served over 81 square miles, 52,000 acres, 4,100 residents, and 2,500 homes, outbuildings, and businesses. It was formed by LAFCO in 1984. A proposition was placed on the ballot to establish a benefit fee of $50 per household. In November 1984, 72 percent of the voters in the district approved the benefit fee.

The district leased land from the water district. Residents had fundraisers such as pancake breakfasts and spaghetti dinners to raise money for a fire station. Almost 2,000 letters were sent out to the community the first year of fundraising and $6,000 was donated. In 1983, construction of the fire station began with volunteer labor. It was mostly built on weekends.

Kevin Dubler became district chief in 1999 and served until his retirement in 2012. Rick Marinelli took his place as district chief. In 2019, the interim chief of the Julian-Cuyamaca Fire Protection District was Mike Van Bidder.

In November 2006, a proposition to create a second annual benefit fee of $50 was placed on the ballot for the purpose of accumulating funds to build a new fire station. Nearly 74 percent of the voters in this general election approved the benefit fee.

A new station was constructed and placed into service in May 2017 on land bequeathed in 2009 by Frances Mosler, a local resident. The Mosler estate deeded 6.4 acres to the Julian Cuyamaca Fire Protection District. The deed states: "If district permanently abandons the fire station, title to the subject property shall automatically vest in the conservancy or the conservancy's assignee of this right of reverted."

In 2015 Chief Rick Marinelli approached JKA Architecture to design a station for half the cost of a typical new fire station. A pre-engineered metal building was used for a detached apparatus bay. The station includes turnout lockers, extractor room, three offices, training room, day room, kitchen, public and crew restrooms, and bunks that can house up to fourteen crew members during a major fire event. The training room, dayroom, and kitchen were designed to be flexible and can be used as both meeting and living spaces. A copper colored standing seam metal gable roof tied the station and the apparatus bay together. The 6,232-square-foot station was built for $2.27 million.

In 2013, the board of directors of JCFPD announced to the residents that the district, due to poor financial standing, was considering an offer from the County of San Diego. The board proceeded to vote on whether to dissolve. The vote was 2 to 2 (1 absentee), therefore, it did not pass and JCFPD remained independent.

Between 2013 and 2017, JCFPD purchased a new rapid attack engine, purchased a new ambulance, and built a new station. The department had twelve vehicles and two fire stations (Julian Fire Station 56 and Cuyamaca Fire Station 57).

In 2017, San Diego County Fire made another offer to assume fire protection and emergency medical services for the community. The subsidy from the county to JCFPD in 2017 was $1,559,000. In April 2018, the board voted 3 to 1 (1 absentee) to pass a resolution to enter into negotiations with LAFCO to dissolve JCFPD. The three board members signed an agreement with Cal Fire for interim service that would displace the volunteer organization and begin dismantling JCFPD.

In November 2018, voters rejected Proposition QQ, which had been placed on the ballot to raise property taxes for fire protection from $50 to $200. The measure failed by a vote of 976 to 836. The five members of the board of directors who were in office of the Julian-Cuyamaca Fire Protection District in November 2018 were against dissolution.

In December 2018, the San Diego County Board of Supervisors voted to hold a special election on March 19, 2019, to determine the fate of the volunteer fire department. Only the 2,482 registered voters in the district could vote on Measure A.

The measure passed with the approval of 55.56 percent of the voters, dissolving the Julian-Cuyamaca Fire Protection District and merging it with the San Diego County Fire Authority.

CALLS RECALLED:

*1970: The Laguna Fire killed eight people, burned 175,425 acres, and destroyed 382 homes countywide. In 24 hours, the fire burned from Mt. Laguna into the edge of El Cajon and Spring Valley.

*2002: In July 2002, the Pines Fire in the area of Vulcan Mountain and Julian burned 61,700 acres and destroyed 37 homes, 116 other structures, and 165 vehicles near Julian. Two fire engines were destroyed. The fire was started when a National Guard helicopter hit a power line.

*2003: On October 28, 2003, the Cedar Fire reached Julian and destroyed dozens of homes in the community. Two Julian firefighters, Nick Rogers and Bill Everett, who were fighting the fire lost their homes. A Julian-Cuyamaca Firefighter Relief Fund was established to help them. The fire burned 273,246 acres, 2,232 homes burned, and fourteen civilians and one firefighter died.

*2007: The Witch Creek Fire burned 197,990 acres from Julian to Rancho Bernardo. Two civilians died and 1,265 homes were destroyed.

*2010: A fire was extinguished in about 30 minutes at the Whispering Winds Catholic Church facility at 17606 Harrison Park Road in July 2010. The church was not damaged.

LA JOLLA RESERVATION FIRE DEPARTMENT

The La Jolla Indian Reservation covers 8,822 acres and lies beneath the southern rim of Palomar Mountain. To the east of the reservation, one finds Lake Henshaw and the vast cattle grazing lands beyond that, to the west lies the Pauma Valley and Rincon reservations, and to the south is the township of Valley Center. The reservation is about 2,800 feet above sea level and receives a dusting of snow in the winter months. The reservation for the La Jolla Band of Luiseño Indians was established by Ulysses S. Grant in 1875.

The La Jolla Band of Luiseño Indians own the La Jolla Trading Post located at 22003 Highway 76 in Pauma Valley. The facility includes a deli, a store, and a gas station. In August 2018 the La Jolla Trading Post added 75 slot machines in a 2,500-square-foot gaming area inside their original building

The fire department is one of a group of county reservations that joined together to form a consortium. Although the departments—San Pasqual, Pala, Mesa Grande, Rincon, Sycuan, and Campo—do not have contiguous borders, their cooperation covers many areas of support. Such areas of sharing may include mutual aid responses, training, and equipment needs. Once some of the reservations got casinos they pulled out of the consortium because they are, of course, economically sound.

The paid firefighters are of the Luiseño tribe. In the past, the Bureau of Indian Affairs gave the department $5,000 a year. The apparatus is located on State Route 76, northwest of La Jolla Boulevard, at 1304 Harolds Road, Pauma Valley. Like many of the reservations, the fire department is overseen by a tribal council. There is a population of 700 Luiseño Indians with 475 tribal members and non-members living within the boundaries of the reservation.

The department was formed in 1976. Chief Kevin Kephart (1976-1984), Juan Reed (1984-1993), and Wesley Ruise, Sr. (1993-2016) have served as chiefs. Wesley Ruise, Sr. worked for the U.S. Forest Service for 35 years. His son, Wesley Ruise, Jr., the current chief, worked for the U.S. Forest Service for 28 years, The two sons of Wesley Ruise, Jr., Wesley Ruise III and Tyler, are hotshots for the U.S. Forest Service. Norma Ruise, the widow of Wesley Ruise, Sr., said, "I'm proud of the way the family has followed in the footsteps of my husband. They have trained a lot of men that have come from the city to get experience. Their time at the La Jolla Reservation Fire Department has been a stepping stone for their careers."

Chief Wesley Ruise, Sr.

The fire department started by responding to all emergencies on a refurbished red 1975 Model 60, a former United States Forest Service brush engine that was modified to carry medical equipment and light rescue tools. It had a fully enclosed cab. The tank held 500 gallons of water which fed a 380-gpm pump. There were two 150-foot hardlines on the rear of the engine, and it carried 1,000 feet of 1-1/2 inch hose. The chief responded to calls in a 1985 Chevrolet Scottsdale. The department refitted a flatbed with a 400-gallon tank and auxiliary pump for additional coverage in the district.

Now the department has Engine 78, a 2007 Spartan Metro star/Smeal engine donated by the McCormick Foundation that holds 500 gallons of water, a 1997 International diesel brush rig that holds 500 gallons of water, and Patrol 78, a 2015 ford F-550.

The department received a grant of $482,000 from the U.S. Department of Transportation (DOT). The La Jolla Reservation had to provide matching funds of $52,000 to receive the full grant. In August 2015, the reservation approached the the San Diego Regional Fire Foundation for assistance in obtaining the matching funds. With additional donations of $51,000 from San Diego Gas & Electric and $1,000 from another source, the reservation had $534,000 to purchase equipment such as fire hose, protective clothing, and breathing apparatus.

In March 2019, the reservation received a grant through the Federal Emergency Management Agency to repair damaged facilities and to remove debris caused by heavy rains, flooding, and mudslides the previous month.

The firefighters respond to about 120 calls a year. They are dispatched by Cal Fire at Monte Vista.

Highway 76 runs directly through the reservation. It brings thousands of tourists on their way to the Palomar Mountain Observatory, the recreational areas of Lake Henshaw, and then on to the Anza-Borrego Desert. Also, the La Jolla Reservation has its own attractive recreational facilities in the popular La Jolla Zip Zoom zipline and the La Jolla Indian Campground. This provides county residents and tourists with a family atmosphere of camping, water sports, and the sheer enjoyment of cold fresh water running through the rocks and boulders.

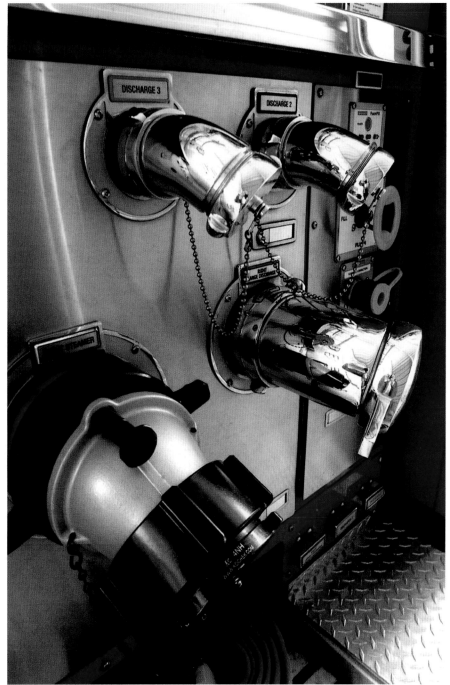

CALLS RECALLED:

*1999:   A fire in October 1999 was started by trash burning at the La Jolla Indian Reservation that got out of control. Gregory Pacheco, a 20-old firefighter from Picuris Pueblo, New Mexico, was killed while fighting the blaze at the Cleveland National Forest when he was struck by a 40-pound falling boulder and fell 140 feet down a hill on October 5, 1999. Since 1996, he had been a federal firefighter with Penasco Number Five, a Native American hand crew from the Carson National Forest in Taos, New Mexico. A memorial to him is on the East Grade Road on Palomar Mountain overlooking the La Jolla Indian Reservation. Tribal members of the La Jolla Indian Reservation, the Palomar Mountain Fire Department, the U.S. Forest Service, and other agencies paid for a bronze plaque, designed by Bob Hayward, to place at the memorial. The fire burned 7,800 acres.

*2007:   The Poomacha Fire started on October 23, 2007, at 3:13 p.m. on Highway 76 in Pauma Valley when a structure fire spread to the nearby brush. Within 15 minutes the fire grew to 500 acres, Ninety-two percent of the reservation was damaged and 50 homes destroyed. The fire joined with the Witch Creek Fire to the south. There were 379 (137 Cal Fire) firefighters on the fire, 7 fire crews (2 Cal Fire), 13 (4 Cal Fire) engines, 2 helicopters, 1 dozer, and 4 water tenders. The fire destroyed 138 homes, 1 commercial property, and 78 outbuildings and burned 49,410 acres. The cost of the fire was $20.6 million.

*2019:   In August 2019, the Red Gate Fire burned 5 acres along State Route 76 and Red Gate Road.

LA MESA FIRE DEPARTMENT

La Mesa is located nine miles east of San Diego with 9.1 acres and a population of 60,021.

The city began as a citrus farming community. Robert Allison named the natural springs in the city "Allison Springs" in 1869. The name was changed to La Mesa Springs after the arrival of the San Diego and Cuyamaca Eastern Railroad in 1889, then on February 16, 1912, La Mesa Springs was incorporated into the city of La Mesa.

In 1908, the residents of La Mesa were advised "Persons who desire to have the protection of the fire company will make it more convenient for the department in case of fire if they will be sure to have a 1-1/2 inch reducer on their faucet near the house. It will pay you to have this attended to at once, because you cannot tell when you may have to use it."

In 1910, a hand-drawn hose cart was purchased at a cost of $147.50 and 150 feet of fire hose was purchased for $46.75.

On April 24, 1914, the La Mesa City Council appointed James Ross Orsborn as city marshal as well as fire marshal. On October 8, 1915, the following men were appointed to the department: Harry L. Smith, chief; F.W. Jackson, assistant chief; J. Frank Robertson, secretary; D. Frank Park, engineer; and Preston Smith, J. Tom McCarthy, John A. Sigler, Dwane Oliver, Harry H. Hill, J. Tom McCarthy, Dwane Oliver, and Harry H. Hill, firefighters.

On September 24, 1915, a volunteer fire department was formed. In December 1915, George Vanderburg was appointed assistant chief to replace F. W. Jackson. Homer Hurlburt, Luther C. Gordon, and W. B. Smith joined the department on April 13, 1916. Then, on October 13, 1916, Harry H. Hill resigned and Eugene Thomas took his place. Harry Smith resigned as city marshal on February 13, 1920.

In April 1915, a Moreland fire truck was purchased for $2,275. It was housed in an old livery shed which was located on the south side of Lookout Avenue (now La Mesa Boulevard) about 80 to 100 feet east of Date Avenue. A year later, the chassis of the Moreland fire truck was exchanged for a heavier one, a 2-1/2 ton chassis.

La Mesa adopted Ordinance #17 which prohibited the exploding of fireworks in the city on June 22, 1917.

On May 14, 1920, Luther C. Gordon was appointed the volunteer fire chief. On June 11, 1920, D. F. Park, H. Smith, C. H. Smith, Rube Levy, and George Miller were selected as firefighters. A month later, John Schlotler, Byron Canon, Bert Lott, and Austin Lott joined the department. On October 12, 1920, Harry Smith was electrocuted from defective electric pads.

La Mesa Volunteer Fire Dept., 1916. Courtesy of La Mesa Historical Society.

On April 24, 1924, the following appointments were made for a two-year period: L. C. Gordon, fire chief; R. Levy, assistant fire chief; and Austin Lott, engineer.

In April 1927, bids were submitted for a firehouse and shed at a cost of $4,595.

A year later, the fire truck was moved into a building owned by the California Division of Forestry (CDF) on the northeast corner of Date Street and Lookout Avenue. CDF kept a fire engine at the site to use to fight fires in the county outside the city boundaries. The livery shed that was used to store the fire engine on Lookout Avenue was demolished.

In July 1930, a reorganization meeting of the La Mesa Fire Department was held and new by-laws adopted. The following appointments were made: Luther C. Gordon, fire chief; Raymond Lyles, first assistant chief; Jim Glen, second assistant chief; and Bud Rethwich, captain.

In April 1922, a REO fire truck with a 1-1/4 ton chassis was purchased for $5,000. In 1931, a Chevrolet truck with a front-mounted 500-gpm Barton pump that was put together by Yankee Motors in Los Angeles was bought.

When the new WPA (Works Progress Administration) building for CDF was completed in 1937, the two La Mesa trucks, the REO and Chevrolet, were housed in sheds on state property that faced Orange Avenue, between Date and Nebo Streets.

The newly renovated firehouse on Nebo Street was occupied in February 1938. The 1931 Chevrolet and one of the two cab-forward GMC County/State owned fire trucks occupied the two stalls of the new fire station. Much of the equipment from the REO was transferred to the GMC fire truck.

In March 1939, George Robeson became a volunteer fireman. George Robeson owned and operated La Mesa Sheet Metal Company, located just across the alley from the Nebo Drive fire station.

In June 1941, the department purchased a new 1941 Seagrave fire engine with a 500-gpm pump. Former Chief Luther Gordon and his wife, Julia, drove the new fire truck from the factory in Columbus, Ohio, to La Mesa. When the National Board of Fire Underwriters and the La Mesa firemen tested the new 1941 Seagrave fire truck at Little Murray Reservoir in August 1941, it passed all the tests. The fire engine was sold to Harbison Canyon Volunteer Fire Department in February 1968.

Thomas William "Bill" Orsborn joined the La Mesa Fire Department as a volunteer in 1945 and in 1950 was drafted into the United States Army during the Korean War. When he was honorably discharged in 1952, Orsborn returned to the La Mesa Fire Department. During his career with the department he advanced through the ranks and retired after 38 years as deputy chief. He attended Grossmont High School graduating in 1946 and attended San Diego State University. He died on January 11, 2019, at the age of 90.

The La Mesa Fire Department purchased a 1942 Seagrave fire engine equipped with a 750-gpm pump in March 1947. The truck was purchased from the Defense Plant Corporation as war surplus. It was used at Ryan Aeronautical during World War II. The fire engine was sold to Lemon Grove Fire Department in February 1968.

In March 1949, a Chevrolet fire truck for fighting grass fires and for quick-attack on house fires was put into service, replacing the 1931 Chevrolet truck. The new truck was built by Captain George Robeson with the help of several of the firemen who worked on it at Robeson's sheet metal shop. It carried 500 gallons and was equipped with a 150-gpm gear pump driven from a power take-off so it could pump while on the move. The 1931 Chevrolet fire truck was sold as surplus to a private party in May 1949.

In May 1952, a new Fire Station #1 opened at 8034 Allison Avenue to replace the old Nebo Drive station. Chief Ray Lyles and his wife, Erma, occupied an apartment above the station. A. W. Lyles, Ray Lyle's dad, lived downstairs.

La Mesa purchased a 1955 Van Pelt fire engine on a Kenworth chassis with a 1,000-gpm pump in October 1955. Also in October 1955, Fire Station #2 was opened at 8834 Dallas Street in north La Mesa.

In September 1962, La Mesa purchased two new 1,250-gpm Van Pelt pumpers with Hall-Scott 935-cubic-inch engines. In December 1967, the city purchased an American La France 90-foot Aero Chief elevated platform with a 1,500-gpm pump.

The city purchased a Navy surplus International Harvester pickup and placed a foam generator and a light water unit on it for fighting fuel fires in 1969.

In February 1976, the city bought a new American LaFrance fire engine with a 1,250-gpm pump. The fire engine was driven from the factory in Sommerville, South Carolina, by two La Mesa Fire Department personnel. In July 1977, the city purchased a new American LaFrance fire engine with a 1,500-gpm pump. Again, the fire engine was driven from the factory by two La Mesa Fire Department personnel.

In March 1978, La Mesa purchased a 1978 American LaFrance fire engine with a 1,500-gpm pump. This pumper was a demonstrator and was delivered to the fire station by a sales representative.

Mike Morris was hired in October 1979 to service both police and fire department vehicles. He worked out of the shop at the rear of Fire Station #1 on Allison Avenue. In 1980, he led a team of firemen who built a new brush truck to replace the 1949 Chevrolet, and in 1982, the firemen built a new light water and foam unit on a new

Chevrolet chassis to replace the worn-out International Harvester pickup. The trucks were fabricated at La Mesa Sheet Metal Shop and at Fire Station #1.

James Orrin "J. O." Orsborn was selected as chief in 1981. Prior to graduating from St. Augustine High School in 1945, his career began as a volunteer fireman with the La Mesa Fire Department at the age of 15 in 1941. Four years later, his brother, Thomas William "Bill" Orsborn, joined the department. Chief J. O. Orsborn was involved with the California Fire Chiefs Association, Fire Training Officers Division, and Pioneer Hook & Ladder Museum in San Diego. Chief Orsborn retired in 1990 after 46 years of service. He passed away on May 11, 2007, at the age of 81.

In 1982, dispatching for the fire department moved from the La Mesa Police Department to the multiple fire agency dispatch center at El Cajon Fire Department. Fire stations in the East County were renumbered 1 through 19. La Mesa fire stations became Stations 11, 12, and 13.

In August 1987, La Mesa purchased a new 100-foot aerial truck to replace the 90-foot Snorkel purchased in 1968. The truck was manufactured in Ephrata, PA, by L.T.I., Inc. In November 1990, the city purchased two new Pierce fire engines to replace the 1977 and 1978 American LaFrance engines. A year later, the city purchased a new Pierce fire engine to replace the 1976 American LaFrance engine. The American LaFrance was moved into reserve.

Chris Carlson became chief of the department on April 8, 1991 at the age of 34. He had been head of the Turlock Fire Department in Northern California for five years, beginning in 1986. His firefighting career began in 1977 with the Solana Beach Fire Protection District, working as a firefighter, fire engineer, and fire marshal. From 1981 to 1986, he worked as a fire marshal for the Rancho Santa Fe Fire Protection District. He attended Point Loma High School. He retired in 1998.

In June 1995, the city purchased a new rescue truck to replace the light water and foam unit which had been used as a rescue truck since 1982.

In July 2000, La Mesa purchased a new Pierce fire engine to replace Engine 11, a 1990 Pierce, which was moved into reserve. In May 2006, the city acquired a new Pierce fire engine to replace Engine 12. A new Pierce 100-foot aerial truck was put into service on August 20, 2009.

In April 2002, the city took delivery of a new Office of Emergency Services (OES) engine to replace OES-192, a 1975 engine. OES engines are used on major fires throughout the state and funded by OES.

In March 2004, La Mesa voters approved Proposition D, the fire, police, and emergency service measure, authorizing the city to sell $25 million of general obligation bonds for needed improvements to fire and police stations.

In August 2004, the city begin delivery of Paramedic Assessment Engine Company services.

Ryan Lopez, Brent Baum, Jason Runkle, and Dean Sergent deliverd a healthy baby boy at the driveway of Station 11. Courtesy of La Mesa Fire Department.

February 29, 2008, was the official launch of the Fire Department Centennial Celebration. Events were held throughout the year to celebrate 100 years of service.

On September 28, 2008, constant staffing model (vacant positions are filled by personnel on an overtime basis) was implemented. On July 1, 2009, La Mesa Firemen's Association became La Mesa Firefighters Local 4759.

Dave Burk, who had over 25 years of experience with the La Mesa Fire Department, was appointed fire chief in June 2004. While he was chief, El Cajon, La Mesa, and Lemon Grove entered into a shared duty chief agreement in July 2009. Chief Burk retired on December 24, 2009.

On January 1, 2010, El Cajon, La Mesa, and Lemon Grove entered into a joint exercise of powers agreement to create the Heartland Fire & Rescue for organizational management of fire protection, fire prevention services, emergency medical services, and community emergency preparedness. All three cities had previously approved the agreement at recent council meetings held in each city. The 14 chief officers of the three cities was reduced to 11. One fire chief is the leader of the three cities. The expected savings was $560,000 among the three cities without a loss of service to the public.

Mike Scott was appointed the Heartland Fire & Rescue chief in October 2009. He had been the chief of El Cajon since 2005. Chief Scott began his career with the department in 1984 as a firefighter/paramedic. During his 28 years with El Cajon, he was one of the original California Task Force-8 Urban Search and Rescue team members in California. He started as a technical rescue specialist and deployed to the Northridge Earthquake in 1994 and to the Atlanta Olympics bombing in 1996. Scott transferred to the Canine Division where he was partnered with a devoted black Labrador, Billy, in November 1998. Chief Scott and Billy became the second canine search team in the county to be certified by FEMA. They served several local missions before being deployed to Ground Zero shortly after the 9/11 terrorist attacks in New York. Chief Scott retired on July 29, 2012.

Rick Sitta, who earned a commendation for bravery in the 2003 Cedar Fire, was selected as chief for Heartland Fire & Rescue in August 2012. Between 2003 and 2010, he had been a fire division chief in El Cajon and Coronado. In January 2010, he was appointed deputy fire chief of Heartland Fire & Rescue. Chief Sitta retired on August 12, 2016.

Colin Stowell became chief of Heartland Fire & Rescue in December 2016. He had worked for the San Diego Fire-Rescue Department for 28 years. He was appointed chief of the San Diego Fire-Rescue Department by Mayor Kevin Faulconer on August 13, 2018. He joined the San Diego Fire-Rescue Department in 1988, promoted to captain in 2002, battalion chief in 2007, deputy chief in 2012, and assistant chief in 2015. He earned an Associate of Fire Science from Miramar College, a Bachelor of Science in Public Administration from San Diego State University, and completed the Executive Fire Officer Program at the National Fire Academy.

Chief Stowell was responsible for four operating budgets as well as capital improvement projects for Heartland Fire & Rescue. He handled contract negotiations and oversight and was accountable to three city managers and city councils.

From August 11, 2018, to October 20, 2018, Mike Chasin served as interim chief of Heartland Fire & Rescue. Chasin began his career as an emergency medical technician at University of California, Los Angeles in 1989. In 1997, he was hired by the city of El Cajon as a firefighter-paramedic and has served there as engineer, captain, fire marshal, and division chief.

On October 20, 2018, Steve Swaney was appointed to lead the Heartland Fire & Rescue. He had been a division chief for Heartland Fire & Rescue since 2013. Chief Swaney began working with the El Cajon Fire Department in 1985. He also served as the fire chief for the Julian Cuyamaca Fire Protection District. He obtained an Associate of Fire Science from Miramar College and participated in paramedic training at the University of California San Diego. He is a 2016 graduate of the Leadership East County. Swaney has a Bachelor of Science in Management from California Coast University.

Besides serving Heartland Fire & Rescue, Chief Swaney is a certified Federal Emergency Management Agency canine evaluator and is a lead instructor for the FEMA Canine Search Specialist School. He started working with a chocolate Labrador named Sherman in 1997. Chief Swaney and his dog, Sherman, were in New York within 24 hours of the Twin Towers collapse to aid in rescue efforts. They were also deployed to Hurricane Katrina in New Orleans and Hurricane Rita in southeast Texas in 2005, Hurricane Ernesto off the Atlantic Coast in 2006, and the Torrey Pines Bluff collapse in 2004. After Sherman retired in 2006, Swaney continued rescue work in San Diego with two other rescue dogs, Icon and Tank.

To summarize, the chiefs of La Mesa Fire Department include: Harry L. Smith (1915-1920); Luther C. Gordon (1920-1939); Raymond "Ray" Lyles (1939-1965); Robert O. Saver (1965-1981); James "J. O." Orsborn (1981-1990); Chris Carlson (1991-1998); Douglass Matter (1998-2004); Dave Burk (2004-2009); Mike Scott (2009-2012); Rick Sitta (2012-2016), Colin Stowell (2016-2018), and Steve Swaney (2018-).

In 2015, La Mesa Captain Eric Danell retired after 31 years with the department. While off duty during the Cedar Fire in 2003, he and another firefighter went to Julian to help a retired fire chief. At 11 p.m. the wildfire surrounded them. They only had a small pump and two hoses connected to a water tank. When the smoke and heat became overwhelming, Danell put his face down in the dirt, trying to breathe. The house was the only one that wasn't destroyed in the area.

In 2016, Captain William "Billy" Doig received the 2016 Department of the Year Award and was honored by the La Mesa Chamber of Commerce in its ninth annual Salute to Heroes event. He began his career with the La Mesa Fire Department in 2004. Captain Doig coordinated the La Mesa Firefighters Pancake Breakfast, La Mesa Fill the Boot Drive, led the La Mesa team in the annual 9/11 Memorial Stair Climb, and helped raise awareness for the Burn Institute.

For over 35 years, the La Mesa Fire Department has hosted the Fire Explorer Post 2328. The program is open to young adults ages 15 to 21. It shows the Fire Explorers what a career in the fire services is like. Fire Explorers meet twice a month for the first six months. Explorers are considered to be Probationary Explorers during this time period. They are given five classroom lectures followed by five hands-on meetings. Each lecture has a quiz that is given the following month. Upon successful completion of each quiz and a final manipulative exam, the Fire Explorer is eligible to begin riding along on the fire engine.

There is a staff of 45 personnel serving La Mesa. The operations division in the La Mesa Fire Department includes 1 division chief, 12 captains, 12 engineers, 6 firefighters, and 6 paramedic firefighters.

In 2019, only 6% of the calls were fire-related, with 87% being medical-related emergencies. Heartland Fire & Rescue implemented call triage as one way to meet the needs of the community. Call triage prompts 911 dispatchers to ask callers for more information other than just basic information so that the department can determine whether or not to send an emergency vehicle. Since this program was implemented, medical-related calls have decreased by 16%.

On August 6, 2019, the La Mesa Fire Department received a new OES Engine 406 to replace an older one.

Heartland Fire & Rescue's fire stations in La Mesa are:

Station 11 is located at 8054 Allison Street. The original station was built in May 1952. In September 2004, a groundbreaking ceremony was held for Station 11 and administrative headquarters. A ceremonial demolition was held in January 2005 to mark the start of construction for the new station, a dedication ceremony was held on July 31, 2006, and a community open house was held on August 5, 2006. The station was designed by JKA Architecture and completed at a cost of $6.4 million.

The 19,500-square-foot station houses 12 firefighters, an emergency operations center, and administrative offices. The administrative portion of the facility includes fire administrative personnel offices, conference rooms, break room, and an Emergency Operations Center/Training Room. The site design includes space for public and private vehicle parking, landscaping and an emergency generator. It is staffed by a captain, an engineer, and a firefighter/paramedic. The station houses Engine 11, a rescue engine, and truck. It responds to medical calls, structure fires, brush fires, vehicle fires and accidents, rescues, hazardous material incidents, and public service calls.

Station 12 is located at 8844 Dallas Street. On June 24, 1998, La Mesa dedicated the station which replaced the old Station 12 at 8834 Dallas Street that was opened in May 1955. The old station was in the path of the extension of State Route 125. The station is staffed by a captain, an engineer, and a firefighter. It houses a medic engine and reserve rescue engine.

Station 13 is located at 9110 Grossmont Boulevard. It was remodeled in 2010 using funds from voter-approved Proposition D. It was opened in 1962. It is staffed by a captain, an engineer, and a firefighter. The station houses two engines, one owned by the California Emergency Management Agency (Cal EMA). On August 6, 2019, OES Chief Brian Marshall presented a ceremonial key for OES Engine 406 to Chief Swaney.

The City of La Mesa has a great fire department with personnel who work hard to provide quality fire suppression and emergency medical services to residents of the community.

CALLS RECALLED:

*1962: In June 1962, Dale Reeser died after being stricken with a heart attack while on a fire call at Little Flower Haven. He was buried in his hometown of Farmer City, Illinois.

*2011: In May 2011, a two-alarm fire fire occurred in a four-story condominium building off Baltimore Drive causing $1 million in damages. Thirty-two firefighters responded from La Mesa, Lemon Grove, El Cajon, San Miguel Consolidated Fire Protection District, Santee, and San Diego.

*2011: Heidi Durfey, 24, died after her SUV with her three young children inside rolled backward 60 feet and ran over her. The tragedy occurred on the driveway of her home in the 8700 block of Glenira Avene. She became caught under the SUV as it rolled and was dragged beneath the vehicle. Firefighters, with help from a neighbor, were successful in lifting the car and freeing the young mother, who suffered head, chest and abdomen injuries. She was transported to Sharp Memorial Hospital by hospital in acute status but died a short time later of her injuries. The children were not injured.

*2015: In December 2015, a fire in a home in the 9300 block of De Camp Drive caused $400,000 damage. Crews contained the flames within 10 minutes.

*2017: A small brush fire broke out on Alvarado Road in June 2017. Crews had the fire extinguished in 35 minutes.

*2017: In August 2017, a fire erupted in the kitchen of Wong's Golden Palace on University Avenue. It took firefighters 15 minutes to extinguish the blaze. The fire caused $300,000 damage.

*2018: On November 19, 2018, several Heartland firefighters were deployed as part of the San Diego USAR team, California Task Force 8, as part of the search and recovery efforts at the Camp Fire.

*2019: A fire at a residence on Maple Street in La Mesa caused $800,000 damage.

*2019: Heartland Fire & Rescue responded to about 22,000 calls.

*2020: On May 30, 2020, the Chase and Union Banks and Vons at the La Mesa Springs Shopping Center were set on fire by protesters about 11:30 p.m. The Randall Lamb Associates' building, a Vons delivery truck, and a Heartland Fire & Rescue vehicle were also burned. Despite the Randall Lamb Associates' building burning to the ground, the owners gave $5,000 to help other businesses to rebuild. The protest was in response to the shooting of George Floyd in Minnesota.

*2020: In July 2020, firefighters responded to a second-alarm fire at a home in the 7450 block of Mohawk Street. Forty firefighters from the Heartland, San Miguel, and San Diego Departments fought the blaze. The fire caused $200,000 in damage.

LAKE CUYAMACA VOLUNTEER FIRE DEPARTMENT

Mr. R. W. Waterman, who became governor of California, bought the Stonewall Jackson Mine in Cuyamaca in 1886. By 1889 Cuyamaca City, located on the southeastern shore of Lake Cuyamaca, had a general store, hotel, post office, bank, and school. The mine closed down shortly after Governor Waterman died in 1891. Today people enjoy fishing, hiking, and camping in the area.

After the Laguna Fire in 1970, twenty-three volunteer fire departments were established with the support of the San Diego County. The county withdrew financial support in 1974.

Realtor Al Sprague was the chief of the Lake Cuyamaca fire department for 15 years. Eighteen firefighters participated in interstation training with the Julian Volunteer Fire Department as well as separate training.

In 1981, under the leadership of Chief Sprague of the Lake Cuyamaca Volunteer Fire Department and Chief Larry Hutchinson of Julian Fire and Rescue, the Julian-Cuyamaca Fire Protection District (JCFPD) was created. In 1984, LAFCO (Local Agency Commission Organization) board members formed the JCFPD. In November 1984, voters approved an annual benefit fee of $50 per household. The board of directors was made up of residents from both Julian and Lake Cuyamaca.

The Julian-Cuyamaca Fire Protection District was an all-volunteer fire department, except for a part-time chief and secretary. JCFPD had a total of 52 firefighters: 12 experienced volunteers who served as officers, and over 50 reserves. The reserves were trained firefighters gaining practical experience, all were emergency medical technicians.

Kevin Dubler became district chief in 1999 and served until his retirement in 2012. In November 2006, a proposition to create a second annual benefit fee of $50 was placed on the ballot for the purpose of accumulating funds to build a new fire station in Julian. Nearly 74% of the voters in this general election approved the benefit fee.

An initiative to replace the Julian-Cuyamaca Fire Protection District's annual benefit fee with a parcel tax was defeated on November 6, 2018.

The Esperanza Investment Group, chaired by Ed Prout, donated land for a station and the Fletcher family donated land for a parking lot. In 1985 a two-story building was added to an existing structure at 34520 Engineers Road, Station 57. Now it is Cal Fire Station 51.

The fire department had a 1991 1500-gpm pumper purchased by the JCFPD for $247,000 from Beck Fire Apparatus in Cloverdale, California; a 1988 Bronco purchased out of station funds for $20,000; a one-ton 1987 Ford rescue truck purchased by the JCFPD; and a 1957 International brush rig that was a military truck.

In 1991 a black and white cat looking near death showed up at the fire station. After the fire department paid the veterinarian bills for the cat and built a cat door for it, the cat, named Flame, decided to make the station his home.

The Lake Cuyamaca Fire Belles, nicknamed the "Ding-a-lings," organized fundraising, prepared food for the firefighters, and helped in many other ways. The 30 women met at the station the third Saturday of each month. The Fire Belles successfully managed without officers. Their 1992 events: March 14—a potluck dinner; May 9 and 10—a run marathon and Chile cook-off; May 24—annual breakfast; June, July, and August—bingo; July 4—rummage sale; September 5—barbecue and auction; October 17 and 18—art, craft, and food fair; December 6—turkey dinner; and December 31—party at the station.

Mary Sprague, a Fire Belle and wife of Chief Sprague, described volunteer firefighters in this way:

A Tribute to the San Diego County Volunteer Firefighters

Tall, short, round, and looks like a beanpole
Looks real pretty in a sweater or grubby after a day on a regular job
Hair? Yes and no
Went to school to become a butcher, a baker, or candlestick maker
Teacher, steno, or exec!
Trained in first aid, CPR, and as an EMT
Can carry a hose or run the pumps
Set up chairs, polish engines
Chase rattlers, scale a cliff, and fill a bag of sand
What a personality!
Mad when the incident is caused by carelessness or booze
Sad if there is loss of keepsakes
Smiles a lot and sheds a tear
Brassy, bossy, quiet, kind, and tender
Can work with CDF, ASTREA, and Life Flight
Gives of oneself for mutual aid
Has personality conflicts
Makes lasting friendships
Who has a lot of paperwork
Maps, mileage, letters, names, and numbers
Let me tell you more!
Oh! Oh! There's the tone! Listen!
"… responding with 1, 2, or more"
From the Mexican border to Rainbow country
Should we get the coffee and donuts ready?
There's a volunteer firefighter in my house and I'm glad!!!

In 2013, the board of directors of JCFPD announced to the public that, due to poor financial standing, JCFPD was considering an offer from the county to take over the district. The board proceeded to vote on whether to dissolve. The vote was 2:2; and therefore, did not pass and JCFPD remained independent.

In 2017, the board of directors announced that the county had made another offer to dissolve the district and assume fire protection and emergency medical responsibility for the community.

In December 2018, the San Diego County Board of Supervisors voted to hold a special election on March 19, 2019, to determine the fate of the volunteer fire department. Only the 2,482 registered voters in the district could vote on Measure A.

The measure passed with the approval of 55.56 percent of the voters, dissolving the Julian-Cuyamaca Fire Protection District and merging it with the San Diego County Fire Authority with staffing by Cal Fire.

CALLS RECALLED:

*1992:   One of the calls that hurt the hearts of the firefighters occurred on April 13, 1992. Barbara Winn, a Cuyamaca resident, was killed in a head-on car collision. Her husband set up a memorial fund in her memory for the Lake Cuyamaca Volunteer Fire Department.

*1992:   Jimmie Mastro, who lived on Engineers Road in Cuyamaca, was 20-feet up a ladder cutting a limb of a tree when he lost control of his chain saw and it made a deep, jagged cut in his upper right arm. Although he was bleeding profusely, he was able to climb down the ladder and apply pressure above the cut. His neighbors rushed him to the Lake Cuyamaca Volunteer Fire Department in their truck. Life Flight flew Mastro to UCSD Medical Center, where he was in surgery for five hours. He would have lost his arm without the help of the Lake Cuyamaca firefighters and the Life Flight crew. Jimmie Mastro said, "They gave me a new lease on life."

*2003:   During the Cedar Fire nine Cuyamaca firefighters, including Bob Garner, Christina Hays, and Chris Wilburn, lost their homes. Battalion Chief Carl Schweikert lost his auto repair business and his home. Firefighter Carolina Finch lost her two-story redwood home. Captain George Hatton and Firefighter Dave Southcott also lost their homes. A Julian-Cuyamaca Firefighter Relief Fund was established to help them. Ninety percent of Cuyamaca was destroyed in the fire. The fire burned 273,246 acres, 2,232 homes burned, and 14 civilians and one firefighter died.

LAKESIDE FIRE PROTECTION DISTRICT

Lakeside is 21 miles east of San Diego, covering 50.5 square miles, with a population of 62,834.

The El Cajon Valley Company was started in 1886. The company, consisting of E. W. Morse, G. H. Mansfield, O. S. Hubbell and I. M. Merrill, laid out the town of Lakeside and built the Victorian Lakeside Inn for $50,000 in 1887. The famous inn brought guests from throughout the country to Lakeside. It was demolished in 1920.

In 1923, Lakeside's first hose cart was made by Tom LaMadrid out of an old Model T frame. A few years later a two-wheeled cart was made and used until about 1949. Property owners were charged $5 annually for fire protection.

A fire bell was at the corner of Maine Avenue and Lakeshore Drive until 1928. It was then moved to a lot next to Valley Bank and moved again when a parking lot was built. No one knows where the bell is now.

In 1945, the fire protection committee consisted of James Haptonstall, John Wilkinson, Charles Newbury, and O. E. Holm. Chief Louis Paraquette led a crew that included Rupert Linley, Jack Hayes, C. O. Langlois, Charles Newberry, and Bob Hoffman.

In July 1946, a new fire truck equipped with pump and hose was purchased for $2,500. The department consisted of Hugo Clapp, chief; Ed Harrison, assistant chief; and firefighters Freddie Prindle, Merton Ankrum, Ormand Mitchell, Bob Williams, Louis Parquette, James Haptonstal, John Wilkinson, and Chuck Newbery. The firemen were paid $2 for each call in 1950.

A coalition was formed in 1959 to promote a fire protection district, including the Lakeside Farm Bureau, Wintergardens Civic Council, Eucalyptus Hills Land Owners Association, Lakeside Chamber of Commerce, and Riverview Farms Group. The Lakeside Fire Protection District was established in 1963.

The wives of the Lakeside firemen spent two days in October 1970 picketing the fire station in support of the request of their husbands to have higher wages. In 1980, voters approved assessing a fee for fire service.

County Service Area (CSA) No. 69 (Heartland paramedics) provides Advance Life Support (ALS) ambulance transport service within Santee and the unincorporated East County communities of Pepper Drive, Bostonia, and Lakeside. It was formed in 1974 to provide ambulance transport service within approximately 63 square miles of unincorporated East County. The western portion of the CSA was included in the 1980 incorporation of Santee but remained in CSA No. 69.

Lakeside's first station. Courtesy of Lakeside Historical Society.

Courtesy of Lakeside Historical Society.

Lucille Moore, who was elected in 1976 to represent District 2 on the San Diego County Board of Supervisors, said: "The people of the district have a right to expect good service from today's firefighters. But they must never forget that they must pay for the outstanding service they receive in terms of tax dollars. Contrary to popular opinion, the job of the firefighter is often unromantic, tedious, filled with constant training, assignments, and upgrading of skills and techniques. A fire department such as Lakeside is the best insurance a homeowner or a businessman can possibly get."

Ramon Ibarra, owner of Lakeside Service and Tow at 10116 Maine Avenue, has restored the Lakeside Fire Station that existed at the site in 1955, including replacing the Mobil Pegasus sign on the roof. Ed Harrison, who established the Lakeside Fire Department, once owned the gas station. He and his brothers served as volunteer firemen while living in the yellow house on the corner of Laurel and Maine Avenue.

In December 1984, a Van Pelt engine with a 50-foot telescoping ladder and an automatic nozzle was purchased at a cost of $207,000. In 1989, a 5,200-square-foot administrative office building was built on Parkside Street.

In 1992, Lakeside approved a $40 a year fire fee. Property owners were asked to vote on an amended special tax (benefit fee), Measure Y, in the November 3, 2020, general election. The district has not increased its benefit fee to fund firefighting and EMS in 40 years. There were 40.22% yes votes and 59.78% no votes in the election.

The Lakeside Fire Protection District provides service to the communities of Lakeside, Eucalyptus Hills, Moreno, Winter Gardens, Lakeview, Johnstown, Blossom Valley, Flinn Springs, Pepper Drive, Wildcat Canyon, and other areas of unincorporated El Cajon.

The district was an original participant in the Heartland Mutual Aid Pact and operates the longest running paramedic program in San Diego County. In July 1975, the first mobile intensive care paramedic ambulance in the county went into service at Santee Fire District Station 1. The crew consisted of one Santee and one Lakeside firefighter/paramedic.

Firefighter/paramedic Patrick Sellers and the Lakeside pit crew won the 2015 Burn Institute's Firefighter Demotion Derby at the San Diego County Fair in Del Mar in 2015 in a 1974 Cadillac Coup de Ville.

Firefighter/paramedic Corey Scott Palmore died unexpectedly on November 8, 2015, while off duty. He worked for several years as an EMT and then paramedic in San Diego for American Medical Response before becoming a reserve firefighter for the Lakeside Fire Protection District in 2010 and in 2013 he was hired full time. His father, Chuck, is a captain in the district.

The fire chiefs of the department include: Louis Paraquette (1945), Hugo Clapp (1946), Ed Harrison ((1946-1974), Patrick "Pat" F. Culkin (1974-1992), Darrell Jobes (1992-1993), Thomas Ace (1999-2003), Paul Heinz Stein, interim chief (2003), Mark Baker (2004-2010), Andy Parr (2010-2016), and Donald Butz (2016-).

Patrick F. Culkin was chief for 18 years. He was previously a firefighter for Convair and a volunteer firefighter in Poway in 1962 and 1963 before joining Lakeside's department in January 1965. He worked his way up through the ranks as engineer, captain, and fire marshal.

Darrell Jobes at the age of 38 was hired to be chief of Lakeside Fire in 1992 at a salary of $75,000. He resigned in 1993 to return to Bostonia. He had raised cows in Descanso and became a volunteer firefighter in Bostonia at the age of 19. He served as chief of Bostonia from 1981 to 1992. He said, "It (firefighting) takes a unique individual because you have to go from a dead sleep to full mental capacity in thirty seconds or one minute and by that time you're rolling out the door."

Thomas Ace was appointed chief on July 1, 1999. Chief Ace, from Wilkes Parre, Pennsylvania, was in the U.S. Navy for 10 years before he joined Lakeside as a paramedic in September 1979. He served as deputy fire marshal and division chief before becoming chief. He retired in September 2003, then became a forensic fire investigator for 17 years. He received a Specialized Certificate in Fire Protection from the University of California, San Diego. He graduated from Camp Hill Senior High School in 1965. On October 24, 2020, Chief Ace, 73, died by suicide.

Paul H. Stein was the interim chief in Lakeside in 2003. In 1999, he retired from the Santa Monica Fire Department after a 31-year career in the fire service. He has a Bachelor of Science in Management from the University of Redlands.

Mark Baker served as fire chief from 2004 to 2010. He was fired by the Lakeside Fire Board of Directors on January 26, 2010, by a 3-2 majority. In 2012 he was elected to serve on the board of the department.

Andy Parr's fire career with Lakeside covered 37 years. He was selected chief in 2010. After retiring from Lakeside in 2016, he served as EMS/Fire Liaison for the County Health and Human Services Agency. In March 2017, he became the Administrative Leader of the County of San Diego EMS Office (LEMSA). From May 2016 to March 2017, Chief Parr was the EMS Fire Liaison for San Diego EMS. He received a Bachelor of Science in Public Fire Administration from San Diego State University in 1989.

Donald Butz was appointed fire chief of Lakeside in October 2016. Previously, he was a division chief with the Lakeside Fire Protection District and then fire chief of Viejas from October 2005 to September 2016. Chief Butz has been in the fire service for over 40 years. In September 2014, he became president of the San Diego County Fire Chiefs Association. From September 1999 to September 2006, he was deputy chief for the Rancho Santa Fe Fire Protection District. From 1988 to 1999, Chief Butz was a fire marshal/fire captain with the San Miguel Consolidated Fire Protection District. He has a Master of Science, Leadership, Disaster Preparedness, and Executive Fire Leadership from Grand Canyon University, Bachelor of Science in Management from University of Phoenix, and Associate of Fire Science from Miramar College.

The governing board of the Lakeside Fire Protection District has five members elected to serve four-year terms. The directors set district policy and provide direction to the chief about the operation of the district. The board is comprised of the following members: Jim Bingham, Tim Robles, Mark Baker, Pete Leibig, and Bob Robeson. The budget for 2017-2018 was $13,827,426. The budget for 2018-2019 was $19,886,770. The budget for 2020-21 is $19,191,743.

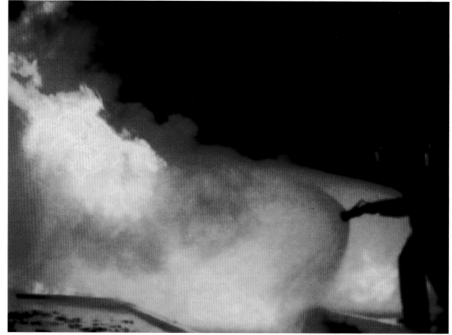

Chief Donald Butz leads a staff of 55 personnel, including three division chiefs and a fire prevention officer. The division chiefs are: John Hisaw, Operations; Humberto Lawler, Logistics, Training, and Facilities; and Bernard Molloy, EMS and Community Risk Reduction. The fire prevention officer is Jeremy Davis. The administrative staff includes Madeline Smith, finance director; Janise Bocskovits, executive assistant; Mukhtar Bari, human resources director; and Stefanie Trompeter Rolon, accounting specialist.

The captains are: Lance Buford, Matthew Buzzell, Jose Corona, Chris Downing, Jamie Hazlewood, Jon Jordan, Justin Loffredo, Ian Lowe, Chuck Palmore, Marc Poynte, Steve Russo, and Eric Stamm.

The engineers are: David Csik, Nathan Fox, Danny Leetch, Shawn McKenna, Brian Moore, Josh Raczka, Steve Schleif, Richard Smith, Joe Vasquez, Brent Watte, Chris Williams, and Robert Williams.

The firefighter/paramedics are: Michael Assof, Anthony Cano, Shane Daunis, Ernie Flint, Jesse Iglinski, Shannon Johnson, Chad Murray, James Paterson, Clinton Pierce, Patrick Sellers, Andrew Shaba, Matthew Shields, Nate Silva, Brandon Stanard, Bing Tom, and Jarrett Williams.

The Community Emergency Response Team (CERT) program trains residents to manage utilities and put out small fires, provide medical aid, search for and rescue victims, organize themselves and others to be effective in disaster situations, and collect disaster information for first responders.

The Logistic Volunteer Group (LVG) established in July 2011 is a senior program to provide assistance in the activities of the department including driving district vehicles, delivering mail, providing assistance at incidents, and representing the district at public functions.

The Reserve Firefighter Program was initiated in 2010. Reserve firefighters ride on apparatus and CSA No. 69 ambulances and perform all of the duties as the regular fire crew, including fire suppression, public education, station maintenance, and the

response to medical emergencies including providing advanced life support. After an initial training period, reserve firefighters, under supervision, work a minimum of two shifts per month on apparatus.

In January 2020, a program was initiated to train first responders to recognize human trafficking and report it to law enforcement. About 3,000 firefighters from 40 departments will receive the training. Chief Butz said, "We know this training will make a difference in protecting victims of human trafficking."

The department has four paramedic engine companies, one rescue company, two wildland engines, and two advanced life support paramedic ambulances. The district received in 2020 a new Spartan dryside tanker which has a Freightliner M2106, Hale MBP 750-gpm pump, 2,000-gallon tank, 10-gallon foam cell, and stainless steel body.

The firefighters respond to calls from four stations.

Station 1 is located at 8035 Winter Gardens Boulevard in the southern section of the district. It provides first response to the Winter Gardens, Pepper Drive, Riverview areas as well as automatic aid to El Cajon, San Miguel Fire & Rescue, and County Service Area (CSA) No. 115. The firehouse is home to one paramedic engine company (E1) and one brush engine (BR1). In 2017, E1 made 2,170 runs and BR1 made 81 runs.

Station 2 is located on 4.8 acres at 12216 Lakeside Avenue in Lakeside. It serves the northern areas of the district including Eucalyptus Hills, Moreno, Wildcat Canyon, and Highway 67. It provides automatic aid response to the Barona Fire District and unincorporated San Diego County. This station has one paramedic engine (E2), one 65-foot KME Telesqurt aerial (202s), one paramedic ambulance (Medic 2), and one patrol vehicle (patrol 2). In 2017, E2 made 2,881 runs, E202s made 22 runs, and M2 made 3,641 runs.

The two-story 24,000-square-foot station was completed in December 2011 at a cost of $15.2 million and opened in early 2012. The county supervisors funded the station with $14.5 million in redevelopment funds. It can house up to 10 firefighters. Areas include an apparatus room with two drive-through bays, 10 bunk rooms, fitness area, kitchen, dayroom, shop, dispatch and administrative spaces. The building design also includes the administrative offices for the department, as well as a board room/training room. The station can support a strike team of 20 personnel. There is space for hose drying facilities, an emergency generator, and a 1,500-gallon emergency fuel tank. JKA Architecture designed and provided construction administration services. It replaced the 44-year-old Station 2 in Eucalyptus Hills.

Station 3, located at 14008 Highway 8 in El Cajon, was remodeled in 2020. It serves the southwestern area of the district and provides automatic aid to El Cajon, Alpine, and Viejas districts. It houses one paramedic engine (E3), one rescue truck (R3), and one paramedic ambulance (M3). In 2017, E3 made 1,908 runs, R3 made 224 runs, and M3 made 3,097 runs.

Station 26 is located at 15245 Oak Creek Road in El Cajon. It serves the eastern section of the district including Blossom Valley, Finn Springs, and the Dunbar Lane area. This station was built by Cairo Construction Company in 1990. The station includes a paramedic engine (E26) and a state OES engine (OES305). In 2017, E26 made 965 runs and OES305 made 15 runs.

Each year the firefighters of Lakeside participate in the San Diego 9/11 Memorial Stair Climb. They join 1,300 first responders from throughout the county in climbing 110 flights of stairs at the Hilton San Diego Bayfront, the same number as in the twin towers, wearing the name of a fallen emergency responder whose life was lost on that day. The climb is in memory and honor of each of the fallen 343 New York firefighters, 23 New York police officers, and 37 New York Port Authority heroes, and to raise awareness of the sacrifices made by firefighters everywhere.

An important member of the fire department who will never be forgotten is 10-year-old Bella, a purebred black Labrador retriever, who died on February 24, 2020. Bella and her handler, Engineer Richmond "Rich" Smith, were part of US&R California Task Force 8 (CA-TF8), an urban regional fire team that does search and rescue. The members are deployed to assignments such as the Camp Fire in November 2018, Hurricane Lane in Hawaii in August 2018, and Hurricane Katrina in August 2005.

The highly trained fire personnel work hard to provide the best possible service to the community.

CALLS RECALLED:

*1949:   The Lakeside volunteer firemen extinguished a brush fire in the back of the Lakeside Grammar School. The fire spread over three acres after starting from trash burning in a nearby yard. Crews from the State Division of Forestry and Santee assisted the Lakeside firemen.

*1977:   On January 26, 1977, the home of Theodore Lambson on Muth Valley Road was destroyed by a fire. Damage was $50,000.

*1984:   A fire caused by an arsonist began on September 6, 1984, burning 3,200 acres near the San Vicente Reservoir.

*2003:   The Cedar Fire killed 14 civilians and 1 firefighter and injured 113 people. In Lakeside, 30,000 acres burned. This fire that started on October 25, 2003, and was not contained until November 3. It destroyed 2,232 homes and burned 273,246 acres in the county.

Sadly, 12 people living in Wildcat Canyon and Muth Valley in the northern part of Lakeside, who had little warning that the fire was approaching, died in the fire. On October 24, 2015, the Cedar Fire Historical Monument adjacent to the Lakeside Fire Administration headquarters and Station 2 at 12216 Lakeside Avenue was dedicated to pay tribute to those who died in the fire. The Lakeside Fire District donated the land and the community worked for more than a year to fund, plan, and build the remembrance. Artists and survivors created four murals made from the remnants of the destruction, including pieces of pottery and glass that were the sole remnants of some homes. It includes a map of the Cedar Fire. The walkway contains the names and dates of past wildfires with space for future fires. James Hubbell designed the concept of a stone bench and table surrounded by native plants.

The monument lists the people who perished in the fire: Galen Blacklidge, 50, Moreno, teacher, died while trying to escape in her vehicle; Christy-Anne Seiller-Davis, 42, Alpine; Gary Edward Downs, 50, Lakeside, small-business owner, died while trying to escape on Wildcat Canyon Road; John Leonard Pack, 28, Lakeside; Quynh Yen Chau Pack, 28, Lakeside; Mary Lynne Pearce, 54, Lakeside, nurse, died in the area of Barona Indian Reservation; Steven Rucker, 54, Novato, firefighter, died in Julian; Stephen Shacklett, 54, Lake View Hills Estates, construction superintendent, died in a motor home on Much Valley Road near Moreno; James Shohara, 63, correctional officer, died while trying to escape on Lake Vicente Drive in Moreno; Solange Shohara, 43, Lakeside, correctional officer, died while trying to escape on Lake Vicente Drive in Moreno; Randy Shohara, 22, Lakeside, died while trying to escape on Lake Vicente Drive in Moreno; Robin Sloan, 45, Lakeside, Wall-Mart employee, died in the area of the Barona Indian Reservation; Jennifer Sloan, 17, Lakeside, student, died in the area of the Barona Indian Reservation; Ralph Marshall Westley, 77, Lakeside, retired retail clerk; and an unknown migrant worker found mid-December in the I-15, SR-52 area.

*2007: The Witch Creek Fire in July 2007 killed 2 people and burned 44,150 acres. More than a million people were evacuated from their homes.

*2010: In June 2010, a brush fire on Los Coches Road in Lakeside burned a car and ignited trees. The fire was confined to a quarter of an acre.

*2010: In August 2010, a wildfire in El Monte Valley burned 100 acres.

*2012: The crews responded to 11,163 calls in 2012.

*2013: In May 2013, a fire on Mapleview Street led to voluntary evacuations. The fire started on the top of the hill and moved quickly downhill towards the San Diego River.

*2013: On June 22, 2013, there was a head-on collision on Lake Jennings Road involving a four-door Altima and a four-door Jeep. Two persons were trapped in their vehicles. Lakeside resident Harold Wise IV, 21, the driver of the Altima, was pronounced dead at the scene.

*2013: In December 2013, two dogs died in a house fire on Jackson Hill Lane. Damage to the house was $100,000.

*2014: On May 14, 2014, about 5:20 p.m., the Aurora Fire broke out near Interstate 8 and Aurora Drive. At around 7:40 p.m. on the same day, the fire was 100% contained after it had reached a size of 17 acres.

*2016: Lakeside firefighters assisted Alpine Fire at a fire in a vacant residential structure on Eltinge Drive on the evening of April 7, 2016. Viejas Engine 25 was first on scene reporting smoke from the attic area. Crews forced entry to the home and pulled ceilings to access the fire in the attic. The fire was extinguished in approximately twenty minutes. Firefighters remained on scene for overhaul for two hours.

*2018: In January 2018, the Lakeside crew smelled smoke outside the repair shop behind Station 3 where an engine was parked for routine maintenance. Firefighters found their engine in flames! The $550,000 engine was destroyed along with the tools inside that were worth about $80,000, including four portable radios worth $7,000 each. Division Chief John Hisaw said there appeared to have been an electrical fire that started under the cab.

*2018: Lakeside firefighters responded to the West Fire in Alpine on July 6 at 11:39 p.m. The fire started on the east side of Alpine and quickly spread through residential areas south of Interstate 8. The fire destroyed 34 homes in Alpine and burned 505 acres.

*2018: A blaze at a home on Moreno Avenue in Lakeside in December 2018 sent a woman to UCSD Medical Center and caused $150,000 damage.

*2018:   In December 2018, a cat climbed a tall palm tree but wasn't able to get back down. Crews used an 65-foot ladder to rescue the animal.

*2018:   In December 2018, firefighters rescued a woman found dangling from a second-story window after a fire broke out in an apartment complex on Mapleview Street. Sixteen residents in six apartments were displaced.

*2019:   In November 2019, family and friends at a Thanksgiving gathering on Vista Camino woke up to find the house on fire, All eight people in the house escaped, including Emanuel Penney who had ran back inside to rescue his dog. The Lakeside fire crew had the fire extinguished in 40 minutes.

*2019:   The department responded to 9,611 calls in 2019, including 7,628 medical aids, 149 structure fires, 47 vegetation fires, 90 vehicle fires, 740 traffic collisions, 242 gas break/ hazmat/alarm calls, 77 public service calls, 79 rescues, and 559 other calls.

*2020:   In July 2020, a big rig carrying about 41,000 pounds of raw pork caught fire on westbound Interstate 8 between La Coches and Lake Jennings Park Roads. The rig's brakes overheated, sparking the fire, which spread to the tires and then the semitrailer. The driver was not injured but the trailer was a total loss.

*2020:   In September 2020, Engineer Danny Leetch rested his head on a small table after fighting the Valley Fire for 26 straight hours in 108 degree heat before returning to the fireline. The fire burned 16,390 acres.

*2020:   Crews from Lakeside were assigned to the Creek Fire. The fire started on September 4 in the Big Creek drainage in the Sierra National Forest. Thirty thousand residents of Fresno County and 15,000 residents of Madera County were evacuated because of the fire. It burned 341,722 acres, destroyed 856 structures, and damaged 52 structures.

Lemon Grove Fire Department

Fire truck at Lemon Grove. Courtesy of San Diego History Center.

Lemon Grove is located nine miles east of San Diego and four miles south of La Mesa with an area of 3.88 square miles and a population of 26,969 (2018).

The Kumeyaay once lived where the city of Lemon Grove is now. It then became part of the Mission San Diego de Alcala, founded on July 16, 1769, by Junípero Serra. The mission property became Mexican ranchos in 1834. When gold was discovered in California, the road to the city of Lemon Grove began.

In 1869, sheep rancher Robert Allison bought a large parcel of land, realizing that the area was good for growing citrus. His son, Joseph Allison, filed a subdivision map for "Lemon Grove" in 1892.

In the early 1900s large citrus groves were planted in the area. By World War II, most of the groves were replaced by suburbs. A 3,000-pound plastered lemon was built in 1928 for use in the Fiesta de San Diego Parade. The Big Lemon served as a parade float until 1932. It became a permanent town symbol in 1932.

In 1931, the trustees ordered the Lemon Grove Grammar School closed to Mexican children. The lawsuit, Alvarez vs. Lemon Grove School Board, became the nation's first successful school desegregation case after San Diego Superior Court Judge Claude Chambers ruled in favor of the Mexican-American plaintiff families.

Fire service was handled by the U.S. Forest Service, but there were only six telephones in town to call for assistance. After two homes were destroyed in 1925, residents decided the city needed a fire department. The yearly budget of $600 consisted of donations by property owners. People could have a fire hydrant placed in front of their houses at a cost of $7.50. The hydrant consisted of a 4-inch pipe with a valve mounted on top.

The district purchased a Model T truck with hose and a pump and a 1927 Dodge chassis on which a chemical tank was mounted. But the Model "T" pumper could not make it to the top of some hills in Lemon Grove. A used 1927 Hudson was purchased and a "pushboard" was mounted on the front. The Hudson responded with the Model T and pushed it up the inclines that were too steep for it to navigate under its own power.

Lemon Grove 1987

H. A. Anderson and B. L. Kerfoot served as chiefs during this period and the district consisted of 12 volunteers who were paid $2 per fire response. An electric siren was mounted on the lumber company tower located on the corner of Main Street and North Avenue. The siren was used to notify the volunteers about a call.

After the stock market crash of 1929, the volunteer fire department decreased in size and service. The U.S. Forest Service took control of the equipment and again became responsible for fire protection in 1930. It was 18 years before the residents of Lemon Grove would have a fire department.

Voters approved the Lemon Grove Fire Protection District on June 15, 1950, and a $30,000 bond issue for the purchase of equipment. In January 1951, Ray Carmody was hired as the first paid fireman, followed by Charles M. Hamel and James Sanchez. H. L. "Pappy" Hensley was appointed chief in December 1951.

Fred Dixon succeeded Hensley as fire chief upon Hensley's retirement. In 1976, Robert Adams replaced Dixon as chief. In July 1977, Lemon Grove incorporated as a city and in November 1977 the Lemon Grove Fire District became the Lemon Grove Fire Department. When Chief Adams retired in 1987, Bill Wright was appointed chief. A new fire station was started in 1986 at Central Avenue and School Lane and was completed in June of 1988 under the direction of Chief Wright.

Bill Wright retired in 1996 and was succeeded by Dale Chamberlain who retired shortly before the city contracted for fire service from the San Miguel Consolidated Fire Protection District in November 1997. When the contract for fire service expired in July 2004, the city resumed operation of its own fire department under the direction of Chief Jon Torchia. In June 2008, he became the deputy chief of the North County Fire Protection District in Fallbrook. Chief Torchia retired in May 2012.

A major milestone of the Lemon Grove Fire Department was joining El Cajon and La Mesa Fire Departments on January 1, 2010, in managing Heartland Fire & Rescue. By consolidating, the departments improved services and reduced duplication of resources. The management team includes a fire chief, three deputy fire chiefs, two division chiefs, five battalion chiefs, and four support staff.

Mike Scott was appointed the Heartland Fire & Rescue chief in October 2009. He had been the chief of El Cajon since 2005. Chief Scott began his career with the department in 1984 as a firefighter/paramedic. During his 28 years with El Cajon, he was one of the original California Task Force-8 Urban Search and Rescue team members in California. He started as a technical rescue specialist and deployed to the Northridge Earthquake in 1994 and to the Atlanta Olympics bombing in 1996. Scott transferred to the Canine Division where he was partnered with a devoted black Labrador, Billy, in November 1998. Chief Scott and Billy became the second canine search team in the county to be certified by FEMA. They served several local missions before being deployed to Ground Zero shortly after the 9/11 terrorist attacks in New York. Chief Scott retired on July 29, 2012.

Rick Sitta, who earned a commendation for bravery in the 2003 Cedar Fire, was selected as chief for Heartland Fire & Rescue in August 2012. Between 2003 and 2010, he had been a fire division chief in El Cajon and Coronado. In January 2010, he was appointed deputy fire chief of Heartland Fire & Rescue. Chief Sitta retired on August 12, 2016.

Colin Stowell became chief of Heartland Fire & Rescue in December 2016. He had worked for the San Diego Fire-Rescue Department for 28 years. He was appointed chief of the department by Mayor Kevin Faulconer on August 13, 2018. He joined the San Diego Fire-Rescue Department in 1988, promoted to captain in 2002, battalion chief in 2007, deputy chief in 2012, and assistant chief in 2015. He earned an Associate of Fire Science from Miramar College, a Bachelor of Science in Public Administration from San Diego State University, and completed the Executive Fire Officer Program at the National Fire Academy.

Chief Stowell was responsible for four operating budgets as well as capital improvement projects for Heartland Fire & Rescue. He handled contract negotiations and oversight and was accountable to three city managers and city councils.

From August 11, 2018, to October 20, 2018, Mike Chasin served as interim chief of Heartland Fire & Rescue. Chasin began his career as an emergency medical technician at University of California, Los Angeles in 1989. In 1997, he was hired by the city of El Cajon as a firefighter-paramedic and has served there as engineer, captain, fire marshal, and division chief.

On October 20, 2018, Steve Swaney was appointed to lead the Heartland Fire & Rescue. He had been a division chief for Heartland Fire & Rescue since 2013. Chief Swaney began working with the El Cajon Fire Department in 1985. He also served as the fire chief for the Julian Cuyamaca Fire Protection District. He obtained an Associate of Fire Science from Miramar College and participated in paramedic training at the University of California San Diego. He is a 2016 graduate of the Leadership East County. Swaney has a Bachelor of Science in Management from California Coast University.

Besides serving Heartland Fire & Rescue, Chief Swaney is a certified Federal Emergency Management Agency canine evaluator and is a lead instructor for the FEMA Canine Search Specialist School. He started working with a chocolate Labrador named Sherman in 1997. Chief Swaney and his dog, Sherman, were in New York within 24 hours of the Twin Towers collapse to aid in rescue efforts. They were also deployed to Hurricane Katrina in New Orleans and Hurricane Rita in southeast Texas in 2005, Hurricane Ernesto off the Atlantic Coast in 2006, and the Torrey Pines Bluff collapse in 2004. After Sherman retired in 2006, Swaney continued rescue work in San Diego with two other rescue dogs, Icon and Tank.

The chiefs of the Lemon Grove Fire Department include: Anderson, H. A. (1925); Kerfoot, B. L.; Hensley, H. L. "Pappy" (1951-); Dixon, Fred L.; Adams, Robert (1976-1987); Wright, Bill (1988-1996); Chamberlain, Dale (1996-1996); Torchia Jon (2004-2008); Scott, Mike (2009-2012); Sitta, Rick (2012-2016); Stowell, Colin (2016-2018); and Swaney, Steve (2018-).

In August 2019, the city of Lemon Grove and the Heartland firefighters of Lemon Grove Local 2728 signed a contract through the end of June 2023. Salaries rose starting in the 2020-21 fiscal year with a 1% cost-of-living adjustment, that will rise to 2% in 2021-22, and 3% in 2022-23. Fire personnel's retirement contributions are 1% in 2020, another 1% in 2021, and 1% in 2022. The contract includes an increase to the firefighters health insurance plan from $150 per month to $350 per month. Lemon Grove also increased the life insurance from $10,000 to $100,000 per employee.

The Lemon Grove City Council agreed on budget cuts for the 2020-21 fiscal year. The closing of businesses because of the coronavirus pandemic made cuts into the city's sales tax revenues. The deficit meant that for the Lemon Grove Fire Department there would be no Emergency Operations Center satellite phones; a reduction in personal protective gear, self-contained breathing apparatus, and tools and supplies; and no Trauma Intervention Program. The city will have a deficit of $800,000 by the end of 2020-21 and a nearly $1.2 million budget deficit by the end of 2021-22.

Heartland Fire & Rescue received a class 1 rating from the Insurance Services Office (ISO) in 2015! Of the 58,000 fire departments across the United States rated by ISO, only 98 have a class 1 rating. The ISO surveys fire departments on fire suppression service, examining water availability, equipment, deployment, training, personnel, and risk reduction. Districts are ranked 1 through 10, with a class 1 rating presented only to those districts that score 90 or higher out of a possible 100 points.

For eight years, the department has released goats in open fields in 8.5 acres to eat heavy brush. This helps to reduce fire danger and provide defensible space in the community. Environmental Land Management provides 100 adults and 100 young goats in the spring to clear the brush in terrain too difficult for machinery.

Station 10 is located at 7853 Central Avenue. The staff includes: 6 captains, 6 engineers, and 6 firefighter/paramedics. The staff is supervised by a deputy chief as well as a division chief. The station is a baby safe surrender site. A sign is displayed by the station's main entrance indicating that it is. The station houses Medic Engine 10, a 2014 Pierce Arrow XT PUC, Medic Engine 210, and American Medical Response Unit 257.

The Lemon Grove firefighters are committed to keeping residents safe.

CALLS RECALLED:

*1890:   A fire started by a locomotive on the route between Lemon Grove and Spring Valley burned hay crops. The San Diego, Cuyamaca, and Eastern Railway (S.D,C. & E.) paid $1,603.14 in damages to ranchers.

*1925:   Two homes were completely destroyed by fire.

*1961:   A fire destroyed the last citrus packing shed of Lemon Grove and two adjacent buildings. The packing house was built in 1891 north of the railroad tracks in Lemon Grove.

*2016:   In January 2016, a house fire on Costada Court killed a 63-year-old man and caused $300,000 in damage.

*2018:   In May 2018 at 5:10 p.m., a fire that ignited in some palm trees on San Altos Place threaten about 20 homes. The fire damaged power lines and burned railroad ties used by the San Diego Trolley. A water-dropping helicopter was used, and firefighters from Lemon Grove, La Mesa, San Diego, and San Miguel had the fire extinguished in about 40 minutes.

*2018:   In November 2018 at 2:30 p.m. a two-story house on Buena Vista Avenue near Central Avenue was damaged by a fire. The 12 people who lived in the house weren't injured.

*2020:   In May 2020 two brush fires broke out along eastbound state route 94. The firefighters quickly extinguished the fires.

LIFE FLIGHT

Life Flight was initially formed on March 17, 1980, by the University of California Medical Center. In 1986, it became a trauma-shared helicopter service of a consortium of Palomar Hospital, Scripps Hospital, Sharp Hospital, Rady's Children's Hospital, and Mercy Hospital.

In 1986, physicians on Life Flight were replaced by flight nurses because of the cost and availability of physicians. The helicopters were Bolkow 105s with a speed of 150 miles per hour. Life Flight could have a helicopter in the air within five minutes. Two helicopters were in service twenty-four hours a day, seven days a week. Bell 206, Aloutte 3, Bell 222, and BO helicopters were used. After 1992, German-made medium-sized BK 117s were flown. Life Flight 1 was based at UCSD Medical Center, Life Flight 2 was based at Palomar Airport, and Life Flight 3 was only available on weekends as a backup.

The pilots and mechanics for the aircraft were on contract. From 1980 to 1989, Life Flight contracted with Evergreen Helicopter. In 1989, Life Flight contracted with Omni Flight.

When the alarm sounded and volunteer firefighters in San Diego County were dispatched to a possible trauma, part of the response was "Life Flight on standby." To the volunteers responding to an emergency those four words were both comforting and motivating. They knew that a highly trained team of medical professionals would provide a rapid response and on arrival give lifesaving advanced life support.

The firefighters prepared a landing site and fire protection. They met the helicopter, relayed information, and assisted the Life Flight crew with their gear and with patient care. The firefighters also helped the Life Flight crew load patients in the helicopter.

"Life Flight"—the two words literally tell what the crew did. The very sight of the chopper—"the bird"—coming in for a landing brought a sense of hope for the patient and pride at being part of something special.

The medical crew went from responding to thirty calls a month in 1980 to 145 calls a month in 1992. A flight nurse and a paramedic or a flight nurse and a physician responded to emergency calls. They were trained in aeromedicine with critical care and emergency care expanded skills to practice the scope of medicine.

Phil Moomjean, who was the head flight nurse since its beginning, said, "The volunteers are a good group of people. They are enthusiastic, have a good sense of mission, and they care about their community. It's nice to work outside the formal hospital environment with the volunteer fire departments, regular fire departments, and law enforcement agencies."

The San Diego County Sheriff's ASTREA (Aerial Support to Regional Enforcement Agencies) has nine Bell helicopters based at Gillespie Field in El Cajon, three of which respond to fire suppression and rescue operations.

In 1996, Mercy Air acquired Life Flight San Diego. The emergency helicopter service has operated in Southern California for 30 years. A nurse and a paramedic provide advanced trauma care during a flight. The helicopters fly at 130 mph.

A CALL RECALLED:

*1992: An example of the important service that Life Flight provided occurred on October 21, 1992. Jimmie Mastro, who lived on Engineer Road in Cuyamaca, was twenty-feet up a ladder cutting a limb of a tree when he lost control of his chain saw and it made a deep, jagged cut in his upper right arm. Although he was bleeding profusely, he was able to climb down the ladder and apply pressure above the cut. His neighbors rushed him to the Lake Cuyamaca Volunteer Fire Department in their truck. Firefighters from departments on the same dispatch system were listening to the Cuyamaca firefighters call Life Flight. They knew it was a serious call when the Cuyamaca volunteers did not cancel Life Flight after treating Jimmie Mastro. Life Flight flew Mastro to UCSD Medical Center, where he was in surgery for five hours. He would have lost his arm without the help of the Cuyamaca firefighters and the Life Flight crew. Flying him to a hospital was the safest and most appropriate action. Jimmie Mastro said, "They gave me a new lease on life."

Mesa Grande Reservation Fire Department

The Mesa Grande Reservation is located in eastern San Diego County near Santa Ysabel. It includes 1,803 acres and has 800 members, not all who live on the reservation.

The Mesa Grande Band of Diegueno Mission Indians are descendants of the original aboriginal peoples who occupied San Diego County. Their ancestors have occupied the region for over 12,000 years.

Between 1850 and 1875, settlers took possession of Native American land. The tribal people were removed if they were located within a half-mile of any non-Native San Diego residence. Native American children were excluded from California public schools.

In 1875, President Ulysses S. Grant established the Mesa Grande Reservation. Executive orders in 1883 and 1891 increased the acreage of the reservation.

The fire station is located at 26000 Mesa Grande Road. The tribal council has applied for grants to fund the fire department but was only offered apparatus and not staffing. The tribal members could not afford to pay salaries. Consequently, the Mesa Grande Reservation is not licensed or certified. However, the department has a 2000 fire engine and a 1999 fire engine that are used on the reservation.

Visitors Sandy Stroehlein and Beverly Silvers at the Mesa Grande Reservation Fire Department

MONTEZUMA VALLEY VOLUNTEER FIRE DEPARTMENT

Off of Montezuma Valley Road (Highway S-22)—eighty miles northeast of San Diego, eight miles southwest of Warner Springs, and nine miles southwest of Borrego, at an elevation of 3,985 feet—is Ranchita with its population of 572.

In the late 1800s, the community was called Canada de la Verruga. William Johnson Helm (known as "Weid") became the first settler when he built an adobe house near a spring west of Ranchita. He and his wife, Mary Mason from Julian, raised a large family. He was renowned for fathering twins at the age of 75.

Weid Helm's brother, Chatham, homesteaded on land of the Cahuilla Indians and lived there for over 25 years. He once had a feud with Bill Fain in which they exchanged gunfire—27 shots were fired—with no one killed.

Paul Sentenac had a camp at Yaqui Well. The property was later purchased by George Sawday and leased to Ralph Jasper. In 1920, Jasper bought Weid Helm's ranch and lived there well into his eighties.

Work on the Montezuma Valley Road from Ranchita to Borrego started in September 1954 and was completed in June 1964. John H. Bye was the construction supervisor of the project. Foremen Ben McManama and Carl Randall were often the only county employees on the job, supervising prisoners from Montezuma Honor Camp. They used 160,000 tons of dynamite to carve a way down San Ysidro Mountain. It was estimated that 570,000 cubic yards of dirt and rock were excavated during the building of the road. The road cost about $500,000 to build.

Ben McManama, a lifelong resident of Ranchita, became the first fire chief of the Montezuma Valley Volunteer Fire Department in 1975. His great-grandfather drove the Butterfield Overland Stage through Ranchita, and his grandfather homesteaded in San Felipe. He recalls that he "hit the ground a few times" while breaking horses before going to work for the San Diego County Road Department in 1962, where he worked for 25 years. Besides being the fire chief, he was active in most of the community activities in Ranchita. Chief McManama died on June 10, 2002, at the age of 77.

Other members of the fire department were Assistant Fire Chief Daniel "Dan" McManama, Captains Steve Howard and Tom Peck, and firefighters Allen Bushman, Tammy Cooter, Dee DiPaolo, Alan L. Hatcher, and Mark Steffens. In 1985, Alan Hatcher became a certified California State firefighter. The firefighters responded within 12 minutes to emergencies in the 36-square-mile district.

One of the firefighters, Francis Bushman, died on March 23,1982, at the age of 55. Bushman's wife, Agnes, helped with fundraisers and his son, Allen, was a firefighter with the department.

Leo Gene Razee, who also died in 1982, was the postmaster at Ranchita for 22 years and one of the original directors of the fire department. The name of the post office, which opened about 1900, was changed in 1935 from Verruga Post Office to Ranchita Post Office. In April 1982, Ben McManama spearheaded an unsuccessful drive to save the post office.

The department became a CA registered 501 (c) (3) non-profit corporation on August 8, 1977. The total revenue for 1977 was $16,645.

After Mary Crawford and L. W. Lindberg arranged for a site for a station, the department used its savings plus $10,000 from HUD (Housing and Urban Development) to build a cinderblock building at 37370 Montezuma Valley Road in 1984. Almost $32,000 was raised to complete the purchase of 9.7 acres next to the fire station for a parking lot, a landing site for Life Flight, and a place to build a community hall.

A diesel fire engine with a 600-gallon water tank was purchased for $90,000 with funds from a Community Block Grant that was arranged by HUD. The department also had a 1988 750-gpm International four-wheel drive, a 1965 Dodge rescue rig that was purchased from Borrego Springs Fire Department for $1,500 and a 1964 Jeep pickup.

The Montezuma Valley Volunteer Fire Department was the first fire department in the county to become self-sufficient. The source of revenue for operating expenses and purchase of equipment was fundraisers. The Fire Sirens planned many of the activities. The annual events included an egg hunt on the Saturday before Easter, a July 4 barbecue, a rummage sale on Memorial Day weekend, a pit barbecue in August, and a Christmas bazaar. The department also had monthly Saturday pancake breakfasts.

Fundraisers recalled:

On April 2, 1983, the department made $611 from a spaghetti dinner and auction.

A letter soliciting money, mailed on December 17, 1983, raised $1,315.

The proceeds from the 1984 Memorial Day rummage sale was $2,500.

On July 4, 1984, there was a potluck at the Montezuma Valley station benefiting both the Montezuma Valley Volunteer Fire Department and the Shelter Valley Volunteer Fire Department.

At the fifth annual pit barbecue in August 1983, one of the prizes was half of a prime beef. In 1984, the proceeds from the pit barbecue were $1,794.95 from food sales and $2,259 from raffle tickets. At the seventh pit barbecue in August 1985, the department earned $2,500. It served 370 adults and 34 children at the event. Realtor Bill Wharton, who has lived in the area since 1973, won the Ranchita General Store sign in the auction.

In December 1984, the department had $12,000 in its money market account and $1,000 in its checking account.

At a fundraiser for the equipment fund on June 25, 1988, $1,087 was netted.

The Montezuma Valley Volunteer Fire Department joined the San Diego County Fire Authority in 2008. The county spent $800,000 improving the station's engine bays, sleeping quarters, showers, and kitchen.

Firefighter Efrain Carillo was one of the firefighters honored by the San Diego Regional Fire Foundation in 2013. That same year the foundation gave $278,000 in grants to San Diego County's rural fire departments.

In 2017, Adam Lambert was replaced by Jeremy Rooster as the battalion chief for the unincorporated area of Ranchita.

On August 19, 2017, the fire company had a 40th anniversary party with live music and pizza.

Ranchita Station No. 58 houses a Type 6 engine designed for rapid fire attack; Water Tender 58 that carries 2,000 gallons of water and is outfitted with a 750-gpm pump; and an ambulance equipped with heavy extrication and stabilization equipment as well as rope rescue equipment.

In January 2019, Ranchita Station No. 58 became staffed 24 hours a day, seven days a week with Cal Fire personnel. By the end of 2019, the department transitioned from basic life support emergency services to advanced life support/paramedics emergency services.

CALLS RECALLED:

*1943: A young boy very carefully started a fire. His family put it out with water that they carried in buckets from a creek.

*1971: A boy from a boarding school in Ranchita started a brush fire in July 1971 that burned 15 acres in Montezuma Valley. The volunteer firefighters and 80 men from the CDF (California Division of Forestry) extinguished the fire.

*1975: A 2,000-acre fire that started at Los Coyotes Indian Reservation in July 1975 threatened Ranchita.

*1981: The firefighters assisted CDF at a fire on May 2 that burned 400 acres in Tub Canyon at Anza-Borrego State Park. The fire spread rapidly to within one mile of homes.

*1981: A 40-acre fire on May 21, 1981 in Culp Valley was extinguished by CDF with the help of the Montezuma Valley Volunteer Fire Department and other units. The heat from the exhaust of a motorcycle was the cause of the blaze.

*1981: The volunteer firefighters requested Life Flight for an accident on November 25, 1981. Stephen Carpenter of Ranchita suffered head injuries and a broken leg when he lost control of his dune buggy. He died on December 10, 1981.

*1987: The firefighters saved a man who had a heart attack. They gave him CPR until Life Flight arrived at the scene.

*1987: Along with CDF and U.S. Forest Service, the Montezuma Valley firefighters responded to a fire which burned 72 acres on July 30, 1987.

*1988: Five people were injured in an automobile accident on Montezuma Valley Road on March 28, 1988. Life Flight and ASTREA (Aerial Support to Regional Enforcement Agencies) helicopters transported the victims to hospitals.

*1992: At a fire at S&S Farms on January 16, 1992, at 2:56 a.m., 250 rare Yucatan pigs were cremated. The loss of the pigs and one of two farms totaled almost $400,000. Tom Salayer and his father, owners of the farm, could continue their operation because the firefighters saved the pigs in the second barn. Mutual aid came from Julian Volunteer Fire Department, Warner Springs Fire Department, Intermountain Volunteer Fire Department, and CDF. One of the visiting firefighters stepped on a dead pig!

*1992: In July 1992, the Montezuma Valley Volunteer Fire Department and CDF responded to a fire north of Montezuma Valley road that was caused by lightning. During that same month, the volunteers rescued Roger Brass from the roof of his mobile home, where he was injured while making repairs.

*2017: In October 2017, a 25-acre brush fire was caused by gunfire.

*2018: In May, an airplane crashed in Ranchita causing a 12-acre fire near Volcan Mountain.

MT. LAGUNA VOLUNTEER FIRE DEPARTMENT

Mt. Laguna, at 6,100 feet above sea level, towers over San Diego County like a giant behemoth. Its panoramic view of the desert floor is breathtaking, the dense forests of pine trees spectacular, and the air so clear and clean it gives the lungs cause to celebrate.

Mt. Laguna is a tiny community of about 60 people that accommodates three million visitors a year to this popular recreational area. Among the many activities are camping, hiking, and horseback riding. There are about 3,000 people who have vacation homes in the community.

The Mount Laguna Observatory was dedicated in 1968. It has five telescopes: the 1.06-meter MLO telescope, the 0.6-meter Clifford Smith telescope, the 0.52-meter Reginald Butler telescope, and the 1.25-meter Claud Phillips telescope.

The Mt. Laguna Volunteer Fire Department was formed in 1976 to respond to incidents in a 15-square-mile area. Fire chiefs included Walt Foster, Doug Baird, Jay Grover, Bette Truitt, Bert Nelson, and Dennis Sherman. The department responded to about 75 calls a year. Walt Foster and Doug Baird have passed away. Jay Grover retired from the fire service. He worked for the San Diego Observatory for many years. Dennis Sherman is also retired.

Besides being dedicated to public service, Chief Bette Truitt established Dragonwhispers Harp Supplies. The harps she made are owned by some of the leading harp players in the world. She developed a superior sharping lever for harps, the Truitt Lever.

In November 2012, Susan "Sue" Raimond, assistant chief for the Mt. Laguna Volunteer Fire Department, received a Lifetime Achievement Award from the San Diego Regional Fire Foundation for 26 years of service to her community. She joined the Mt. Laguna Volunteer Fire Department in 1986 and served on it until its dissolution in May 2020. She is currently active as a chaplain. Sue Raimond is on the board of directors for the San Diego Regional Fire Foundation. Originally set up to serve the needs of the volunteer departments, the foundation now more broadly serves the region of fire service and needs they may have.

A five-member board of directors made up of citizens and firefighters administered the fire department. The department operated on a budget of about $17,500 a year. A small budget from San Diego County was supplemented by fundraisers such as an annual dinner/dance on the third weekend in September at the Shriner's Camp. Fire Chief Dennis Sherman said, "We sell pancakes to put bandages on people for free."

The Mt. Laguna firefighters have a fire station centrally located at 10385 Sunrise Highway about a quarter of a mile from the general store, near the 22.5 marker. It has two bays with a day room, office, and storage area.

A light-duty 1968 Chevy rescue rig and a Dodge Ram utility truck were dispatched on medical aid at traffic accidents. A 1961 1,000-gpm Pirsch and a 1956 750-gpm GMC pumper were dispatched to structural fires. The volunteers also had a 1967 International brush rig, a 1972 1,000-gallon water tender, and a 1967 1,300-gallon water tender. Both of their water tenders were retrofitted with Class A foam.

Now San Diego County Fire Authority purchases equipment for the Cal Fire personnel at San Diego County Station 49. The department is staffed 24 hours a day, seven days a week. Station 49 houses Engine 49 (2017 International 7400), Patrol 49 (2016 Ford F-550), and Rescue 7489 (2005 GMC C8500).

The geography of Mt. Laguna is a paradox of nature. To the eyes of a visitor, the scenery provides beauty, relaxation, and serenity. To the eyes of a firefighter, nature provides a potential for treachery, violence, and death.

Along the Sunrise Highway, hundreds of feet down, cars have gone over the side that require extensive rescue operations. The steep rugged terrain would be a formidable challenge to the most seasoned of mountain climbers and heavy rescue personnel. The Mt. Laguna firefighters receive extensive training to meet the challenge. Rappelling, knots, specialized equipment, and teamwork are mandatory for these hazardous and physically demanding incidents.

The Cal Fire staff of the department coordinates their operations with the San Diego County Sheriff's Department and the United States Forest Service which has a station nearby. Air medical transport and its personnel are, as always, indispensable for trauma victims.

Once again, to the eye of the visitor, the wind blowing through the trees is a peaceful and tranquil experience. To the firefighter, a wind-blown timber fire can consume all in its path—wildland, animals, and humans. The 1970 Laguna Fire was just such a conflagration. It destroyed hundreds of thousands of acres of woodlands, homes, and cost some human lives.

To the visitor, the snowy winter landscape brings memories of white Christmases and fun in the snow. To the firefighter, the same scene brings memories of tire chains and an engine company hampered by nature and increased dangers.

The Mt. Laguna firefighters are dedicated "mountain people." They covet their individualism and their privacy. They serve "city people" mostly and maintain a good reputation at what they do.

The firefighters of Mt. Laguna understand that, although they live in harmony in this land of mountains and places, when the forces of nature meet the forces of the fire service, it is at best an uneasy relationship!

CALLS RECALLED:

*1970: The strong Santa Ana winds caused an oak tree to fall on a power line on the morning of September 26, 1970, at the intersection of Kitchen Creek Road and the Sunrise Highway in the Laguna Mountains igniting dry annual grass and pine needles. The fire was reported by two deer hunters to U.S. Forest Service Officer George Abbott in the Laguna Mountains. Within 24 hours the fire burned in a southwest direction, approaching the outskirts of El Cajon and Spring Valley. The fire burned 4,000 acres per hour and moved 32 miles in 30 hours. The Laguna Fire wasn't contained until October 3, resulting in 5 deaths, destroying 1,400 structures, including 382 homes, and burning 175,425 acres. The five people who died in the fire were believed to be undocumented immigrants and were never identified. There were 117 homes in Harbison Canyon, 114 homes in Crest, 40 in Jamul, and 111 in other East County communities that were destroyed. At the time, it was the second largest fire in California history. The damage cost was approximately $40 million, including $5.6 million for lost of homes. After the fire siege, FIRESCOPE was implemented, a concept in multiagency fire suppression coordination.

*2013: The Chariot Fire burned 7,000 acres in the Cleveland National Forest in July 2013, destroying 100 cabins and a dining hall in the Al Bahr Shrine Camp.

NATIONAL CITY FIRE DEPARTMENT

National City is located five miles south of San Diego on San Diego Bay. It covers 9.5 square miles and has a population of 61,653.

National City was originally part of the 26,000-acre El Rancho de la Nation, which was purchased by Frank Kimball and his brothers Warren and Levi. The Kimballs cleared land, built roads, constructed a wharf, and brought the railroad to the city.

The National City Firemen's Club was formed on September 10, 1887. Hose carts and a hook and ladder rig were housed in a building at the corner of 16th Street and Taft Avenue. Another hose cart was located in a building at 8th Street and National Avenue. In 1910, the first fire station was built and was located at 13th Street and National Avenue. It was used until 1954. The station was torn down in 1966 to make way for the civic center.

The National City Firemen's Club became incorporated on April 27, 1911. On April 6, 1912, the city purchased a Seagrave pumper that cost $6,000. It carried 1,200 feet of 2-½ inch fire hose and a 40-gallon tank of chemicals. An 80-horsepower air-cooled engine could propel the apparatus at speeds up to 40 miles per hour. National City was one of the first cities in the state to buy a motor-driven vehicle. In 1913, the firemen served a city with a population of 3,200. There were about 150 volunteers who had little training in firefighting. There was a great deal of confusion, and a fire had usually gained such headway by the time they arrived on the scene and got organized that there was little chance of saving a building.

In 1922, the city hired its first paid fire chief, W. S. Carvell. He continued as chief until February 8, 1924, at which time James A. Bird was appointed fire chief.

Captain Martin E. Fernberg retired at the age of 55 on January 1, 1955. His service began as a volunteer in 1923. On his first day as a fireman he reported for duty at 12:00 a.m. and at 12:01 a.m. he was driving a 1912 Seagrave to a grass fire on 41st Street.

Captain George Ellis joined the department in 1946 following a tour of duty with the Army in World War II. He was promoted from fireman to engineer in 1950 and to captain in 1956. He was a graduate of Sweetwater Union High School. Captain Ellis retired in 1959.

In 1925, a Seagrave 750-gpm class B pumper was purchased and the original 1912 pumper was retired. In 1935, the pumper had a complete overhaul by Seagrave mechanics. Lack of funds prevented making an overhaul sooner. The 1925 Seagrave pumper is no longer in service but is occasionally used for parades and social events. The Seagrave, which has the original engine in it, is housed at Station 34 and is a fine example of antique apparatus and a tribute to the care and maintenance given it by generations of firefighters. Another pumper with a 500-gpm capacity was added in 1931. A Dodge pick-up was purchased in 1936. An E and J inhalator and resuscitator was purchased in 1936 for $350. The instrument was used in cases of drowning, electric shock, heart failure, and

National City Fire Station and first Seagraves fire pumper, located at 13th Street and National Avenue. Men pictured in group L.A. Weisser, P.t. Mizony, W.A. Sharp, K.V. Langford, Ed Reed, H. Wood, R.E. Miner, Phil Evans, Harry Linder, Claude Bullen, A.K. Patterson, Rico Martijo, N. Wade, L. Blanchard, W. Markham, Kyle W. Alexander, George E. Miner (Chief), Jack Alexander, Dave Strahl, Joe Packard. Original picture donated by: Paul Mizony

suffocation when breathing was stopped. By the reversing of a lever the machine could be changed from an inhalator to a resuscitator. It was almost impossible to injure the patient because it tripped itself at four pounds of pressure and the average person can stand 15 pounds. Members of the department had first aid cards and the radio and telephone operators, licenses.

In 1928, some of the volunteer firemen were: W. C. Simms (later paid fireman who retired in 1960 as assistant chief), Milton McCool, Devere Field, Bill Rooney, Raymond Eller, Sam Babcock, Martin Fernberg (later paid fireman who retired in 1954 as captain), Raymond Smith, and M. S. Taylor (later a policeman in Chula Vista who retired in 1964 as a police captain). The paid personnel were James A. Bird, chief (later city manager, retired in 1962), Ray Amos, assistant chief (who died in 1934), and Cliff Bailey, captain (appointed assistant chief in 1935, chief in 1950).

By 1935, the department had five paid firefighters. During the 1940s more staff and equipment were added. In June 1941, Chief James A. Bird attended a meeting to start a fire prevention campaign. The civic leaders in the county were concerned about the heavy growth of grass and brush due to excessive rains. In 1940, there were seven regular men and four call men to respond to calls. Those on active duty

were: James A. Bird, chief; J. Clifford Bailey, assistant chief; William C, Simms and Martin E. Fernberg, captains; and Ben E. Diffenbaugh, Leland B. Bacon, and Walter R. Towsley, firemen. A club room, furnished by the men themselves, and a dormitory were upstairs at the fire department. The club room had a library, a radio, and a pool table.

In 1954, Fire Station #1 was constructed at the corner of 16th Street and "D" Avenue. It was demolished in October 2003. In 1961, Fire Station #2, located at 2130 Tidelands Avenue, was built to house a four-person engine company.

The Fire Prevention Bureau was established in February 1956. Engineer Richard Harrold was assigned as the first fire inspector. In 1959, the department hired its first full-time dispatcher, Kay Nielsen.

In 1978, Dispatcher Carol Ann Grove, 37, left the National City Fire Department to become Chula Vista's first woman fire inspector. She dispatched calls for National City for 11 years. Grove wrote a communications manual for the National City Fire Department and taught classes to other personnel about efficient communication during emergencies. She has a fire science teaching credential.

In April 1968, Assistant Chief Leland B. Bacon succeeded retiring Chief J. Clifford Bailey. Also in 1968, National City Fire Department became the first department in San Diego County to initiate the system of having three shifts. Captain Kenneth Joyce was selected to fill the new position of battalion chief.

Three diesel-powered pumpers were put into service in the 1970s. In 1980, dispatching was transferred to the Chula Vista Police and Fire Dispatch Center.

American Medical Response (AMR) provides basic and advanced life support service. National City Fire Department started a paramedic program on January 3, 2007, with the first paramedic response taking place at 8:09 a.m. When the fire personnel arrive at a scene, they can start life support services before AMR ambulances arrive. When AMR ambulances arrive, they assist ambulance crews to provide care to the patient. In most instances, a paramedic is on all the fire units.

For 10 years the National City Firefighters Association Local 2744 hosted a Tower of Terror Haunted House. The haunted house was located in the first level of the drill tower at National City Fire Station 34 where firefighters scared individuals through torture chambers and caves. There were also displays of equipment used by firefighters and information about what to do in the event of a fire. The enhanced regulations of the California Fire and Building Codes now require that a sophisticated fire alarm and fire sprinkler system be installed in the tower in order to comply with today's safety standards. The training tower was built for operational firefighter training and the addition of such a system is financially unfeasible and the system would not hold up to the rigorous conditions associated with live fire training.

James Catanzarite retired in 1975 after 25 years as a captain with the department. He worked for the department for 30 years. Captain Catanzaarite died at the age of 65 in 1986.

Sherman Peters received the St. Florian Fire Service Award as Firefighter of the Year in 2001 after serving the National City Fire Department for 18 years. After he retired he became a volunteer with the Eagle Police Department in Ada County, Idaho, beginning in February 2013.

Assistant Fire Chief William C. Simms served the fire department for 37 years. He was a lifelong member of the California State Firefighters Association. He died at the age of 86 in 1988.

In 2014, the National City Fire Department joined the Burn Institute in providing smoke detectors for seniors 62 years and older. The Burn Institute provides the smoke detectors to the fire department and the the department has local service clubs install the devices. A smoke alarm reduces the risk of a person dying in a house fire by 50%.

Picture was taken in front of original National City Fire Station 1, located at 13th and National Boulevard.

In June 2019, the National City Council approved a measure requiring out-of-town drivers who cause serious accidents to pay for their emergency service response. The National City measure created a contract with Fire Recovery USA, a private firm responsible for billing and collecting funds on behalf of the city. The charges could range from $275 for a basic fire response to more than $2,000 for large scale hazardous material cleanup.

In June 1989, the department purchased a Seagrave Commander pumper which is still used now as a reserve engine. Also in 1989, the city's emergency medical defibrillation (EMT-D) program was implemented.

In 1992, a Beck engine was put into service and is still used as a reserve engine. In 1994, dispatching was transferred to Heartland Communications Facility Authority.

In 2004, a new Pierce engine was placed into service, and in 2006 another Pierce engine was purchased.

On November 3, 2009, the department placed a Pierce Arrow XT 105-foot aerial ladder into service. On June 17, 2019, a Pierce pumper was delivered to the department. It has an Arrow XT chassis, Detroit Diesel DD13 engine, 505 hp, foam and water tank, and a 500-gallon tank.

Chiefs include: George Miner (1912), W. S. Carvell (1922-1924), James A. Bird (1924-1941), J. Clifford "Cliff" Bailey (1950-1968), Leland B. Bacon (1968-1973), William Wright (1973-1979), Richard B. Bridges (1979-1983), Randy L. Kimble ((1983-2004), Roderick Juniel (2004-2010), and Francisco "Frank" Parra (2010-).

Cliff Bailey was appointed assistant chief in 1935 and chief in 1950. He implemented new policies. For the first time uniforms were required to be worn by all full-time firefighters. He had the firemen map every business and industry in town. Chief Bailey was instrumental in establishing the fire science program at San Diego Community College. This program was the beginning of higher education for firefighters in the county and has become essential in order to do the job of a modern day firefighter. Chief Bailey became the president of the California Fire Chiefs Association in 1965 and was a member of San Diego City College's Fire Science Advisory Committee. As a 15-year-old Missouri farm boy, his first job in the county was feeding the furnace at Scripps Ranch near Del Mar. Four years later he was hired by the National City Fire Department. In three years he was made captain. He said, "Then we just shoved a hose through the window of a burning house or building and let the water run until everything flushed out the front door." Chief Bailey died September 10, 1991, at the age of 85.

Roderick "Rod" Juniel was selected as chief in June 2004. He served as chief of the Denver Fire Department from March 2001 until 2004, when the city's new mayor replaced several officials. Chief Juniel spent nearly 30 years with the Denver department and was its first black chief. In Denver, Juniel led 950 firefighters and oversaw a budget of $100 million.

The director of emergency services is Frank Parra. Chief Parra, who is a lifelong resident of National City, served as a council member from November 2002 through April 2010. On April 6, 2010, he became chief of the National City Fire Department. He graduated from Sweetwater High School in 1981 then attended San Diego State University and transferred to University of California San Diego Emergency Medical Services Training Institute for his paramedic training. He worked for 33 years in emergency medical services, as a field training officer, operations manager, dispatch manager, and director of operations for San Diego Medical Services. At San Diego Medical Services he was in charge of a $50 million budget and 400 field paramedics and emergency medical technicians.

The Fire Operations Division is composed of 3 battalion chiefs, 9 captains, 9 engineers, and 18 firefighters.

Fire administration and fire prevention are located at 1243 National City Boulevard. The Fire Administration Division has a director of emergency services, a management analyst, an administrative secretary, and a senior office assistant. The Fire Prevention Division has one fire marshal, one deputy fire marshal, and one fire inspector.

The department has three stations:

Station 31, located at 2333 Euclid Avenue in the southeast portion of the city, was opened in February 1984. It houses Engine 31 (2019 Pierce Arrow XT) and an AMR ambulance.

Station 33 is located at 2005 East 4th Street at U Avenue near El Toyon Park in the northeastern section of the city. It houses Squad 33 (2016 Ford F-550 custom-built pickup equipped with a 150-gallon water tank and paramedic equipment). The squad has a captain and firefighter/paramedic to respond to emergency medical calls.

A mobile home with a metal garage structure was opened to support a squad that helps decrease response times in the northeastern quadrant of National City. The mobile trailer costs the city about $54,000. Annual costs of the program include $172,000 in overtime to staff the team, $4,800 in facility maintenance and utilities, and $1,500 in fuel and vehicle maintenance. Besides a large carport for Squad 33, there is a carport for the National City Police Department's mobile command vehicle.

In March 2014, a response time survey showed that the area had longer response times than other parts of the town. Prior to having a squad, response time in the area averaged 4 minutes and 51 seconds per call. With the squad response time was decreased to 3 minutes and 15 seconds. Funding for the squad was made possible by voter approved Proposition D, a one-cent sales tax measure that funds the city's public safety. In addition, the department received a $25,000 grant from the Alliance Healthcare Foundation to help with the purchase of equipment. On October 10, 2017, the department started responding to calls from Station 33. The squad has a captain and firefighter/paramedic to respond to emergency medical calls.

Station 34, located at 343 East 16th Street, was dedicated in June 2005. A fire station that was constructed at the same site in 1954 was demolished in October 2003. The two-story station designed by Jeff Katz Architecture has over 19,500 square feet with a 5,000-square-foot training tower and four drive-through apparatus bays. The total cost of the project was $6,749,000. It houses Engine 34 (2011 Pierce Arrow XT); Truck 34 (2016 Pierce Arrow XT); an AMR ambulance; and B-57 (battalion chief vehicle); and reserve apparatus.

Also featured in the station are offices, a fitness room, eleven individual bunk rooms, a kitchen, dining room, day room, history room (which displays the 1925 Seagrave pumper and memorabilia from the history of the department), and a community room.

The five-story training tower features a live burn room and smoke generation throughout the building. The drill yard has a 27,000 gallon underground water tank with its own pump system that supplies two training hydrants, an auto extrication training area, and larger ventilation prop with the ability to change the pitch/angle of the "roof". It is used for training not only National City personnel but fire personnel from fire agencies throughout the county.

Each year the community and the first responders of the fire department gather for a breakfast on September 11 for a remembrance ceremony. After the flag is raised, some firefighters who were part of San Diego's Task Force that was sent to New York as part of the rescue effort speak about that day in 2001.

The National City Fire Department provides outstanding service to the residents of the city.

CALLS RECALLED:

*1924: The Spreckels wallboard factory at 24th and Harrison Streets burst into flames. Tank cars full of acid next to the factory blew up.

*1927: The Central School auditorium which was built in 1906 was destroyed by a fire.

*1930: The National Theater was destroyed inside by a fire.

*1940: The firemen responded to 135 calls.

*1941: In July 1941, a short in the wiring resulted in a fire in a sedan which the owner had purchased less than two hours earlier.

*1945: A fire in Old Town at 23rd Street and Cleveland Avenue resulted in $500,000 damage. A building built by Frank Kimball was destroyed.

*1945: In June 1945, a 40-acre brush fire in the Paradise Valley community was fought by the National City Fire Department and the California Division of Forestry.

*1946: On December 24, 1946, R. E. Smith of 2565 J Avenue was revived by Captain William C. Simms and Firefighter Robert Bates using an inhalator and resuscitator. He was taken to Paradise Valley Hospital. Smith said there was some doubt he would have lived through the attack if it had not been for the equipment and quick action of the firemen. William C. Simms became a paid fireman who retired in 1960 as assistant chief.

*1949: A fire which started at the Tahiti Bar burned a half block before it was extinguished. The Knights of Pythias hall which was built in 1897 was destroyed in the fire.

*1950: There were 215 calls in 1950. Of these alarms 28 were to homes, 75 were to grass fires, and 34 to automobile fires. Property losses totaled $15,793 and contents loss was $20,786.

*1956: In September 1956, a pump containing 11,000 gallons of gasoline was knocked off its foundation, broken electrical wiring caused it to burn. The fire crew used a water fog hose nozzle to save Old Town from a major disaster.

*1958: In January 1958, an apartment building on J Avenue was damaged and the Lovell Cabinet Shop burned.

*1958: The department answered 284 calls for a fire loss of $46,210. There were 34 fires in buildings.

*1990: In September 1990, My Hue Gregor, 45, was working late at her clothing contract business at 2434 Southport Way when a fire broke out. The front of the small store was in flames and there was no back door. She died an hour later.

*1994: In January, the National City Fire Department sent a three-men crew on an engine to assist with rescue efforts at the Northridge earthquake. Fifty-seven people were killed and 8,700 injured in the earthquake.

*1995: Captain Issac Hollis pulled firefighter Debbie Rosasco to the ground when her gear was set ablaze while on a call. Fumes from an overturned gasoline can got inside Rosasco's turnout coat. She overturned the can while hosing down a burning couch.

*2009: The department responded to 4,928 calls in 2009.

*2014: In July 2014, a person was injured in a RV fire and was transported to UCSD Medical Center. The fire started in the engine compartment.

*2015: The department responded to 8,759 calls.

*2016: The personnel responded to 8,379 calls in 2016. The fire incidents were: residential fires, 24; other structure fires (other than residential), 4; vehicle fires, 18; rubbish, grass, wildland fires, 55; equaling total fire responses, 101; total fire loss, $752,400. Other incidents were: emergency medical responses (ambulance, EMS, rescue, etc.), 4,296; false alarm responses (malicious or unintentional false calls, malfunctions, bomb scares, etc.), 115; mutual aid or assistance responses, 2,333; hazardous responses (arcing wires, bomb removal, power lines down, etc.), 15; hazardous materials responses (spills, leaks, etc.), 18; all other responses (lockouts, courtesy, smoke scares, etc.), 1,501.

*2018: In October 2018, a man was arrested for starting fires in National City.

*2019: Part of a duplex burned on East Fifth Street in February 2019. A neighbor rescued a dog before the arrival of the firefighters.

*2020: The department responds to more than 10,000 calls a year.

NORTH COUNTY FIRE PROTECTION DISTRICT

The North County Fire Protection District covers 92 square miles, serving the communities of Fallbrook, Bonsall, and Rainbow, with a population of about 55,000. The district also provides emergency medical services for 40 additional square miles outside the primary service area.

The 13.57-square-mile unincorporated area of Bonsall is bordered by the Fallbrook to the north, Oceanside to the west, and Valley Center to the east. It was originally called Mount Fairview and had a post office by that name from December 28, 1871, to December 28, 1880. It has a population of 4,341. It is home to the San Luis Rey Downs Training Center for thoroughbred racehorses and other equestrian facilities.

The 21-square-mile unincorporated area of Rainbow is just south of the Riverside County line and 60 miles north of San Diego. It has a population of 1,832. Rainbow is renowned for its nurseries.

Fallbrook is located south of Riverside County and east of Camp Pendleton. Its neighboring communities are Bonsall to the south, Pala to the east, and Rainbow to the northeast. It covers 17.6 square miles and has a population of about 33,021.

The Vital Reche family settled in the area in 1869. They named the community Fall Brook after their former homestead in Pennsylvania. From the 1920s through World War II Fallbrook was known for growing olives, but then became known for its avocado groves and nurseries.

In the late 1880s, a bucket brigade was used to fight fires. The only water supply was from well windmills and tanks. In 1914, Henry Ellis was named the fire warden of Fallbrook. In 1921, John Clark became the first California Division of Forestry (CDF) fire warden assigned to Fallbrook. When a fire occurred, Clark would hand out canteens, wet sacks, shovels, and other equipment to anyone in sight and direct them to fight the fire. In 1926, a hose cart was purchased. It was pulled to a fire by available manpower and used with the newly installed water system on Main Avenue. Water for the new mainline came from a reservoir located on what is now the east end of Dougherty Street. A Model A Ford fire truck was acquired in 1928 under the auspices of the California Division of Forestry (CDF). It was stored at the Tex Maze's garage. Vic Westfall was Fallbrook's first volunteer fire chief. In 1931, the Model A truck was relocated to a California Conservation Corps Camp. Carl Palm was then the volunteer fire chief and the assistant chief was William G. "Bill" Thurber.

James Warner and Bill Thurber at packing house on College Street, 1942.

Fallbrook V.F.D. 1942-43

In 1927, the Fallbrook Chamber of Commerce appointed a committee to organize a fire department. The department was called the Fallbrook Local Fire Protection District when it was founded in 1930. A 1930 Dodge fire truck was purchased in 1931 and stored at Marr's Garage. Three years later the fire truck was moved to a new CDF station at Red Mountain.

Bob Aaberg was elected chief in 1942. Fallbrook received a 1941 pumper trailer, fire hose, ladders, and a pump kit from the office of Civil Defense. A 1938 V8 Ford chassis, donated by the Fallbrook High School, was converted into a fire truck at the high school bus barn by volunteer firemen. The department used a 1942 Packard as an ambulance.

In 1945, Carroll Huscher became the volunteer fire chief. Chief Huscher served as president of the Fallbrook Chamber of Commerce when it was incorporated in 1949.

Assistant Chief William G. "Bill" Thurber left for two years of Army service in 1945. During this time, the volunteer fire department fell apart and the pumper was sold. When Bill Thurber returned from the Army, he organized the Fallbrook Volunteer Fire District, and a certificate signed by 13 volunteers was recorded with the county recorder's office on April 26, 1947. Thurber served as chief from 1947 to 1976. He drove a 1951 Willy's (M-38) jeep in the 1950s as his primary response vehicle, with his Dalmatian "Lady" alongside him, to answer alarms. Chief Thurber died on July 29, 1996. His wife, Mary Ellen, died on December 19, 2003. She retired as head nurse at Fallbrook Hospital in 1975.

In May 1947, a war surplus General Detroit triple combination fire truck was donated by the Fallbrook Chamber of Commerce and the Fallbrook Rotary Club. It was housed at Bill Thurber's welding shop at 1019 South Main Avenue.

Jack Wilborn Cornell was an early member of the Fallbrook Volunteer Fire Department. He graduated from Fallbrook Union High School in 1936. After serving in World War II, Cornell returned to Fallbrook and started a radio repair service, later called Cornell's TV and Electronics. In 1948 he obtained an army surplus radio set and kept it operating while the fire truck maneuvered along wet or dusty rough roads.

In April 1948, an E&J resuscitator was purchased with donations made by the residents and the Fallbrook Rotary Club. In July 1948, the fire department began using shortwave radios between units, units to station, and from units to aircraft.

The volunteers purchased an old Waco biplane to spot brush fires. In 1949, Chief Thurber let the department use his one ton 4x4 military truck, which was converted into a water tanker.

A financial committee was set up with the Chamber of Commerce in 1949 asking each club in town to have a representative on this committee. Four people attended the meeting and the decision was made to educate the public about the advantages of becoming a local fire district. The Fallbrook Local Fire District was formed in 1953. Under the Fire Protection District Law of 1961, the Fallbrook Local Fire District was changed to the Fallbrook Fire Protection District.

The first full-time paid fireman, Ralph Lash, was hired on August 13, 1957. All trash burning was banned after July 1, 1968, by order of the San Diego Air Pollution Control Board. Chief Bill Thurber said that his department would not be permitted to issue any burning permits.

Ed Pollock with display of equipment on a Fallbrook engine, June 1947.

In 1987, the Fallbrook Fire Protection District merged with the Rainbow Volunteer Fire District (CSA-7) to form the North County Fire Protection District.

In 1989, the district implemented the Emergency Medical Defibrillator Program. A year later, it implemented the Alternate Advanced Life Support Program, having one paramedic and one EMT on an ambulance while also having one paramedic and one EMT on an engine. Previously there were two paramedics on an ambulance which was more costly. It was the first single paramedic program in San Diego County.

In July 2003, a consultant was hired to compare the district to national standards in the fire service. In July 2004, the dispatch center was closed and the district joined the dispatch center in Rancho Santa Fe. It is now called the North County Dispatch Joint Powers Agency (NCDJPA), commonly referred to as NorthComm, and is the emergency dispatching organization for nine fire agencies—Rancho Santa Fe, Carlsbad, Del Mar, Encinitas, North County, Oceanside, San Marcos, Solana Beach, and Vista.

The district participates in the "boundary drop" program with other northern San Diego County fire agencies. Under the program, the closest available unit is dispatched to emergencies.

The Fallbrook Fire Safe Council (FFSC) was established in November 2002 (nine months after the area's Gavilian Fire), a non-profit 501c organization focused on three wildland urban interface fire disaster areas: prevention, preparedness, and recovery. The Fire Safe Council has published an evacuation map in English and Spanish and has obtained grants and donated money to conduct public education. It has obtained $800,000 to clear brush in Fallbrook, Bonsall, Rainbow, and De Luz.

Some of the grants that the district has received are: a $1.1 million SAFER (Staffing for Adequate Fire and Emergency Response) grant to staff an additional ambulance for a 2-year period, a $945,000 SAFER grant to assist with recruitment and retention of volunteer firefighters, a $205,000 AFG (Assistance to Firefighters) grant to purchase an ambulance, a $100,000 Fallbrook Healthcare District grant to purchase an ambulance, a $108,000 Neighborhood Reinvestment Grant to purchase a new radio system and breathing air compressor, and a $30,000 Fallbrook Healthcare District grant to purchase a 12-lead EGK and Autopulse CPR device.

Ed Sprague was deputy fire chief of the department from May 2012 to July 2015. He worked for the Carlsbad Fire Department from September 1986 to May 2012. He is an assistant professor for Palomar College. Chief Sprague has a Bachelor of Arts and a Master of Public Administration from San Diego State University.

The chiefs of the department are: Vic Westfall (1928-1931), Carl Palm (1931-1942), Bob Aaberg (1942-1945), Carroll Huscher (1945-1947), William G. "Bill"

Thurber (1947-1976), Andrew "Andy" Vanderlaan (1976-1995), Ed Burcham (1996-2003), William "Bill" Metcalf (2003-2015), and Stephen Abbott (2015-).

Andy Vanderlaan became the fire chief when Bill Thurber retired in 1976. He spent two and one half years as a firefighter for the Covina Fire Department and nine and

Captain Burt Ranlinson leaves his cafe "on the double" as the alarm sounds in Fallbrook

Fallbrook Volunteer Dept. 1059 Main Street lined up for parade in 1955.

one half years at the Huntington Beach Fire Department before coming to Fallbrook as the assistant chief. When Chief Vanderlaan retired in 1995, he became the leader of the Western Fire Chiefs Association. He has been on the board of the San Diego County's Local Agency Formation Commission (LAFCO) since 1996. In 2013 he was the chair for LAFCO and is the vice-chair for the 2020 LAFCO board meetings.

Ed Burcham took Vanderlaan's place as chief in 1996. He retired from the district in 2003 after nearly 42 years of service.

William "Bill" Metcalf was the chief from June 2003 until December 2015. He started his career in the fire service in 1974. As a member of the International Association of Fire Chiefs, Metcalf served as the chair of the Emergency Management Committee, vice-chair of the National Centers Task Force, vice-chair of the National Fire Service Mutual Aid Response System Task Force, member of the Homeland Security Council, secretary for the EMS section, and president in 2014. On November 3, 2014, he became chairman of the board of Emergency Services Consulting International.

Stephen Abbott was selected to be the fire chief/CEO by the board of directors on September 8, 2015. He began his career in the district in 1990 as one of the first paramedics, becoming a shift battalion chief, an emergency medical services chief,

then a division chief for administration from September 2014 to July 2015, and deputy fire chief from July 2015 to September 2015. Chief Abbott completed his final year with the Southern California Incident Management Team 2 in 2015, where he served for two fire seasons as a planning section chief. He is president of the San Diego County Fire Districts Association.

Steven "Steve" Marovich was selected to be the deputy chief of the Administrative Division in January 2017. He served the district for 33 years—firefighter/paramedic beginning in 1987, captain paramedic from June 2008 to April 2014, battalion chief from April 2014 to July 2015, and division chief from July 2015 to January 2017. He was an adjunct instructor at Palomar College from September 1988 to December 2017. Chief Marovich received an Associate of Science in Paramedicine from Palomar College and a Bachelor of Applied Science in Fire Services Administration from Cogswell Polytechnical College. He retired on November 24, 2020.

The North County Fire Protection District Board of Directors is the governing body for two divisions, Fallbrook and Rainbow. It consists of five members elected at large. The Rainbow division has an advisory board that coordinates operational activities and makes recommendations to the North County Fire Protection District Board. It consists of five members elected at large. In December 2020, the board of directors are Ruth Harris, Bob Hoffman, Fred Luevano, Ken Munson, and John Van Doom. The executive assistant and board secretary is Loren Stephen-Porter.

The Administrative Division is responsible for records, finance, facilities, human resources, and information technology. Keith McReynolds, the division chief of administration, previously served as a captain and as a battalion chief. The division covers human resources, facilities, IT oversight, maintenance, policies and procedures, and training. Personnel in the division includes Nancy Goss, human relations/finance specialist; Charlie Swanger, administrative specialist; Dan Nieto, mechanic III; and Todd Parmalee, mechanic II.

Kevin Mahr is the division chief for Operations and EMS. Chief Mahr has worked for the department since October 1993. Previously he was a captain with the department. Emergency response services includes fire suppression, medical services, ambulance transportation, hazardous materials response, and public assistance. Mary Murphy is the medical services officer. The battalion chiefs are Greg Mann, Barry Krumwiede, and Brian Macmillan. The division has 15 captains, 15 engineers, 15 firefighter/paramedics, 12 single role paramedics, and 12 single role EMTs. There are 60 full-time emergency services personnel, 14 support personnel, 20 reserve firefighters, and 33 volunteer firefighters.

Cheri Juul, the finance manager, is responsible for the budget, grant oversight, payroll, and workers' compensation.

Dominic Fieri became the fire marshal responsible for the Fire Prevention Division in 2019. The division covers arson investigation, plan checks, and fire prevention. The division works closely with the Fallbrook Fire Safe Council and the Community Emergency Response Team (CERT). The fire protection specialists are Lars Beeghley and Aaron Murg.

Every station has a Type 1 engine which is designed to fight structure fires and respond to medical emergencies. The district also has three Type 3 engines designed for brush fires and three ALS ambulances. On May 31, 2019, the department received a Pierce pumper with an Arrow XT chassis, Cummins L9 engine, 450 hp, 1,500-gpm pump, foam and water tank, and 500-gallon tank.

Station 1 at 315 E. Ivy Street in Fallbrook was originally built in December 1963 as the headquarters. It has a battalion chief, one captain, one engineer, one firefighter/paramedic, one single-role paramedic, and one single-role EMT. It houses Engine 111, Brush 111, Battalion 111, and Medic Ambulance 111.

Station 2 is at 2180 Winterwarm Drive in Fallbrook. In December 1963, the district, through federally matching funds, constructed a station at 2180 Winterwarm Drive, now known as Station 2. It has one captain, one engineer, and one firefighter/paramedic. It houses Engine 112 and Brush 112.

Station 3 at 2309 Rainbow Valley Boulevard in Fallbrook was built in 2008. The original Station 3 was opened in 1976 to serve the Olive Hill area. It has one captain, one engineer, and 30 volunteer firefighters. It houses Medic Engine 113, Medic Squad 113, and Water Tender 113.

Station 4 at 4375 Pala Mesa Drive in Fallbrook has one captain, one engineer, and two firefighter/paramedics. It houses Medic Engine 114, Brush 114, and Medic Ambulance 114. In 1979, the original Station 4 opened in the Monserate Mobile Home Park to serve the Pala Mesa area.

Station 5 at 5906 Olive Tree Road in Bonsall opened in 1982. It has one captain, one engineer, one firefighter/paramedic, one single-role paramedic, and one single-role EMT. It houses Engine 115, Medic Ambulance 115, and OES 306.

In 2014, a new Station 5 was built on a 2.7-acre site. The 8,931-square-foot facility was designed by WLC Architects, Inc. to accommodate seven firefighters. It was made with a combination of plaster and stone veneer in keeping with the dominant materials of the adjacent homes. Simplified Craftsman detailing was added in selected areas to help reduce the scale of the building.

Four of the five stations need to be replaced. Two stations are almost 60 years old and two are nearly 40 years old. Proposition A, the establishment of community facilities district 2019-02 special election on October 24, 2019, fell 10 percentage points short of meeting the required two-thirds vote for passage.

Donald "Don" McLean Jr. was was born in a hospital that once existed on Main Avenue, graduated from Fallbrook High School, and spent his career with the North County Fire Protection District, retiring as a captain. "I went to school to be a history teacher and ended up being a firefighter," he said. "I'm pretty glad about the way things turned out."

The Fallbrook Firefighters Association Memorial Sculpture was dedicated on September 11, 2004, in front of Station 1 at 315 E. Ivy Street. A life-size bronze sculpture depicts a firefighter and a boy with a dog. Also there is a flagpole cast with granite plaques on four sides. One side of the flagpole is engraved with the words of the firefighters' poem in memory of the 343 members of the New York Fire Department. The other three side pay tribute to local firefighters. In front of the statue is: "Some gave all, FDNY, 9-11-01, never forget."

CALLS RECALLED:

*1890:   In 1890, the second block on Main Avenue burned to the ground.

*1896:   In 1896, the school built on Hill Street (now South Mission Road) in the 1870s burned, with all records of the school lost.

*1968:   In November 1968, Fallbrook real estate broker Mark Gallacher died when his Cessna 150 monoplane crashed into Rock Mountain.

*2002:   The Gavilan Fire started in a De Luz canyon and was pushed by strong Santa Ana winds into northern Fallbrook on February 10, 2002. It destroyed 43 homes and burned 5,763 acres. More than 650 firefighters and 100 fire engines were assigned to the fire. Dorothy Roth and Russ Kortlever, whose insurance had lapsed the day before the fire, did not get a new home until 2007. Sid Morel, fire marshal and division chief of the North County Fire Protection District, offered to organize volunteer labor to clear the property and rebuild their home. The volunteer help came from the district's Fire Explorer program for high school students, the Community Emergency Response Team coordinated by the district, and local businesses.

*2003:   District personnel helped to fight the Cedar and Paradise Fires in other areas in the county.

*2007:   The Rice Fire started burning on October 22, 2007, at 4:16 p.m. and was not fully contained until November 1, 2007, at 6:00 p.m. It was caused by a dead tree limb falling on a downed power line. All of Fallbrook was ordered to evacuate. It burned 9,472 acres, destroyed 240 homes, injured five people, and cost $6.5 million. There were 1,095 personnel on the fire at its peak, 112 engines, 6 helicopters, 12 dozers, and 17 water tenders. North County Fire Protection District, U.S. Forest Service, Oceanside Fire Department, California Conservation Corps,

Camp Pendleton Fire Department, and Carlsbad Fire Department fought the blaze.

*2014: In May 2014, the Highway Fire started near Old Highway 395 north of White Lilac Road. The fire burned 380 acres and threatened the Monserate Mobile Home Park. The cost of the fire was $916,692.

*2014: The Tomahawk Fire started on May 14 at 9:45 a.m. on the Fallbrook Naval Weapons Station. Crews from North County Fire, Cal Fire, Orange County Fire, Oceanside Fire, and the San Diego Sheriff's Department assisted the Camp Pendleton fire crews. It burned 5,367 acres.

*2017: The Lilac Fire in December 2017 threatened Bonsall, Fallbrook, Oceanside, Vista, and Camp Pendleton. It started as a small brush fire off of Interstate 15 at 11:15 a.m. on December 7 and wasn't fully contained until December 16. The fire destroyed 157 buildings, burned 4,100 acres, and injured seven people. The fire burned the San Luis Rey Training Center, destroying eight barns and killing 46 horses. The cost of the fire was $8.9 million.

*2018: The Rock Fire burned 207 acres in the northern part of Fallbrook in July 2018.

*2018: In July 2018, crews quickly stopped a small brush fire from spreading near Gopher Canyon in Bonsall from spreading.

*2018: An arsonist was arrested in November 2018 for causing a five-acre brush fire adjacent to State Route 76 and Ramona Drive near Bonsall.

*2019: The North County Fire crew was at a traffic accident on January 29, 2019 on Interstate 15 north of Mission Road in which a car was wedged under a semi-truck. There were no injuries.

*2019: Firefighters responded to a structure fire on La Canada Road at 7:41 a.m. on January 29, 2019. They had the fire extinguished by 9:30 a.m.

*2019: On February 2, 2019, a man who was walking along the shoulder of Old Highway 395 in Bonsall was killed by a hit-and-run driver.

*2019: Eighty percent of the calls were for medical emergencies in 2019.

*2020: On August 24, 2020, a car and a pickup truck had a head-on collision on East Mission Road, killing one driver.

OCEANSIDE FIRE DEPARTMENT

Oceanside is a coastal city in San Diego County, 36 miles north of San Diego with three and half miles of beaches, covering an area of 42.2 square miles and with a population of about 176,000. The city is renown for its 1,954-foot wooden pier which has been rebuilt six times. Many people come to the city to visit the Mission San Luis Rey de Francia, built in 1815, which is the largest of the California missions.

Andrew Jackson Myers settled in the San Luis Rey Valley in the late 1870s. He received a homestead grant for the land which is now Oceanside. A railroad between Los Angeles and San Diego was built in the early 1880s and the train traveled over his property. Soon businesses sprung up in the town and by 1886 Oceanside had a population of 350. After Camp Pendleton was established in Oceanside in 1942 for the U.S. Marine Corps, the city grew quickly.

A volunteer fire department was formed in 1888. Volunteers hurried to a fire bell tower located at First and Freeman Streets. They would read the location of the fire off of a chalkboard and take the hose carts and wooden ladders to the fire.

In 1909, the city approved buying one 40-gallon two-wheeled roller-bearing chemical wagon, one two-wheeled roller-bearing hose cart, 100 feet of 2 1/2 in. fire hose, and 10 Sentry hand chemical extinguishers.

In 1925, the city purchased a 1923 American LaFrance Type 65 class B pumper equipped with a 40-hp motor and a 400-gpm pump for $8,500 and stored it at the Oceanside Garage on Hill Street owned by Fire Chief Ernest White. In 1926, the fire department was called the Oceanside Engine Company Number One. The second engine purchased was a 1932 Model B Ford with 350 gpm.

The firemen had a baseball team and a firehouse dog named Blackie.

A fire station was built at the intersection of Third and Nevada Streets in 1929 to house the fire department and the police department. The two departments shared the station for almost 40 years. The police moved to a station on Mission Avenue in 1968. The site was the former homestead of Andrew Jackson Myers, the founder of Oceanside. Walter Johnson was selected to be chief to lead a crew of 18 volunteers. In 1930,

Station 1 at 714 Pier View Way. Built in 1929, one of the nation's oldest working stations. Courtesy Oceanside Historical Society.

1929 Oceanside, L–R: R.J. Bullard, H.B. Davis, John Todd, fire chief Walter Johnson, assisstant chief Lee Jennings, Gus Mullam, Ernest Taylor.

Courtesy of Oceanside Historical Society

Oceanside had a population of 4,200. In 1939, Oceanside purchased a new Mack fire truck; in 1946, a front-mount pump Dodge engine; and in 1948, a Type 85 Mack. The department's first engine, the 1923 American LaFrance, was retired in 1948.

Harold B. Davis was a volunteer firefighter for 10 years. While he was a volunteer, he became a police officer with the Oceanside Police Department. Davis was made an honorary member of the fire department.

In 1939, Richard Trotter and John W. Todd became the first full-time paid firefighters. A year later Todd died after a ladder fall. He had been a volunteer first lieutenant with the Oceanside Fire Department for 10 years. The firemen helped his wife and five children get settled in a new home.

The annual budget for personnel in 1942 was $585. In 1952, the department bought a new 1,000-gpm Mack engine that was in service for thirty years! It became known as the White Whale in the 1970s because the city manager ordered that all Oceanside city vehicles be painted white. All the other fire apparatus of the department remained red. In 1981 it was bought by a man in Oregon, then in 2005 it was put up for auction on eBay. The Oceanside Firefighters Association bought it for $6,000 even though it was in bad condition and covered with rust. In July 2005, Joe Brown, the son of a former Oceanside volunteer fireman, drove his flatbed to Oregon to pick up the engine. Richard "Hatch" Baxter, who as a fire engineer drove the Mack for many years, went with him to Oregon. The engine was called F4 because it was the fourth apparatus purchased since the labeling system for apparatus was initiated. The firefighters spent hundreds of hours restoring the engine and then Manheim Auto Auction in Oceanside painted it red. The engine is dedicated to Hatch Baxter, who died in 2008.

In 1976, the department began providing paramedic services to the community. A new rank was created, firefighter/paramedic. After a 1963 Seagrave was used for 20 years, it was donated to the Cabo San Lucas Fire Department. The firefighters in the 1960s liked to go to Cabo to fish. Brad "Sunfish" Anderson and Hatch Baxter spent two months every year for 15 years fishing marlin and camping there. In 1977, the first aerial ladder was purchased, a 100-foot Van Pelt, for $206,000. It had an Oshkosh Low Profile chassis, one of only two ever built.

The Oceanside Fire Department was one of the first in the country to use MDTS (Mobile Data Transmitters) in all apparatus.

Chiefs of the Oceanside Fire Department include: W. H. Fultz (1893-1896), John Shuyler (1897-1900), F. B. Shuyler (1900-1905), L. W. Stump (1906-1924), Ernest White (1924-1928), Walter Johnson (1929-1959), John Billings (1959-1962), Richard Trotter

(1963-1972), Jack Rosenquist (1973-1983), Tom Moore (1983), James Rankin (1984-2001), Jack Francis (1987-1988), James Rankin (1988-1991), Dale Geldert (1992-2001), Robert Osby (2002-2004), Rob Dunham (2005-2006), Jeff Bowman (2006-2007), Terry Garrison (2007-2009), Darryl Hebert (2009-2016), and Rick Robinson (2016-).

L. W. Stump, who was selected as chief in 1906, gave the volunteer firemen permanent job assignments, such as nozzle men, hose men, and ladder men.

Walter Johnson was the first paid chief of the Oceanside Fire Department. He was promoted from assistant chief to chief on October 10, 1929, a position he held until his retirement in 1959. Johnson, who was born in Chicago on January 1, 1894, moved with his family to Oceanside in 1908. After his father died in 1935, Walter Johnson and his brother ran the 296-acre family dairy farm in San Luis Rey Valley until it was sold in 1943. He was a forest ranger for five years before joining the Oceanside Fire Department. During his tenure, fire stations 1 and 2 were built and the fire apparatus upgraded. His firefighters built a spring-loaded aerial ladder on a swivel called Truck 5. Chief Johnson served on the California State Fire Advisory Board from 1944 to 1947 and headed many state and county organizations. He was well-loved and was renown for wearing a cowboy hat around town and in parades.

The Oceanside Fire Department celebrated the 90th anniversary of Chief Johnson becoming the first paid chief in 1929 with a ceremony in front of Station 1 which opened in 1929. Firefighters and staff wore cowboy hats for the commemoration. Members from Chief Johnson's family were at the celebration, including his daughter Marjorie Breen, granddaughters Jill Reilly with husband Bob, Linda Weseloh with husband Peter, two great-granddaughters, and a great-great-grandson.

Richard Trotter, one of the two first paid firefighters with the department, was appointed chief in 1963. Chief Trotter initiated the department's first emergency medical technician and ambulance program. He retired in 1972 after serving the department for over 40 years.

In 1973, Jack Rosenquist was promoted to chief. After graduating from Oceanside High, Rosenquist served in the Korean War. He returned to Oceanside in 1954, becoming a firefighter and working his way up to fire chief. Under his leadership, the department started an EMT and ambulance program in 1972 and then four years later a paramedic service. Chief Rosenquist retired in 1983 but stayed involved with fire prevention programs. He also served as a board member of the Oceanside Boys and Girls Club. He died in 2002 at age 71.

Robert Osby worked for 43 years in the fire service before being hired as chief for the Oceanside Fire Department in 2002. He was previously a chief for the Inglewood, San Jose, and San Diego Fire Departments.

Terry Garrison was selected chief in 2007. He left California to return to his home in Arizona in 2009. He was chief of the Houston Fire Department from 2010 to 2015 when he left to return to his hometown of Glendale, Arizona, becoming the city's chief on November 2, 2015. Garrison holds a Bachelor of Science in Fire Science Management from Ottawa University and a Master of Educational Leadership from Northern Arizona University.

Darryl Hebert was appointed chief in December 2009. He worked 26 years for the Oceanside Fire Department, working his way up the ranks from firefighter to engineer, captain, battalion chief, and training and safety division chief from January 2006 to March 2007. He retired in May 2016. He has a Bachelor of Science in Management from California State University, Long Beach, and an Associate of Arts and Sciences in Fire Science/Firefighting from Palomar College.

Rick Robinson served as interim chief of the department from June to October 2016 before becoming chief on November 16, 2016, at the age of 61. Chief Robinson retired from his position as a battalion chief with the Orange County Fire Authority for the cities of San Clemente, Dana Point, San Juan Capistrano, and Mission Viejo in 2013. He started his career in firefighting in Escondido. At the time he began working in Orange County, he and his wife bought a home in Oceanside. He holds a Bachelor of Arts in Technical Education and a Master of Arts in Organizational Management. He is also a graduate of the National Fire Academy's Executive Fire Officer Program.

In February 2005, the department received a $345,583 grant from the Department of Homeland Security Firefighters Grant Program to upgrade or purchase emergency medical services equipment on its ambulances. The money was used for monitors that alert paramedics if a breathing tube is inserted incorrectly or CPR is not working and small computers that are called electronic mobile emergency medical data collection and reporting system.

The department received the Lifeline EMS Gold Level Award from the American Heart Association in August 2020. It is the sixth consecutive year that the department has earned the award which measures metrics success in the rapid identification and treatment of heart attack victims.

The Oceanside Fire Department has 128 employees, including fire chief (Rick Robinson); deputy chief (Joe Ward, deputy chief of operations, training, and lifeguards); three division chiefs (Pete Lawrence, division chief of administration; David Parsons, division chief/fire marshal; and Terry Collins, division chief of training); three battalion chiefs (Jessamyn Specht, A shift; Scott Stein, B shift; and

Greg deAvila, C shift), EMS manager (Lynne Seabloom, RN, EMT-P); 30 captains; 27 engineers; 45 firefighter/paramedics; 29 emergency medical technicians; one fire safety specialist/investigator; five fire inspectors, one fire plans examiner; one assistant training officer; and administrative support staff.

Joe Ward was appointed deputy chief in August 2015. He has a Bachelor of Arts in Fire Service Administration from Cogswell Polytechnical College.

Station 1 at 714 Pier View Way was built in 1929 at a cost of $15,341 and opened on October 3, 1930. It was listed on the National Registry of Historic Places in 1989 as one of the nation's oldest working stations. The two-story station with a 50-foot tower was the first building designed by Irving J. Gill. In September 1971, the station was named the Walter Johnson Fire Station in memory of Oceanside's first paid chief. The building has been modified several times and won't be used too much longer because there isn't room for a ladder truck.

The fire bell in front of Station 1 was purchased in 1906 from G. S. Bell Company. It was first located in a bell tower at First and Freeman Streets. In 1921, it was moved to Fourth and Cleveland Streets. The bell was replaced by an electric siren in 1926. When Station 1 was opened in 1930, the bell was put into storage. In 1969, Chief R.

W. Trotter located the bell and had it mounted in front of Station 1 where a fish pond had been for many years.

Station 2, located at 1740 South Ditmar Street in south Oceanside at the corner of Ditmar and Cassidy Streets was opened on January 15, 1953, at a cost of $37,879.

Station 3, located at 3101 Oceanside Boulevard at the intersection of Oceanside Boulevard and El Camino Real, opened on October 10, 1962, at a cost of $66,400. The original station was located at the eastern edge of Oceanside.

Station 4 is located at 3990 Lake Boulevard. The original station 4, located at 2797 College Boulevard, opened on October 1, 1971, at a cost of $35,805. In 1991, Station 4 was relocated to Lake Boulevard to serve the southeastern area of the city.

Station 5 is located at 4841 North River Road. It opened on October 7, 1973, at a cost of $93,522 to serve the northeastern area of the city.

Station 6, located at 805 North Santa Fe Avenue at the intersection of Mesa Drive and North Santa Fe Avenue, was built in the late 1990s.

Station 7 at 3350 Mission Avenue, which was opened in July 2008, houses up to eleven firefighters. It replaced a temporary 20-year-old station that was opened on Jones Road in the 1990s. The 18,000-square-foot station, designed by JKA

Architecture, cost $7.25 million. Areas include an apparatus room with four drive-through bays, bunk rooms, fitness area, kitchen, day room, and shop. The site includes space for fueling facilities and an emergency generator.

Station 8 at 1935 Avenida Del Oro, on the east end of Oceanside Boulevard, was opened in March 2006.

The stations house seven engines, one tiller truck, five ambulances, three Type III brush engines, one Type VI brush engine, one water tender, one command vehicle, one command and interoperability trailer, one incident support trailer, one mass casualty response vehicle, and one confined space trailer.

On March 31 2020, the department received a 2020 Pierce Type III wildland pumper with a CumminsL9 engine, 350 hp, 500-gpm pump, foam and water tank, and 500-gallon tank. On October 19, 2017, Oceanside received a Pierce pumper that has a Quantum chassis, Detroit diesel DD13 engine, 505 hp, a Command Zone electrical system, a Husky 3 foam system, a 1,500-gpm Pierce PUC pump, and a 500-gallon tank. On December 27, 2018, the department received a similar Pierce pumper. The department has two new Type III wildfire engines.

Firefighters train for structural and wildland firefighting, confined space rescues, emergency medical incidents, vehicle extrication, hazardous material situations, and more. Oceanside Fire Department is the only department in the zone that holds full fire academies for new hires. New hires spend a minimum of eight weeks full time additional training, starting with physical conditioning.

Chiefs and command officers attend the Oceanside Fire Department Command Training Center. The Blue Card program is used to develop the skills of members of the management team. Oceanside is only one of three Blue Card command training centers in California. Fire officers complete 50 hours of online training before being evaluated in a simulation laboratory. The evaluation process is completed over a three-day period. The program is designed to supervise local National Incident Management System (NIMS) Type 4 and Type 5 events. It teaches hazard zone operations.

The props used for the command training of routine and large-scale incidents include 16 interactive consoles, instructor console to run the incident, big screen monitors, dispatch console, and separate room for first in incident commanders.

Reach Air Medical Services, an emergency medical helicopter service, opened a base in Oceanside in 2013 in partnership with the Oceanside Fire Department. Reach 16 moved into a facility at the fire department's training center on June 26, 2017.

North County Dispatch JPA, commonly referred to as North Comm, provides fire and medical emergency dispatch.

The department has a senior volunteer program of men and women who assist with non-firefighting duties such as fire safety education, special events, public service requests, office work, fire station tours, and residential inspections.

Captain Mark Finstuen, who works for the Oceanside Fire Department, and Stu Sprung, who worked for the Oceanside Fire Department in the early part of his 17-year fire service career and is an executive board member of the Firehouse Museum, published a book titled "Oceanside Fire Department" in 2010. Captain Finstuen is a past president of the Oceanside Firefighters Association and the historian of the department.

In 1923, the Oceanside Fire Department was the second department in the state to enroll in the California State Firefighters Association with 100% membership. The Oceanside Firefighters Association, IAFF Local 3736, has over 100 members. It has an active charity and community committee. Beginning in 1956, the Oceanside Fire Department began having an annual firemen's ball to benefit the Police and Fire Benevolent Fund. For three years, starting in 1984, the firefighters hosted a rodeo at the San Luis Rey Downs. The association sponsors an annual surf contest that is attended by firefighters from throughout Southern California. The proceeds from it go to Casa De Amparo, a local home for abused children.

The fire personnel work hard to provide the best possible service to the 176,000 residents and the many visitors to the city of Oceanside in time of need.

CALLS RECALLED:

*1896: The South Pacific Hotel burned on June 13, 1896. The beautiful seaside resort was built in 1887 at Third and Pacific Streets.

*1959: On April 29, 1959, a laundry at 202 South Cleveland Street caught fire. Crews in three Oceanside engines and Truck 5 responded to the incident, laying over 2,000 feet of hose and using 500,000 gallons of water. Firefighters from Carlsbad and Camp Pendleton helped fight the blaze.

*1961: On March 11, 1961, at 6:41 p.m., the Saint Malo Lumber Yard Company on 1702 South Hill Street caught fire. When Captain Lloyd Seal and his crew arrived at the scene aboard F4, there were 100-foot flames from the burning wood. The flames caused a 2,400-volt power line to drop on Chief John Billings and Captain Seal. The chief was able to roll off the live wire. The captain was taken to Oceanside Hospital on North Horne Street for third-degree burns on his left thigh and on both legs. The doctors had to amputate both his legs. A bystander, Fred Pimental, 21, was killed while trying to help Captain Seal when he stepped on an electrified metal gate. It took three hours to get the fire under control.

*1977: At the Lumber Yard Fire in 1977, a new Van Pelt 100-foot aerial ladder was used.

*1987: The Ice House Fire burned for a long time because there was sawdust in the walls of the building.

*1991: The dry goods store of E. Brown was destroyed by a fire.

*1992: Engine 21 was deployed to Los Angeles to assist in firefighting and rescue efforts during the Los Angeles riots.

*1997:   There was a large furniture store fire on South Hill Street.

*2001:   Division Chief Ken Matsumoto was assigned to Ground Zero as part of the San Diego Urban Search and Rescue Team.

*2003:   Captain Mike Young and his crew fought the Cedar Fire.

*2006:   Captain Kurt Edwin Krebbs, 45, died April 9, 2006, after fighting a house fire on April 7, 2006. He earned a Bachelor of Science in Business from Cal Poly-Pomona in 1985, then joined the Rancho Santa Fe Fire Protection District. After working at the Encinitas Fire Department for a short time, he joined the Oceanside Fire Department in January 1989.

*2007:   In 2007, there were over 50 fires caused by arson in the San Luis Rey riverbed.

*2011:   In September 2011, a fire broke out in the music room of Garrison Elementary School. Fortunately, the musical instruments, valued at $30,000, were not damaged. Structure loss was $150,000.

*2012:   In August 2012, firefighters on a ladder truck arrived to rescue a turtle that had been taped to a balloon. But the wind picked up and the turtle was blown to the ground. The turtle was turned over to the Humane Society.

*2013:   In October 2013, a brush fire on the east side of Interstate 5 near Oceanside Boulevard burned half an acre.

*2014:   In May 2014, Cal Fire assisted the Oceanside Fire Department with a 105-acre fire on North River Road and College Boulevard.

*2014:   In May 2014, a mobile home was destroyed in a fire on North Cleveland Avenue. The home was valued at $150,000.

*2015:   The department responded to 20,452 calls, including 881 fires, 15,751 medical services, 1,834 vehicle accidents, 891 service calls, 118 hazardous condition calls, 116 investigation calls, and 860 other types of calls.

*2017:   On December 7, 2017, Santa Ana winds spread a small brush fire near Old Highway 395 and Dulin Road, on the west of Interstate 15, towards Oceanside, Bonsall, and Vista. The Lilac Fire caused 44,000 households to be evacuated. The fire was contained on December 16, 2017. It destroyed 157 buildings, damaged 64 buildings, and burned 4,100 acres.

*2018:   In November 2018, a small brush fire in the dry bed of the San Luis Rey River was extinguished by crews from Oceanside, Vista, and Camp Pendleton. The fire was contained to a half acre.

*2019:   Crews responded to a house fire on Mertensia Street in January 2019. The firefighters arrived within eight minutes and contained the fire to the guest bedroom.

*2019:   In February 2019, a motorhome that was in the parking lot of Walmart caught fire, killing one man.

*2019:   In 2019, the department responded to 21,138 calls.

*2020:   In February 2020, a brush fire in a riverbed spread to a rail bridge. Oceanside firefighters were assisted by crews from Camp Pendleton and Carlsbad.

*2020:   In August 2020, brush engine 8633 was assigned to the Apple Fire in the San Gorgonio wilderness.

OCOTILLO WELLS VOLUNTEER FIRE DEPARTMENT

Ocotillo Wells is a tiny community on the vast desert floor of the Anza-Borrego Desert. Seven miles east one finds the San Diego-Imperial county line, to the north is the Anza-Borrego Desert State Park, to the west is the Borrego turnoff, and to the south of the town lies a large active gypsum mine. The mine is a hundred years old and projected to be used for at least another hundred years. The mine fills 30 railroad cars and 30 trucks daily.

"Ocotillo" is the name of a wildflower that blooms bright red every spring. The word "Wells" comes from the fact that this entire desert area sits on an enormous underground lake.

The 84,000-acre Ocotillo Wells State Vehicular Recreation Area (SVRA) is a motorcycle, four-wheel drive, all-terrain vehicle, and dune buggy use area. It is open 24 hours a day, 7 days a week. The Ocotillo Volunteer Fire Department helped with the clean-up of the area.

The Ocotillo Wells Volunteer Fire Department was originally formed in 1976 but folded in 1982. George "Curly" Bowen, the fire chief in 1982, had hoped to form a community service area. In January 1992 it was reactivated with full community support with 37 members. Of the 266 residents, almost half are retired.

A fire station was built on 2.5 acres at 5891 Split Mountain Road. A HUD (Housing and Urban Development) grant of $122,000 ensured the station's future. The apparatus consisted of a 1954 Van Pelt on a GMC chassis that was donated to the fire department by the San Diego County Sheriff's Department at the Descanso Department of Corrections. It had a 1000-gpm 2-stage pump that held 450 gallons of water. The other piece of equipment was a 1967 Dodge power wagon with a 500-gallon tank. The water was pumped by two 150-gpm Briggs and Stratton engines. It was renovated by local mechanic Dick Tiernan.

The Ocotillo Wells Volunteer Fire Department was incorporated on February 20, 1992. It was funded by the community residents who paid a $12 annual fee.

Fundraising events, such as barbecues, rummage sales, and pancake breakfasts, provided income for the department over the years. For a raffle held December 21, 1999, Ron Wilson donated an ATM at the fundraiser that raised $450 towards the construction of a firehouse. A bake sale on February 15, 1992, raised $800. The mud bog races at Dome Hill, off of State Route 78, put on by the fire department, attracts hundreds of spectators to this unusual annual event. Dune buggies, ATMs, motorcycles, jeeps, and 4 x 4 vehicles were challenged to run the gauntlet of mud for the best time.

Chief Mark Gault, a park ranger in the Anza-Borrego Desert State Park, has a background in firefighting and shared his knowledge to bring training and procedures to the volunteer department.

Jim Holmes, president of the board of directors, stated that with the formation of the fire department, "What we're really trying to do is create unity within the community and develop a focus of interest in area events." He said, "Our goal is to construct a firehouse that can also serve our community as a multipurpose meeting hall." Past board members included Dan Christiansen, Joann Lawrence, Rob Parkinson, Dick Tiernan, Betty Walker, and Jack Ward.

In 2011, the San Diego Fire Authority assigned a patrol vehicle to the department that cost $147,000. In 2013, the department had $170,184, expenses amounted to $29,233, and revenue was $24,639.

Now Ocotillo Wells has a fire department located at 5841 Highway 78, San Diego County Fire Authority Station 54 staffed with Cal Fire personnel, one captain or engineer and two firefighter/paramedics. The station houses Engine 54, a Type II 2015 HME, Patrol 54, a Type VI Ford F-450, and a rescue ambulance that is used to transport patients from off-roads to paved roads to be transported by Mercy Ambulance or Mercy Air.

More than a million visitors a year seek recreational pleasure in this area, including dune buggy drivers, campers, and hikers. Many people get injured riding in their desert vehicles, often with broken ribs, wrists, and legs.

CALLS RECALLED:

*1982:   The Ocotillo Wells firefighters transported two injured motorcyclists to Pioneers Memorial Hospital in Brawley on April 25, 1982.

*1992:   Between February 9 and May 13, 1992, three unoccupied structures burned within a one-mile radius. On February 9 the mobile home of Richard and Kathy Riggins burned; on April 27 the mobile home of Jim Kykendoll burned; and on May 13 a garage, dune buggy, and jeep burned at the home of Doug Burgess.

*2010:   In May 2010, a 24-year-old San Diego man was killed while riding his off-road motorcycle in the Ocotillo Wells State Vehicle Recreation Area. The victim lost control of his motorcycle and was ejected at Shell Reef Expressway at Fault Wash.

*2012:   Augie Ghio, chief of the San Miguel Consolidated Fire Protection Disetrict, lost control of his Harley-Davidson motorcycle at 9:30 a.m. on State Route 78 and was air lifted to Palomar Hospital with serious injuries.

*2017:   On March 3, 2017, three people were injured in a head-on collision on State Route 78. They were transported to a hospital in two helicopters.

*2018:   On February 15, 2018, an ultralight plane was found upside down at the airport in Ocotillo Wells. The pilot suffered minor injuries.

*2018:   Firefighters had to extricate three people from a vehicle and a motor home who were injured in a head-on collision on February 17 at 9:40 a.m. at Wolfe Well Road and State Route 78.

*2018:   On October 17, 2018, a pilot who broke his leg when he made a hard landing at the Ocotillo Airport was transported to a hospital by an air ambulance.

*2018:   On November 24 at 7:00 p.m. two cars collided and burst into flames on State Route 78 near Quarry Road. One of the two people killed was Brett Ann Gregory, an Oceanside Police Department dispatcher.

*2019:   In June 2019, several trailers were destroyed in a fire near Split Mountain Road and Old Kane Springs Road.

PALA FIRE DEPARTMENT

The Pala Reservation was established by the Executive Order of December 27, 1875. The reservation was originally occupied by the Luiseño people.

"Pala" means water when translated from the language of the Cupeños and Luiseños who live and work on the Pala Indian Reservation. In 1903 the federal government relocated the Cupeño Indians from their ancestral home in the village of Cupa (now called Warner Springs) to the valley of Pala. The U.S. government supplied tents and very small houses for the Cupeños. Although the Indians found fertile soil and water in Pala, they would have preferred to stay in Cupa. In 1922, a dam was built across the San Luis Rey River to create Lake Henshaw. The water supply for the Indian community was cut off. There are about 800 homes and commercial buildings on the reservation.

The Pala Indian Reservation is bordered on the north by the San Diego/Riverside county line, west by Rice Canyon, east by the Pauma Valley Indian Reservation, and south by Lilac Road. The reservation sits at an elevation of 2,000 feet, encompassing

over 4,000 acres of forest, 8 acres of lakes, 6 acres of wetlands, and approximately 40 miles of streams.

The first weekend of May the tribal members celebrate the move to Pala with a cultural celebration which is open to the public and has entertainment and exhibits.

The Pala Fire Department was formed in 1978 with only two firefighters and a 300-gallon water tank. By 1980 it had a full-time volunteer department, operating 24 hours a day, seven days a week. It responded to 186 calls in 1991. By 2014, the number of calls had increased to 920 calls, 620 of which were on the Pala Indian Reservation. Less than 200 calls were from the Pala Resort and Casino.

With a large casino having been built on the reservation as well as homes, the responsibilities now are much larger than when the department was formed.

The department covers 20-1/2 square miles, consisting of 13,315 acres and about 650 people. The fire department has established mutual and automatic aid agreements with departments such as Cal Fire, North County Fire, Rincon Reservation Fire Department, Pechanga Fire Department, and Valley Center Fire Protection District.

Anthony Ravago, a Pala tribal member, has been the chief for four years. He started with the department when he was 18 years old. In 2019, Chief Ravago was elected vice-chairman of the tribal council. Previously Robert Smith, who is now the tribal chief, was the fire chief.

There are 30 full-time suppression personnel (including chief, assistant chief, battalion chief, 6 captains, 6 engineers, and 15 firefighters). There are also 15 reserve firefighters. Most of the firefighters are not tribal members. Chief Ravago's staff includes: David Osuna, assistant chief; Douglas Moriaty, battalion chief; Mark Melick, Gary Mercer, Chris Hutchings, and Juan Luna Sr., captains.

All the personnel maintain California State Fire Marshal certification status. The firefighters keep in touch with the residents through lectures, school programs, and a newsletter. Two firefighters on each shift are trained for swift water rescues.

Fifty-two-year-old Elfego Covarrubias, who has been with the Pala Fire Department for 14 years, said, "I feel like I waited my whole life to be a firefighter. When I was a freshman in high school in Fallbrook, the school had a career day. I headed directly to the red fire engine. As a 15-year-old student, I joined a Fire Explorer program and rode on the tailboard of the engine. I love that I have a lifesaving job."

Firefighter Elfego Covarrubias

The original three-bay station across from the Mission San Antonio de Pala was built with grant money, fundraisers, donations, and volunteer labor and was completed in April 1989 for under $70,000.

In June 2008, the Pala Fire Department completed construction of a $9.2 million fire station located at 34884 Lilac Extension Road, at the intersection of Highway 76 and Pala-Temecula Road. It includes a two-story building housing administration, 18 sleeping quarters, six large bays, huge kitchen, weight rooms, training center, family room, and laundry facility totaling 25,061 square feet. Enhancing the dining area, Captain Gary Mercer made a 15-foot dining table out of rare wood and the table is engraved in the center with the department's logo. The training classroom can be utilized as an emergency operation center. There is a five-story training tower with live fire burn rooms.

In 2009, the Pala Fire Station received funding from ARRA (American Recovery Reinvestment Act) to install solar electric panels as a demonstration project. The solar contractor, Good Energy Solar, installed 138 high efficiency LG 310 watt modules onto the metal roof.

In April 2015, the Pala Band of Mission Indians received grant funding from the Department of Energy to assist in the installation and operation of a photovoltaic solar electric generating facility at the Pala Fire Station, and in May 2016, the Pala Fire Station received permission to operate the facility.

The 91.14 kW DC addition to the Pala station provides annual production of 145,896 kilowatt hours of energy to the facility, and will result in a utility bill savings of approximately $52,000 a year.

In the past, the department's first responder for any type of medical incident was a 1991 Ford rescue unit. It carried the Jaws of Life, air bags, and a full complement of medical gear. For structure fire responses, the firefighters had a 1976 1,250-gpm FYI Detroit diesel engine with 500 gallons of water, single stage. It had two 1-1/2 in. preconnects, 1,000 feet of 2-1/2 in. supply line, and 1,000 feet of 1-1/2 in. donut rolls for wildland fires. A 1966 two-stage 1,250-gpm American La France which was fed by a 500-gallon tank had 3-1/2 in. reconnects, 1,000 feet of 2-1/2 in. supply line, and 1,200 feet of 1-1/2 in. donut rolls for wildland fires was also used. The department had a 1962 Dodge brush engine, which had a two-stage 800-gpm mobile pump fed by a 500-gallon tank, held an additional 1,200 feet of 1-1/2 in. of hose for wildland lays. A 1980 Ford water tender, which held 2,500 gallons, pumped 1,250 gallons per minute, had mobile attack capabilities, and carried a mounted deck gun that was taken to fires.

Medical transport was provided by mutual aid with the North County fire departments or Hartson's Ambulance Service out of the city of Escondido. Now American Medical Response is used. Helicopters are used for trauma victims as needed.

In September 1992, the Pala firefighters began a dispatch system with Cal Fire. Now Northcomm provides fire and medical dispatch services.

The department's equipment consists of a 2013 Type 1 KME structure engine carrying 500 gallons of water, a Type 3 brush engine, a Freightliner water tender that holds 1,800 gallons of water, a 2009 American La France Type 1 reserve engine that carries 750 gallons of water, a 1998 reserve International brush rig, and three chief vehicles.

A six-member tribal council administers the fire department. A fee is assessed on all structures. In the past, other monies came from grant money, fundraisers,

donations, and the Bureau of Indian Affairs. The annual budget in 1990 was $125,000.

Directly across from the fire station is the Mission San Antonio de Pala. It was founded in 1816 by Father Antonio Peyri. Its sole mission was to serve the Indians of Pala, and is the only one of the original California missions to survive with this purpose.

The mission school was established in 1958. The school has about 125 students, 80% of whom are Indian. It is the only Catholic parochial school in California which has primarily Indian students.

The mission is a shrine to the people of Pala. Rich in history, its Spanish architecture still stands proudly, gracefully, and with reverence. Over the years the mission has developed a need for some repairs, and the community answered this call for help. The Pala Indians once again gave their labor, effort, and time where it would do the most good for the community and their church.

The Cupeños and Luiseños word for firefighter or fire tender is "tekweus 'ash," and it honors their ancestors and their present day brethren.

CALLS RECALLED:

*2003:   Pala personnel had 631 calls in 2003.

*2009:   In May 2009, three homes were destroyed and 122 acres burned in a fire along Highway 76.

*2010:   On June 23, 2010, at 3 p.m. the Pala Fire burned 106 acres of chaparral off of Highway 76 east of the Pale Resort and Casino.

*2011:   In August 2011, a brush fire burned 300 acres near Pala. More than 600 firefighters fought the fire.

*2016:   In January 2016, a brush fire started on the north side of Highway 76, causing some evacuations.

*2016:   In May 2016, a fire in Pala quickly spread and burned 70 acres on Pala-Temecula Road.

*2018:   In May 2018, the Agua Fire burned 60 acres off of State Route 76 east of Pala Casino & Spa. Over 100 firefighters fought the fire.

*2019:   Eighty percent of the calls for the department are medical emergencies and traffic accidents, especially along Highway 76 and Pala-Temecula Road.

PALOMAR MOUNTAIN VOLUNTEER FIRE DEPARTMENT

Palomar Mountain, one of the highest peaks in San Diego County, is 6,140 feet. The firefighters cover 39 square miles, from Lake Henshaw to Nate Harrison Grade. The Palomar Observatory and Palomar Mountain State Park bring many visitors to the area.

On South Grade Road, a two-lane road to Palomar Mountain with over 20 hairpin turns, there are often motorcycle accidents. East Grade Road is a more gradual climb up the mountain.

Palomar Mountain Volunteer Fire Department was first organized on October 1, 1975, when the County of San Diego decided not to renew the contract with CDF (now Cal Fire) for fire protection in the back country. The county would provide a local volunteer department with a used fire truck and equipment, 240 hours of training, and insurance for the vehicles used. When the contract expired on July 1, 1976, the department took over emergency response services with a crew of 25 volunteers. The elected officers were: Bill Richardson, fire chief; Al Andrews, 1st assistant chief; Bruce Druliner, 2nd assistant chief; LeRoy Bonham, chairman; Otis Kilgore, vice-chairman; and Pat Richardson, secretary/treasurer.

In March 1976 Bill Richardson resigned as chief due to health reasons and took over as secretary and treasurer from Pat Richardson. Richardson wrote letters to property owners about funding and the reasons to support the department. He wrote the by-laws and obtained tax exempt status. When it was decided to turn over fundraising to the Friends of the Palomar Mountain Volunteer Fire Department, he also got tax exempt status for the organization. He resigned in October 1980 after five years of service.

Since there was no place to house the equipment, various places served as a station, including the county yard, Bailey's Hotel, the Palomar Observatory, and the Crestline Water Company building.

Through fundraisers and donations enough money was raised to purchase a piece of property centrally located to serve the community. The fire station property, located at the intersection of Crestline Road and East Grade Road, was formerly a gas station and store. After the store burned in the 1930s a house was built on the site.

Fundraisers are an important part of a volunteer fire department's income, and one of the biggest events on Palomar Mountain was the annual barbecue to help support the department. The first barbecue was held on September 3, 1977, at the Skyline Lodge at the end of Crestline Road. On every Saturday of the Labor Day weekend the annual barbecue was held, generating an important part of the department's income.

Pat Richardson and Oliver Brown co-chaired the first annual pit barbecue. Subsequent barbecue chairpersons were: 1978: Pat Richardson and Pearl Schrader,; 1979: Pat Richardson, Doris Bailey, and Katie Beishline; 1980: Jennifer Palm; and 1981: Roy Birdsall. Kay Schmide and Molly Brown organized dances. Aluminum can collections and bingo games generated money. Jo Davis established year-round crafts sales and held weekly get-togethers at Skyline Lodge to make the crafts. The Palomar Mountain Mutual Water Company provided garage space for equipment at no charge.

Past fire chiefs include: Bill Richardson (1975-1976), Steve Barry (1976-1977), Brad Bailey (1977-1978), Harry Schrader (1978-1979), Pat Shelly (1979-1980), Rick Lobner (1980-1982), Karl Bauer, George E. Lucia Sr. (2005-2013), and Cliff Kellogg (2013-2015).

In 1982, the fire personnel were Rick Lobner, chief; Harry Schrader, assistant chief; Kathy Bates, EMT/captain; Will McKinley, Skip Staples, and Keith Oldham, engineers; and firefighters LeRoy Bonham, Will McKinley, Bill Pickard, Bob Hall, Nancy Hall, Jonnie Staples, Jill Staples, Will Cain, Maggie Price, Joe Sims, Helen McKinley, John Black, Bill Pickard, Chris Marszalek, and Russ Day.

In August 2013, Chief George E. Lucia Sr. announced his retirement. Chief Lucia was a firefighter for Woodcliff Lake Fire Department in Bergen County, New Jersey, from 1969 to 1973 before moving to California. Besides being the last operational fire chief for the Palomar Volunteer Fire Department, he was a battalion chief and fire marshal for the Valley Center Fire Protection District for ten years.

Cliff Kellogg followed Chief Lucia Sr. as an administrative chief during the transaction when the County of San Diego and Cal Fire took over and dissolved the volunteers.

Earl Walls did a great deal for the mountain community, serving with the fire department, Palomar Mountain Planning Organization (PMPO), community center, and action committee. His car was hit by a driver who fled the scene of the crash. Walls died four weeks later on November 15, 2012. He served in World War II, graduated from West Virginia University with a degree in engineering, worked for Monsanto, and developed his own company.

Prop L was approved by residents to support the volunteer fire department. In 2011, the county service area providing fire protection to Palomar Mountain was added into the San Diego County Regional Fire Authority. Beginning on July 1, 2016, Cal Fire began staffing the fire department 24 hours a day, 7 days a week.

The County of San Diego contracts with Cal Fire to provide fire and emergency medical services to the community. Station 79, located at 21610 Crestline Road, is staffed by two Cal Fire personnel every day, one who is a paramedic, and reserve firefighters. Captain Dean Kowalski and Battalion Chief Cal Henrie are in charge of the station.

In 2018, the Palomar Mountain Fire Department's board of directors approved the county's plan for remodeling the fire station by removing the large oak tree behind the fire station to make room for the construction of a 2,000-square-foot building for quarters for four to six firefighters, adding an office, installing an emergency standby generator, and widening and paving the driveway. The county paid $1.8 million for the improvements. The station was built in the 1990s on 3.29 acres.

In May 2018, the department received a new water tender that holds 2,000 gallons. Other equipment the department has includes engine 79 received in January 2017, patrol 79 received in 2016, water tender 52, water tender 79, and utility vehicle 79.

The patrol 79 is a quick-attack vehicle to assist Cal Fire operations when a brush fire breaks out in a hard-to-reach area. The patrol is smaller and faster than a larger engine but is equipped with the same lifesaving equipment. It holds up to 200 gallons of water and 10 gallons of foam or gel. In addition to wildfires, the patrol vehicle can be used for structure fires, medical aid, and traffic accidents. It cost $260,000.

The department received an automatic vehicle locator (AVL) from the San Diego Regional Fire Foundation in 2015. AVL allows dispatchers to see where every fire vehicle is located and send the closest unit to an emergency regardless of fire department.

The Palomar Mountain Fire Safe Council, a 501c3 nonprofit corporation, has worked in the area since 2002. It identifies areas of the mountain where lives, structures, and resources are at significant risk due to high fuel loads, writes grants for funding to accomplish the work necessary to reduce the fuel load in those areas, oversees fire safety projects, and educates the mountain community about fire safe practices.

The Community Emergency Response Team (CERT) educates people about disaster preparedness for hazards that may impact their area and trains them in basic disaster response skills, such as fire safety, search and rescue, team organization, and disaster medical operations.

In additional to national CERT training standards, Palomar Mountain CERT members receive training in disasters that may affect the community, such as earthquake, wildfire and snow emergencies. Palomar Mountain CERT members are trained to assist the fire department with public safety, radio communications, and first aid. Palomar Mountain CERT has their own fire engine and is trained to apply Barricade gel to homes that are threatened by fire. A 4-wheel drive Suburban is used to assist the community. The department received a $2,500 grant from SDG&E to fund equipment and supplies for training.

The Palomar Mountain Volunteer Fire Department accomplished much from its beginnings in 1975. The fire personnel, board members, and community members worked diligently to keep the residents, visitors, and mountain safe.

1936

Calls recalled:

*1982: There were 77 service calls in 1982.

*1983: On March 21, 1983, a Cessna 170 B crashed near the Palomar Observatory. The plane fell into a deep canyon, killing the pilot and passenger.

*1987: A man burning avocado leaves started a fire on Palomar Mountain in October 1987 that burned 14,000 acres. The cost of fighting the fire was $2.5 million.

*2005: The fire crew responded to 26 motorcycle injury accidents in 2005.

*2007: The Poomacha fire started on the La Jolla Indian Reservation near Palomar Mountain on October 23, 2007, and was contained on November 9, 2007. It destroyed 138 homes and burned 49,410 acres. Since there were six other fires in the county at the time, the Palomar Mountain crew were on their own for about 48 hours before additional assistance arrived. The firefighters with the help of eight CERT members, worked nonstop to protect the 300 homes on the mountain, none of which were destroyed.

*2015: The Cutca Fire started on July 24, 2015, two miles north of the Palomar Observatory in the Cleveland National Forest. More than 380 firefighters fought the fire. It burned 167 acres.

*2016: There were 96 calls in 2016. Ninety percent of the calls were medical emergencies. The average number of calls per year based on the years 2010 to 2016 was 118.

*2017: Crews responded to six road slides in January 2017 and two medical aids.

*2017: In March 2017, there were three motorcycle accidents and two medical calls.

*2017: In May 2017, one of the calls was a a 6-year-old child who was bitten by a rattlesnake in Palomar Mountain State Park. Another call was for an elderly man doing mining beyond the High Point lookout. A rock rolled and broke his collarbone. It took firefighters 90 minutes to get to him.

*2018: When a tree fell across the South Grade Road, it was only because the department had a paramedic on the mountain that a victim survived.

*2018: In March 2018, there was a paraglider emergency landing on the Mendenhalls' East Grade ranch.

PINE VALLEY FIRE PROTECTION DISTRICT

Thirty-four miles east of San Diego on Interstate 8 is Guatay. The 2,000-acre mountain valley was inhabited by the Kumeyaay Indians. In 1860, sixty-four Indians lived in the area. Guatay is from the Indian word "wah-ti" which means large council house.

Ten miles further east on the same interstate is Pine Valley at an elevation of 4,500 feet. Pine Valley was originally part of the Mexican land grant Rancho Cuyamacha. Charles F. Emery with John Ross built a log cabin in the valley in 1870. Emery's son, Charley, discovered gold in Noble Canyon. Jack and Tom Noble mined the canyon until World War I. Pine Valley is from the Mexican name "El Valle de los Pinos."

The two communities have a population of about 2,000 residents and up to 7,500 visitors on weekends. The valleys are surrounded by the Cleveland National Forest.

In August 1947, the Pine Valley Volunteer Fire Department was formed by the Pine Valley Improvement Club. On June 4, 1962, the department became a fire protection district under Title 19 of the California statues to serve Guatay and Pine Valley.

John Francis Pingley was the fire chief from 1948 to 1964. Chief Pingley was a retired U.S. Navy veteran who received three decorations for meritorious service during World War II. The first was as commanding officer of the U.S.S. Munsee in operation against enemy Japanese forces in the Pacific Ocean area in October 1944; the second, in the same year, was for fighting a fire on a U.S. ship while commander, and the third as commanding officer of a fleet tug in action against Japanese forces during the assault on Iwo Jima and Okinawa from February to May 1945. He died in 1966.

In 1962, Chief Pingley's crew consisted of Ed Osborn and Louis Perma, captains, and R.T. Hadley, Nathan Morse, Conrad Mulhauser, Donald Turnbull, Dale Gowdy, William Russell, Roy Williams, Fred Cox, Sr., Jerry Bilyeu, and Albert Kerrick, firemen. Three of the crew were Red Cross first aid instructors, five had advanced first aid cards, and four had standard first aid cards. The men were often called to highway accidents and emergencies in the nearby recreation areas.

On May 5, 1962, the firemen had their second annual firemen's ball in the Pine Valley clubhouse. It was a formal affair and a queen was crowned during the festivities. Firemen Paul Hatter, Louis Perna, Frank Ferguson, and Jerry Mackey, who were with the Pine Valley Fire Department in its early days, attended the 50th anniversary of the department.

For about 20 years it was the only fire department to respond to calls between Alpine and El Centro.

In the 1990s, the department responded to about 300 calls a year in the 75-square-mile district which encompasses 15 miles of Interstate 8. The firefighters worked for free because the tax base of about $96,000 did not generate enough money to pay them.

Fred Cox Sr., who retired from the department to become a paid fire chief, was the chief from 1964 to 1985. He then became chief of the San Diego Rural Fire District (now known as San Diego County Fire Authority) and in Del Norte County in Northern California from which he retired. He encourage his son, Fred Cox, Jr., to become a career firefighter.

Jim Pilant was chosen to be the fire chief in 1985. Chief Pilant became a firefighter in 1980 because he wanted to be involved in the community. He said, "I can't give a lot of money but what I can give is my time." His wife, Bonnie, also helped out at the fire department; his two children, Jamye and Jason, liked to visit the fire station; and his dog, Bud, had a path beaten between Pilant's home and the station. In addition to working 40 hours a week as a purchasing agent for the San Diego Gas & Electric Company, he worked up to 20 hours a week for the Pine Valley Fire Department. Chief Pilant was president of the Inland Zone Fire Chiefs Association from 1987 to 1992 and a council member for the Watershed Fire Council of Southern California.

The five members of the board of directors were selected in the general elections. They were responsible for fiscal matters and choosing the fire chief. The chief was responsible for the operation of the department. He was allowed by state law to delegate certain duties to the assistant chief and fire marshal.

The department's budget was $87,278 in 1982-83; $131,352 in 1983-84; $85,490 in 1984-85; $102,709 in 1985-86; $105,000 in 1987-88; and $96,000 in 1992-1993.

Members of the department in 1990 were Jim Pilant, chief; Fred "Knute" Cox Jr., assistant fire chief; Tim Halderman, captain/fire marshal; John Koljeski, captain; Aron Cox, engineer; and Rick Williams, Travis Collier, Richard Fries, Chris Goodale, Derick Jarrell, Randy Keller, Ronda McClellan, Craig Neville, Ken Ockle, and Troy Sloan, firefighters.

Fred Cox, Jr., was a volunteer fireman for the district for 13 years, he became a volunteer when he was in high school. He volunteered and worked there for 21 years, promoting through the ranks to include six years as fire chief. Fred Cox, Jr., was hired by the Rancho Santa Fe Fire Protection District in 1990, where he has worked for 30 years. He was appointed fire chief in Rancho Santa Fe on December 1, 2018. In 1998, Cox attended the 50th anniversary of the Pine Valley Fire Protection District. He was reminded by a woman who went to school with him from kindergarten to the end of 6th grade (when her family moved away) that back then his nickname was "Knute."

Craig Neville, who worked at Kaiser Hospital, had been with the department for four years. Richard Fries, who had been a volunteer firefighter for another department for nine years, had been on the department for two years. Rhonda McClellan, a mother and homemaker, had been on the department for two years. Tim Halderman, who worked at the Pine Valley Bible Camp as a facilities operation manager, served on the department for seven years. Bret Davidson, who was a paid firefighter for the El Centro Fire Department, had been on the department for five years.

The firefighters trained every Thursday night from 6:00 p.m. to 9:00 pm. Their training was part of the reason they had an ISO (Insurance Service Organization) rating of 5. The department was the only volunteer fire department in San Diego County with a rating of 5! The ISO classifies fire departments on a scale of 1 to 10. A low classification means lower fire insurance premiums for homeowners. It helped that the firefighters were able to respond within nine minutes to calls that were furtherest away from the station. Both Guatay and Pine Valley have good water systems—the Pine Valley Mutual Water Company has seven wells and four water reservoirs with 1.7- million-gallon storage capacity and the Gautay Community Service District has two wells and one water reservoir with 170,000-gallon storage capacity. There are hydrants every 500 feet in commercial areas and every 300 feet in residential areas.

The 6,900-square-foot fire station built in 1974 was replaced in 2018 by a 13,090-square-foot station at a cost of $8.2 million. The new two-story facility at 28850 Old Highway 80 has three apparatus bays, two sleeping quarters that can accommodate 15 firefighters, a fitness room, and kitchen. The station has diesel pumps on site so engineers don't have to leave the station and drive to Descanso to refuel. The Pine Valley Fire Department is run by Cal Fire and the new station allows for better service to Pine Valley as well as neighboring communities including Descanso, Mount Laguna, and Boulevard.

The first equipment was a Ford pickup and a 1945 International pumper donated by the U.S. Navy. In 1948 the firefighters operated Tex Jones' service station for a week. The profits were used to buy a resuscitator. The department purchased two Ford trucks from Drew Ford of La Mesa that were built into fire apparatus by La Mesa Sheet Metal Works. The 1955 Ford was rebuilt twice and the 1958 Ford was rebuilt three times.

In 1981 a Jaws of Life was donated by the County Employees Charity Organization. In January 1984 a 1,000-gpm Grumman turbo-charged diesel triple-combination pumper was purchased for $83,986. The fire district also had a 1974 1,000-gpm Van Pelt triple-combination pumper, a 1980 250-gpm Indiana mini pumper, and a 1992 750-gpm Rescue 84.

After providing fire and medical services for Pine Valley and Guatay for 70 years, on August 8, 2017, the Pine Valley Fire Protection District was dissolved and joined the San Diego County Fire Authority (SDCFA). The two communities became part of Cal Fire (Station 44). Station 44 houses Water Tender 44 (2016 Freightliner M2 106), Engine 7424 (2007 International 4400), Water Tender 7454 (2007 International 4400), and USAR 44 (2017 Spartan Metro Star).

CALLS RECALLED:

*1898: On October 16, 1898, 400 acres of brush burned in Guatay.

*1941: On August 1, 1941, a fire burned 200 acres at the north end of the valley.

*1970: Six homes were destroyed in Pine Valley during the Laguna-Kitchen Creek Fire in September 1970. Jim Orsborn, a battalion chief for the La Mesa Fire Department, stationed crews from La Mesa, Santee, Lemon Grove, Spring Valley, and Lakeside in Pine Valley to fight the fire. The Laguna Fire burned 150,000 acres and destroyed 223 homes.

*1970: A mother told her young daughter to put a few of her treasures in the car during the evacuation of Pine Valley in September 1970. Later, the mother discovered that the girl had placed a gallon of ice cream on the seat, then protected it by placing other things on top of it.

*1970: Excerpts from the log of the Pine Valley Fire Department.

September 26, 1970:

06:30 Smoke reported.

10:10 Evacuation ordered. Fire units and two pickups leave.

12:00 Call Civil Defense El Cajon, ask for assistance.

18:00 Fire jumps Sunrise Highway.

20:40 Task force arrives from Heartland.

22:30 Unit 2 to Westover's on Lookout Loop. Engulfed and surrounded.

September 27, 1970:

05:45 Winds building approx. 50-70 mph.

05:55 Unit 1 leaving area—heat very intense and front moving fast.

05:58 Fire across Pine Blvd. into meadow.

11:30 New fire coming down from Sunrise.

19:00 Fire front increasing along entire north side of valley

September 28, 1970:

00:30 Men sleeping all over firehouse.

07:30 Valley looking good—some residents returned, more returning. September 29, 1970:

20:00 Secured.

*1980: Thirty-year-old Patrick Lee Vincent, a resident of Guatay and captain in the Pine Valley Fire Protection District, was killed in April 1980. A wrong-way vehicle crashed into his pickup on the Pine Valley Bridge on Interstate 8. Captain Vincent had a Bachelor of Science in Fire Science and was Fireman of the Year in 1978.

*1981: On December 2, 1981, the volunteers administered CPR for two hours to a child who had been struck by a car. The Life Flight physician commended the firefighters.

*1983: The firefighters worked all night to rescue a hiker with a fractured leg below the Pine Valley Bridge.

*1989:   Fog on May 13, 1989, caused an accident involving 20 cars. As cars came up to the accident, they hit the cars ahead of them. The second accident involved 30 cars. Thirty-six people were taken to hospitals, and Interstate 8 between Japatul Valley Road and Pine Valley Road was closed for nine hours. Over 100 emergency personnel and 30 emergency vehicles were at the scene.

*1989:   In June 1989 the fire personnel responded to 13 medical aid calls, 3 vehicle fires, 4 public assistance calls, 3 vehicle accidents, 1 smoke check, 2 brush fires, and 1 illegal burn. This represented a typical month for the fire department.

*1989:   On September 7, 1989, a fire at Guatay and Pine Valley burned over 130 acres. The U.S. Forest Service was assisted by 200 firefighters from Pine Valley, Lake Morena, Campo, Mt. Laguna, Descanso, and the California Department of Forestry

*1992:   When a blaze threatened the Pine Valley Bible Conference Center in Guatay, an ASTREA helicopter picked up Chief Pilant at the location where he worked 50 miles away from Pine Valley and flew him to the fire scene.

*2015:   In February 2015, a man was critically injured in a mobile home fire on Old Highway 80 near Pine Valley Road. He didn't suffer any burns. A helicopter took him to the hospital.

*2017:   In April 2017, a 42-year-old La Mesa man, Joseph DiPari, died from injuries he suffered after he crashed his 2016 Ducati motorcycle on Sunrise Highway just north of Interstate 8. He drifted onto a dirt shoulder and struck boulders along the road.

*2017:   In November 2017, Fire Captain Ryan Mitchell took his own life at the Pine Valley Bridge. (There were 69 firefighters in the United States who died in the line of duty in 2016, but 139 who took their own lives.)

*2020:   On September 5, 2020, the Valley Fire started at Japatul Road and Carveacre Road in the Japatul Valley, southeast of Alpine. As the fire spread, mandatory evacuations were given for Corde Madera south of Pine Valley and evacuation warnings for Pine Valley. The fire was extinguished on September 21. The fire burned 17,665 acres, destroyed 30 homes and 31 other structures, and damaged 11 structures.

POWAY FIRE DEPARTMENT

Poway is in the central part of San Diego County, east of Interstate 15, twenty miles northeast of San Diego, covering 37 square miles. With the growth of Poway from a city of 2,000 people in 1962 to a city of 49,470 in 2020 came the transition of a volunteer fire department to a paid one in 1992.

Today Poway is not the rural farming community of old, but a modern, progressive city that tens of thousands of people call home. Here they live, many commute to San Diego, but all are fortunate to have the protection of the Poway Fire Department. Its dedicated firefighters have earned a well-deserved reputation for professionalism and service that the pioneers and homesteaders of years past would have been proud of!

The name Poway is believed to have been derived from the Native American word "Paquail," meaning "here, the waters meet." Poway Creek is fed from the north by Rattlesnake Creek and Buehler Creek from the south. There is much evidence to conclude that Native American tribes lived in the area, then plentiful with game and water.

Spanish influence played a part in the development of such areas as Los Penasquitos and Rancho Bernardo. However, Poway itself was never part of any Spanish land grant as were many other parts of San Diego County.

Prior to the Civil War Poway was dotted with farms whose main crops were peaches and avocados. During the 1860s and after the end of the Civil War, Poway began to grow with the arrival of settlers from the Midwest and East Coast. Some of the early settlers were Philip Crosthwaite (first white settler, 1858); Louis N. Hilleary (Poway's first doctor, 1883); Castanos Paine (first postmaster, 1870); Solon G. Blaisdell (farmer, 1875); and John Frank (farmer, 1893).

The stagecoach commuters in 1901 would stop at the Half-way Cafe to rest and eat a meal for 25 cents. The area continued to grow and mature with churches, schools, and better roads and services. But it was not until 1954 when the Poway Municipal Water District was founded that residential development started to flourish. The Colorado Aqueduct provided much needed water to the agricultural community and its citizens.

In 1959, the San Diego County Board of Supervisors' task force recommended that Poway Municipal Water District establish a fire department for the fast-growing community. The Poway Taxpayers Association submitted a petition in opposition but the district board approved an ordinance in July 1960 establishing a fire department under provisions of state law. The Poway Fire Protection District was one of five districts in California in 1961 that were formed as part of municipal water districts. On October 9, 1961, three firefighters began their full-time duties with the Poway Fire Department: Jim Westling, Ignatius J. "Iggy" Leone, and Robert Bussee. Shortly afterwards, Von "Rip" Ruple replaced Robert Bussee. They were supplemented by about 20 volunteers.

The directors of the Poway Municipal Water Districts selected Jim Westling as chief. He had worked 23 years for the Minneapolis Fire Department and five and one half years for ARAMCO in Saudi Arabia. His new station wagon served as an ambulance. I. J. "Iggy" Leone and Von "Rip" Ruple were selected as engineers from among 10 applicants. The department had its own emergency phone number, which rang at the water district offices and at the fire chief's home. After office hours for the district, the business number would ring at the station. Short-wave radios were used for communication and to summon the volunteers where there was a fire. The engineer on duty would notify the volunteers by radio and then respond to the fire himself.

A fire station, built on Community Road catty corner from Community Church, opened in October 1961 at a cost of about $18,000. The department began providing emergency services from this station with one fire engine. The new 1961 American La France pumper had a Ford c850 chassis, a 534-inch displacement engine, and a 500-gallon tank. The rig's $15,000 price included hoses, nozzles, tools and equipment. The Poway Firefighters Association purchased and operated Poway's 1959 ambulance. This service was turned over to the fire department due to the rising operating expenses. The remaining $3,062.58 balance owed on the ambulance was paid by the fire department.

As call volume increased, a second fire engine was added in 1964. A second station was built in the northern portion of the district on Lake Poway Road. In 1973, the second engine was moved from Station One into the newly constructed Station Two.

Mutual aid agreements were signed with the U.S. Forest Service, Miramar Naval Air Station, and other departments throughout northern San Diego County.

Glen Olson and Louis E. "Pat" Wills were hired full time in 1966. Wills typifies the type of people in the fire service. Because he loved firefighting he took a large cut in pay to join the department. He worked as a welder for General Dynamics. After he retired from the department he continued to work part-time as a fire marshal for the Poway Fire Department. He was one of 36 call men, or part-time firemen who assisted two full-time engineers and the fire chief during the department's first year. The men shared 12 bulky radios that were capable of receiving only one channel frequency. Call men were paid 75 cents for every fire they fought. Since there was only one oxygen mask available, call men would inhale smoke during a fire. The city's original firefighters were only called upon 35 times to respond to 19 fires and 16 medical emergencies. Willis attended the 40th anniversary of the Poway Fire Department in 2001 at the age of 74. He said, "Volunteer firefighters have an 'espirit de corps' not often found."

In 1974 Bill Bond became the third chief, followed by Bill Toon in 1980.

Each firefighter trained at least 20 hours each month. The department had three fire engines, one aerial ladder truck, and two ambulances.

For $15,000 the department acquired a 1961 750-gpm Ford class A pumper with a 534-cubic-inch displacement engine. In 1964, it purchased a 1964 American La France pumper on a Ford chassis for $15,000 and later a 1,500-gpm Mack.

The Poway Fire Department took delivery of two rescue engines in 1980, two Beck brush engines in 1982, a Beck 1,500-gallon water tender in 1986, an E-One fire engine in 1988, an ambulance in 2001, a Pierce 3,000-gallon water tender in 2002, and a four-wheel drive Westmark brush engine in 2007.

The first fire station at 13050 Community Road was built in 1961 at a cost of $18,000 on land that cost $6,000. Two divisions were set up in the district: Division A west of Community Road, and Division B east of the road. The firefighters had no safety

equipment and only ten radio receivers. Since there was not enough money for all the men to have receivers, each man called one other man when there was an alarm.

An organization for Explorer Scouts, boys between the ages of 14 and 18, was formed by the Firemen's Relief Association in October 1963. The boys in Explorer Post 601 studied first aid, radio equipment, fire trucks, firefighting, and rescue techniques. At that time, Engineer Von Ruple said, "When they reach sixteen and have qualified, they get to spend the night at the station." Explorer Tom Pachman, who became a volunteer firefighter, explained that their goals were "to protect the lives and property of the people of Poway, to keep ourselves physically fit, and to maintain good grades in school." The department also had men on call who were over 18 years of age and were notified to respond in times of emergencies.

The first two Explorer Scouts were Bob Kranz and Bill Briscoe. They were followed by Jim Butler, John Winder, Tim Carle, Steve Harrison, Gary McPherson, Mark Sanchez, John Kring, Marty Larson, Dale Stevens, Lloyd Harrison, Vic Reed, and Alan Samuelson.

Bill Briscoe, an Explorer Scout, became the fourth paid fireman in 1971, and he was promoted to captain in 1973. Briscoe said the support that Chief Westling gave the program led to jobs as firefighters not only in Poway but throughout the United States for many of the young men. The fire department had a reserve force of volunteers who attended local colleges and wanted to become professional firefighters. He pointed out that a fire made no distinction between paid and volunteer, all must be physically fit, mentally prepared, and have a working knowledge of firefighting techniques.

In 1976 firefighter/paramedics began using the ambulance purchased by the Poway Firefighters Association, and in 1998 firefighter/paramedics were assigned to two engines.

In 1978, a bond to relocate Stations 1 and 2 and buy apparatus passed with 79% of the vote. Two fire stations were established in 1980 (Station 1 on 13050 Community Road and Station 2 at 16912 Westling Court), and one station was established in 2005 (Station 3 at 14322 Pomerado Road).

The department's first female firefighter was Cathy Orchard who went on to become a captain in Long Beach and fire chief in Monterey. Another female that worked for the department became a captain in Orange County and the third in the department, Kelly Delotch, is an engineer in Poway.

In March 2016, a new deputy chief position was added to the personnel at the department. It was filled by Division Chief Jon Canavan. Three division chief positions were eliminated and replaced by three battalion chief positions.

In May 2016, Scott Post, Brian Mitchell, and Ray Fried were promoted from captains to battalion chiefs. Scott Post was hired in 1992 and had been a captain since 2007. Brian Mitchell was hired as a firefighter in 2001 and promoted to captain in 2008. Ray Fried was hired in 2000 and promoted to captain in 2014.

The Poway Fire Department was classified as a Class 1/1X department by the Insurance Services Organization's Public Protection Classification program in September 2020, the highest level of recognition available from ISO. The split classification includes a 1X representing an area of Poway that is located far from a fire hydrant. This area is outside the water service boundary area where approved above ground water tanks are allowed in lieu of fire hydrants. This rating places Poway's fire department among the ranks of only 37 fire departments in California and 348 nationwide to earn this distinction. Only four fire departments in San Diego County have earned Class 1 designations. Poway first achieved a Class 1 Public Protection Classification rating in 2014.

The chiefs of the department are: Jim Westling (1961); Pat Wills; Bill Bond (1974-1980); Bill Toon (1980-1989); Mark Sanchez (1989-2019); and Jon Canavan (2019-).

Chief Mark Sanchez retired as Poway's safety services director at the age of 63 in July 2019 after a 48-year-career with the Poway Fire Department. He looks forward to spending more time with his wife, Leisl, and their eight children and nine grandchildren. As a freshman in high school in 1970, Sanchez became a volunteer at the department. He fought several wildfires and the fire that destroyed the Big Bear Market. After graduating from Poway High School in 1973, he became one of eight original full-time firefighters. Two years later, Sanchez and four other firefighters spent five months attending a class run by San Diego County to be certified as paramedics. Chief Sanchez spent 10 years as a firefighter before being promoted to captain to oversee the paramedic program in 1984. City Manager Jim Bowersox interviewed 70 applicants for fire chief in 1990 before selecting Mark Sanchez as safety services director. The Poway Safety Services Department was responsible for the Poway Sheriff's Department and the Poway Fire Department. He oversaw the law enforcement contract with the San Diego County Sheriff's Department. When Chief Sanchez retired, the city manager decided to return the responsibility handling matters relating to the sheriff's department contract with the city to his office.

On July 11, 2019, Jon Canavan was appointed chief of the department. Chief Canavan was raised in San Bernardino. He graduated from St. Thomas Aquinas High School (1978-1982); studied aerospace, aeronautical, and astronautical engineering at California State Polytechnic University Pomona (1982-1983); received a Bachelor of Science in Fire

Protection Administration from Cal State Los Angeles (1986-1989); and graduated from the second Palomar College Fire Academy in 1990. From October 1989 to April 1990, he was a reserve firefighter for the City of Montclair. From April 1990 to January 2003, he served the San Marcos Fire Department, working his way through the ranks to become a captain. From January 2003 to October 2013, he was a division chief and fire marshal for the Poway Fire Department. From October 2013 to December 2013, he was the chief of the Encinitas Fire Department. From December 2013 to April 2016, he was a division chief and fire marshal for the Poway Fire Department; and from April 2016 to July 2019, he was the deputy chief. He taught part-time at Palomar College until 2004. When Chief Canavan began working in Poway, he and his wife with their two sons moved to the city. Chief Canavan is committed to providing the best possible service to the residents of Poway and promoting the health and wellness of the fire personnel.

The senior officers are: Scott Post, deputy fire chief/fire marshal; Brian Mitchell, battalion chief, Training and Safety; Raymond Fried, battalion chief, Operations/EMS; and Rodney Ortiz, battalion chief, Logistics/Support.

The Poway Fire Department has a fire chief, a deputy chief, three battalion chiefs, 48 firefighter/paramedics, three fire prevention staff, two administrative assistants, and one disaster coordinator. Three personnel are assigned to each fire engine, three personnel on the truck, and two personnel are assigned to each ambulance. The department has a constant staffing of 16 personnel per day per division. All fire suppression personnel are assigned to 24-hour shifts and work 56 hours a week.

There are three divisions: Fire Prevention, Fire Administration/Disaster Preparedness, and Operations/Training/Emergency Medical Services.

The three stations are:

Station 1, located at 13050 Community Road just south of Hillery, was established in 1961 and has been at the current location since 1980. It contains the administrative offices. It houses Engine 3711, a 2010 Pierce Arrow XT engine with a 500-gallon water tank, 1,500-gpm pump, and foam. The engine is equipped with radio gear, mapping tools, breathing apparatus, medical treatment devices, hoses, nozzles ,and rope rescue equipment. It cost $525,000 and $25,000 to outfit the engine. At the same time, the same type of engine was purchased for Station 3.

Station 2, located at 16912 Westling Court, has been at the current location since 1980. The second station was opened at Lake Poway in 1973, providing improved service to northern Poway. It houses Engine 3721, a 2014 Pierce Arrow XT.

Station 3, located at 14322 Pomerado Road, was established in 2001 and has been at the current location since 2005. The station was constructed in 2006. It houses

Engine 3713 (2010 Pierce Arrow XT); Truck 3773, a 2006 Pierce Dash; and Medic 3793.

On January 1, 2007, the department's first aerial ladder truck, Truck 3773, was put into service. The 65-foot-long truck cost $1 million. The truck features a tractor-trailer design with a rear cab with an extra steering wheel and a 100-foot ladder that can be extended to the fourth floor of a building. A high-pressure water nozzle is mounted on a swivel at the end of the ladder. The ladder truck can be used to reach across to buildings set back from the street, bridge small canyons and soak burning, one-story structures from above. Equipment for dealing with floods and water damage, and 212 feet of ground ladders that can be laced up the sides or across the roofs of buildings are on the truck.

The personnel come into contact with potential coronavirus patients every day. They are taking extra precautions on calls and clean the stations many times each day. When crews come on duty, they disinfect the entire station, each apparatus, and their dorm rooms. They also clean again at night.

The fire personnel work so, so hard to provide quality service to the residents of Poway.

CALLS RECALLED:

*1962: In March 1962, short-circuited electric blankets caused fires in two Poway residences.

*1962: Three children, ages four, two, and two months, perished in a fire in July 1962. Chief Westling found Mrs. Gleason leaning against a car in shock. The chief said, "After a couple of minutes, one of the fireman heard moaning. We found the father down a little hill. He was badly burned." Gary Gleason suffered from second and third degree burns on his back and feet during his attempt to rescue his children.

*1963: One of the calls in January 1963 made the national news, from the front pages of Philadelphia's The Evening Bulletin to the National Enquirer. Fifteen-year-old Linda Tapp and her horse fell fifty feet into a well that was four feet in diameter. Engineer Von Ruple climbed down the well and rescued the girl with the aid of a parachute harness. Unfortunately the horse had to be destroyed.

*1966: Captain "Iggie" Leone died of a heart attack at a structure fire on February 8, 1966, at the age of 47. He touched the back of Firefighter Lee Main, then fell. He was transported to Palomar Hospital in an ambulance he helped to acquire for the district. Captain Leone founded the Poway Ambulance Service and the Poway Firemen's Relief Association. He was posthumously given an honorary diploma from Poway High School. In an interview published by the high school newspaper in October 1965, Captain Leone stated, "Of the 170 students in the class, I know 169. The one I'm not sure of is myself."

*1966: A fire truck sustained $4,000 worth of damage during a three-acre grass fire. Engineer Glenn Olson did not see a hole hidden by grass. When the engine struck the hole, the gas tank tore loose and flames ignited the gasoline.

*1967: During the Woodson Fire that swept down on Poway from Ramona in October 1967, the firefighters, with aid from other fire departments, worked nonstop day and night. More than 700 firefighters fought the blaze. Crews and equipment came from as far away as Arizona. There were 200 pieces of equipment used to fight the fire which burned 32,500 acres and destroyed 16 homes in Poway. As the flames threatened to surround the Poway High School, the senior boys were asked to fight the fire. More than 300 teenagers took part in fighting the Woodson Fire, reporting for their assignments at the station. Most of the houses burned were in northern Poway near Mt Woodson: five in High Valley, one on Green Valley Truck Trail (now Blue Sky Ranch), one on Green Valley Road (then a road to High Valley) and now part of Lake Poway, and one on Old Coach Road. Three houses in Green Valley were destroyed. To the south, five uninsured rental properties on unpaved Midland, north of Twin Peaks Road, were lost to the flames. Engineers Von Ruple and Glenn Olson suffered severe burns. Olson was loaded into a fire truck from Ramona, transferred to an ambulance, and rushed to Palomar Hospital. Ruple was taken in a fire rig. Both men had to have skin grafting operations.

Residents honored the firefighters from Poway and 23 other agencies at a barbecue at Poinsettia Mobile Home Park. The Poway Chamber of Commerce presented plaques of appreciation to the participating agencies, as well as to Poway High School and Palomar College. The following month, Chief Westling was named Poway's Man of the Year.

*1968: A fire at Sycamore Canyon burned 1,173 acres before 243 firefighters from Poway Fire Department and nearby departments could extinguish it.

*1970: Five hundred firefighters fought the Laguna Fire, including crews from Poway. After the fire, a program called Firescope emerged and a way to manage simultaneous incidents involving multiple agencies. The National Incident Management System (NIMS) was adopted. NIMS provides shared vocabulary, systems, and processes to successfully fight fires.

*1990:   St. Michael's Catholic Church was destroyed by fire.

*2003:   The Santa Ana winds sent the Cedar Fire into Poway on October 25 at 5:00 a.m. The fire spread at a rate of 3,600 acres per hour. There were 15 firefighters to protect 49,000 residents and four available engines to protect homes. Chief Mark Sanchez was relieved to see five Orange County fire engines on Highway 67 that could assist in saving homes. The Cedar Fire destroyed 54 homes and 16 businesses in Poway.

*2004:   A Wendy's fast-food restaurant was destroyed by fire.

*2007:   The Witch Creek Fire started 23 miles east of Poway at 12:35 p.m. on October 21. By October 22 the raging fire spread quickly to Poway, and 7,000 residents evacuated. Fifty firefighters fought the blaze. Eight fire engines from Poway and five engines from San Diego were used to fight the fire. The fire destroyed 90 homes in Poway and burned 7,247 acres. The Blue Sky Ecological Park and Lake Poway Park were affected by the fire. The fire destroyed 1,265 homes, 587 outbuildings, and burned 247,800 acres, and caused $1.339 billion in damages to San Diego County.

*2010:   In February 2010, a couple who lost their home in their San Pasgual home in the 2007 wildfire had a fire in their Poway home. The fire was caused by a faulty refrigerator motor and caused $100,000 damage.

*2014:   On June 20, 2014, Engine 3711 was severely damaged when it was struck at Poway Road and Midland Road by a car. The engine was en route to a call with emergency lights flashing. Evelyn Courtney, a 19-year-old girl who was a passenger in the car, was killed in the accident. The driver was later found to have been under the influence of methamphetamine at the time of the crash. He pleaded guilty to gross vehicular manslaughter.

*2017:   When firefighters responded to a house fire in August, they discovered a couple who had over 100 marijuana plants growing in three bedrooms. The husband and wife's one-year-old child was taken into protective custody and the couple were charged with endangering a child.

*2018:   On January 25, 2018, a man was seriously injured in a recreational vehicle fire. The man was taken by paramedics to the UC San Diego Burn Center.

*2018:   In August 2018, a fire started by electrical wiring in the garage caused an estimated $30,000 damage to a home in the 14900 block of Cinchring Drive in Poway. The firefighters stopped the fire before it entered the living quarters of the home.

*2018:   The department responded to 5,000 emergency calls.

*2020:   In June 2020, a vegetation fire burned 15 acres in Poway. The Poway crews were assisted by firefighters from Santee, Cal Fire, and San Miguel along with two airtankers and one helicopter.

*2020:   In August 2020, the OES rig from Poway was in Napa as part of Strike Team 6840C assigned to the Lightning Complex Fire in northern California and Brush 3763 was part of Strike Team 6430C assigned to the Monterey Fire after working at the Lake Fire. (Firefighters at the Lake Fire were surprised by a bull that came running toward them and chased them down the road.)

*2020:   In September 2020, a two-alarm fire destroyed Wow Auto Care at 12255 Poway Road. It took the crews 50 minutes to put out the fire and they were at the scene for about five hours to mop-up.

*2020: Three different crew changes were on Brush Rig 3763 for seven weeks while fighting fires in northern California. As part of Strike Team 6430C, they were assigned to the Dolan Fire in the Los Padres National Forest about 10 miles south of Big Sur. The Strike Team 6430C was made up of firefighters from Poway Fire Department, San Diego Fire-Rescue Department, and Chula Vista Fire Department.

*2020: On October 4, 2020, there was a large fire in an upstairs apartment building. The fire was attacked quickly with an offensive strategy and contained to the unit of origin. All occupants got out safely and the other three adjacent units were evacuated with minimal damage. Mutual aid was provided by San Diego Fire-Rescue Department.

*2020: The department responds to about 3,500 calls a year.

Rainbow Volunteer Fire Department

The 21-square-mile unincorporated area of Rainbow is just south of the Riverside County line and sixty miles north of San Diego. It has a population of 1,832. Rainbow is renowned for its nurseries.

Rainbow has one of the oldest elementary schools in San Diego County and one of the oldest chapters of the California State Grange.

In 1869 surveyor Peter Larsen filed for the first homestead in Rainbow. He remained in the community for sixty years. By 1883 the Huffstatler, Kolb, Hindorff, and Hind families had also arrived in the valley, and in 1888 James Rainbow and W.F. Gould laid out a town site. James Rainbow, who was a Union Army officer, lived to be 105 years old.

Vallecitos Elementary School was erected in 1884 on ten acres donated by the Rainbow Gould Land Company. The original adobe building was replaced in 1889. When a new school was erected in 1956, Bill Nyholt bought the old schoolhouse for $1 and converted it into a home for his son. There were only fourteen students at Vallecitos Elementary School in 1907 but now there are 190 students.

As a 25-year-old single woman, Ruth Wilson homesteaded one hundred acres in Rainbow Heights in 1927 and cleared twenty acres of the land. She raised goats and shared her goat's milk with neighbors. In 1934 she married Raymond Sanderson. After her husband's death, she continued to live in Rainbow.

When the volunteer fire department was formed in April 1967, its 1941 Seagrave fire engine was housed in a makeshift shelter of plastic siding in Loren Bremseth's yard. Two years later the engine was moved to the school bus barn next to the Rainbow Valley Grange.

Jess Boren became the first fire chief of the Rainbow Volunteer Fire Department in 1967. Loren Bremseth, who was a fire captain at Camp Pendleton for over twenty years, succeeded Chief Boren in 1972. After Bremseth had a heart attack in 1982, he resigned and then assistant chief, Richard Mills, a former Los Angeles Fire Department captain, assumed the position. Dick Bremseth, Loren Bremseth's brother, was assistant chief under Chief Mills.

In 1987 Fred Buck, an electronics engineer for thirty-two years, became the department's top man. He headed the 26-member department that responded to about 235 calls a year. Paramedics from North County Fire District cover the Rainbow area.

In 1976, Charlotte Andre became the first woman to join the department. She was promoted to assistant fire chief in 1991. Chief Andre, who was a senior instructor for the California State Marshal's Office, taught fire control 3, heavy rescue, and live fire training to volunteer and career firefighters throughout the state. In addition to being a fire instructor 3 and Rainbow volunteer assistant fire chief, she managed a fifteen-acre wholesale nursery that she owned.

The department was funded through CSA 7 (Community Service Area 7) taxing district. It had a budget of $12,021 in 1982-83; $43,295 in 1983-1984; $118,000 in 1984-85; and $124,535 in 1985-86. It had an ISO (Insurance Service Office) rating of 6.

On November 14, 1978, a station was dedicated at 6441 Rainbow Heights Road. The structure was donated by Jim Lang on property owned by Jerry Brown. La Mesa Fire Department donated a siren and residents of Rainbow paid for the siren base and flagpole.

This station collapsed during a storm on Halloween night in 1981. Luckily, groundbreaking ceremonies for a new station had been held the month before. A 3,700-square-foot building was constructed for $57,000 on 2.5 acres of land at 2309 Rainbow Valley Boulevard. The station boasted three bay doors, a chief's office, a dispatch room, and a kitchen. Citizens raised $25,000 to complete the interior of the building.

The department had two first-line rigs—both were 1,000-gpm Wards 79s (1990 and 1986) on Ford C8000 chassis. Rainbow also had a 1988 1,000-gpm Wards 79 heavy-rescue rig with pump, a 1992 Ford Victoria command vehicle, a 500-gallon 1962 GMC reserve pumper, and a Chevy suburban light-rescue truck. Earlier equipment included a 1941 Seagrave, an international FT military surplus, and a 1948 Mack with power steering.

On December 31, 1985, the Rainbow Volunteer Fire Department and the Fallbrook Fire Department merged for economic dispatch, maintenance, and inspection reasons. The resulting North County Fire Protection District must have at least one member from the Rainbow Volunteer Fire Department on its seven-member board. Rainbow's Fred Buck was the 1992 chairperson of the board. Tax revenue in Rainbow paid for the Rainbow Volunteer Fire Department's operations.

In 2006-2009, Bruce Fried, an EMT instructor at Palomar College, was chief and assistant chief was Rick Moramarco, a career firefighter with the North County Fire Protection District, who was with the Rainbow department for over thirty years. Moramarco retired on April 12, 2017.

Four volunteers who lived in the district: Chief Bruce Fried; Captain Weaver, an engineer with the San Marcos Fire Department; engineer Jim Beebe, a fire protection inspector with North County Fire; and firefighter Robert Williamson, a machinist in Escondido. Most of the volunteers live outside of Rainbow, coming to the district for training before seeking positions as career firefighters. They spend three eight-hour shifts at the station each month.

Firefighter Cody Lingard was honored by the San Diego Regional Fire Foundation in 2012 for his service to Rainbow.

The department in Rainbow is now Station 3 of the North County Fire Protection District staffed with one captain, one engineer, and thirty volunteers. It has a medic engine, medic squad, and water tender.

CALLS RECALLED:

*1969: Rainbow residents were evacuated during the Walker Basin Fire which occurred on August 22 and 23, 1969. The fire started west of Temecula.

*1978: When the J. Brown warehouse burned in November 1978, Irvin (Jay) Hall died in the fire. He had been sleeping in a trailer near the building.

*1979: Air tankers dropped retardant on a 75-acre fire on Rainbow Peak on June 12, 1979.

*1980: Pack rats built nests in the floor furnace of the Rainbow Community Church. When the furnace was lighted, the volunteers had a fire to extinguish.

*1980: A resident was very happy when firefighters removed a snake from her shower.

*1990: On June 21, 1990, a million-dollar home was lost due to a fire started by combustible oily rags.

*1991: A pregnant dispatcher gave birth one weekend but didn't tell anyone on the department about the event except Chief Fred Buck and Assistant Chief Charlotte Andre. At the following Tuesday night's drill, she showed up looking as if she were still pregnant, thanks to a pillow placed beneath her clothes. During the drill, she feigned labor pains and rushed into the bathroom with the chief and the assistant chief. The firefighter EMTs stood outside anxiously waiting to use their skills while the dispatcher's husband passed the baby to the woman through the bathroom window. She then walked out onto the apparatus floor carrying the newborn who was dressed in a Rainbow firefighter's shirt. Mouths were agape!

*1992: Rainbow's engines 1511 and 1561 were first on the scene on February 26, 1992, when a brush fire burned 313 acres and threatened two homes west of Rice Canyon and north of Highway 76. The fire was started by an agricultural burning that got out of control. Responding to the call were Chief Fred Buck; Captains Rick Moramarco, Bruce Fried, and Rusty Smith; engineer Chris Dunn; and firefighters Mike Matcham, Ed Jones, David Garza, Nick Lutes, Bob Miller, and Bill Van Paepeghem.

*2007: On October 22, 2007, the Rice Canyon Fire moved south from Rainbow, crossing Interstate 15. The fire started when a dead tree limb hit a power line. The fire spread rapidly, burning 9,472 acres.

*2016: On June 4, 2016, a fire moved through the Pala Indian Reservation then through Rainbow towards Temecula.

*2017: Five-year-old Philip Campbell and his 73-year-old father, Roland Phillips, drown in Rainbow Creek. Numerous agencies worked to recover the bodies.

*2018: On September 19, 2018, a two-acre fire that started on Rainbow Heights Road burned two acres.

*2018: A majority of the calls are for medical emergencies and freeway accidents.

RAMONA FIRE DEPARTMENT

Ramona covers 154 square miles and has about 40,000 residents. The Ramona Fire Department is a cooperative agreement between the California Department of Forestry and the Ramona Water District covering over 75 square miles of the Ramona service boundary.

When Helen Hunt Jackson's book "Ramona" became popular in 1884, promoter Milton Santee changed the name of the town Nuevo to Ramona. The Verlaque House, Ramona's first permanent residence built in 1886, was placed on the National Register of Historic Places on August 7, 1991.

In 1928 the first fire station was built on Seventh Street, then in 1952 a new fire station was built by Forrest Holly Construction Company at 222 Ninth Street for $7,500, with room for three engines, an office, and a squad room. Volunteers finished the inside work, making improvements to the station at a cost of less than $600. It was sold to a glass company in 1993 and named the Firehouse Glass Company.

The Ramona Chamber of Commerce formed a Fire Department Affairs Committee in 1931 and appointed the following commissioners to take charge: William Hanigan, who served for 50 years, Charley Wereloh, T. S. Hewlett, George Kayser, and L. P. Coddington. Letters were sent to local residents, soliciting subscriptions for fire protection, and annual donations from a few dollars to as much as $1,200 were received.

The Ramona Local Fire Protection District was formed in 1946, covering 22 square miles. In 1978, the San Diego Country Estates became a part of the Ramona Fire Protection District and a new fire station was added. Proposition 13 brought about financial trouble for the Ramona Fire Protection District. In 1981, the Ramona Municipal Water District offered assistance and the Ramona Fire Department was formed.

The early chiefs of the Ramona Fire Department are: John Barger (1927), William Cannon (1928-1931), C. C. "Cap" Williams (1931-1942), Claude Oakes (1942-1944), Jack Jones (1944-1950), Erwin C. "Barney" Bernhard (1950-1953), Earl Nielsen (1954-1956), Edwin "Ed" Eller (1957-1972), and Rick Robertson (1972-1978). They were followed by Bill Wright, Dan Williams; Von Rupple; John Allen; Karl Diekman (1988-1990); Jack Story; Michael "Mike" Vogt; Saul Villagomez (2012-2016); Steve Foster (2016-2017); Adam Lambert (2017-2018); Larry Converse (2018-2019); and Jeremy Snyder (2020-).

E. C. Bernhard was the first paid chief, earning $450 a month. Under his leadership, the department purchased a 750-gpm Mack pumper.

Earl Nielsen was a member of the Ramona Volunteer Fire Department from 1949 to 1978 and served as chief and commissioner. He owned and operated the Ramona Body Shop for 30 years. Chief Nielsen died on September 15, 1998, at the age of 75.

Ed Eller was elected chief in 1957 and retired in 1972. He became a volunteer fireman in Ramona in 1944. He was born in Iowa and moved to San Diego County in 1922. He owned a poultry ranch in Del Mar in the early 1940s and an appliance store in Ramona in the 1940s and 1950s. Chief Eller died on July 1, 1984, at the age of 74.

In 1962, the department had a National Board Class 6 rating by the Pacific Fire Rating Bureau of Los Angeles.

Darrell Beck, who wrote "On Memory's Back Trail," served the Ramona Volunteer Fire Department from 1959 to 1971. He was a firefighter, engineer, lieutenant, and captain before serving as assistant chief for five years. He initiated the San Diego County Backcountry Fire Engine Association whose 50 members restore antique fire rigs. In 1991, he received a 1935 pumper that originally was purchased in 1937 for the Ramona Volunteer Fire Department at a cost of $2,300 and was called Engine No. 2. In 1973, the Poway Firemen's Association restored the engine and used it in parades. The association acquired a 1945 Chevrolet high-pressure brush rig that was the first truck that Ramona bought new. It was at the Antique Gas and Steam Engine Museum in Vista before being donated to the group.

John Peabody, who lived in Ramona for 51 years, was a member of the department for 23 years. He was a veteran of World War II, serving in the U.S. Marine Corps. He worked for San Diego County for 40 years as a heavy equipment operator. Peabody died on July 15, 1996, at the age of 72.

Gordon "Gordy" Kundel was a captain in the volunteer department. He was born in Nebraska and lived in Ramona for 56 years. He graduated from Ramona High School in 1939 and began flying lessons the day of his graduation. He was the operator of the Ramona Air Field from 1945 to 1955. Captain Kundel died at the age of 58 on October 22, 1978.

Rick Robertson was hired as the fire chief in 1972, and Don Mitchell became the first full-time firefighter in 1974. Robertson was recruited to join the Ramona

Volunteer Fire Department by Chief Jack Jones in 1947. At the time, he was working at Stevens Grocery Store to support his wife and two young sons. The volunteers received $1 a month, provided they showed up for half of the meetings and emergencies. He continued as a Ramona volunteer fireman even when he was hired in 1957 as a firefighter for General Dynamics Missile Testing Center in Sycamore Canyon. He left that job when he had his first heart attack in 1965. In June 1978, at the age of 54, he had a five-bypass heart surgery. "When I was a child, I had only three ambitions: to be a fireman, to move to California, and to own my own home," he said.

Chief Rick Robertson said, "It's a stressful job. The emergency service—I like it because it's helping someone who needs it. It's not the money; there are lots of places you could go to make more per hour. I'm from the old school that says you always help others because some time you may need help yourself." He died in 1997.

About 1924 John Berger, who owned what is now Ransom Brothers, donated a two-wheeled soda-acid tank extinguisher to the town that he kept at the lumber yard, and in 1927 he donated a truck that was equipped with a 50-gallon water tank. Also, in 1927, Charles Weseloh donated a 1923 Dodge truck which had 600 feet of 2 1/2-inch hose.

Courtesy of Ramona Pioneer Historical Society.

The department purchased a 1941 Ford tanker and a 1946 Chevrolet high-pressure engine. On October 8, 1952, the fire department acquired a Mack 750 triple-combination pumper. The tank extinguisher and the 1951 Mack pumper are at the Guy B. Woodward Museum.

In the 1920s, a railroad engine tire was beaten with a sledge hammer to sound the alarm for calls. In July 1962, the commissioners of the department approved paying $10 a month to wives of the fire personnel who assisted in maintaining the alarm system. Four women each served 72 hours a month, including Kitty Robertson, wife of the chief. They answered emergency calls at home, pushing a button to set off the siren at the station. The first firefighters to reach the station would call the woman on duty to find out the nature of the call.

A letter to the editor of the Ramona Sentinel written by Chuck Fields described the Ramona volunteers:

"On December 4, 1973, I witnessed our Ramona Volunteer Fire Department moving to answer a fire call. Very impressive!!

"Being a retired professional firefighter, the opportunity to observe response time, which is the elapsed time between alarm and the "rolling" of sufficient manned equipment and supervision, was quite exciting.

"It is indeed a tribute to the individuals and a rarity to this city dweller to watch public-spirited people responding so readily. I am sure Norman Rockwell would have been pleased to put this scene on canvas had he been a witness to today's series of events; as follows:

"The siren at the fire station starts to sound. From this point on a flurry of concerted activity unfolds: from a car repair garage, a man erupts on the dead run; while from the grocery store across the street, an aproned man appears, also on the run. Activity can be seen within the fire station. Outside, an ambulance slips into a space under a tree. From this surge of activity, the first fire truck is 'manned and rolling'. The siren starts to wind down. Men are still appearing on foot and in cars

from all directions and from relatively distant locations and businesses in town, all are moving 'on the double' followed by the fire chief's vehicle. Immediately the third fire truck takes its place at the station entrance in readiness on standby.

"Elapsed time for 'rolling' the first truck, forty-five seconds; the second truck and fire chief's vehicle rolling time, two minutes, forty-five seconds. Exceptionally fine time for any volunteer fire department. I say 'Well done.'

"The community of Ramona is indeed fortunate to have such obvious dedication to the public safety as displayed this day."

In 1981 the Ramona Fire Department became part of the Ramona Municipal Water District. The district contracted with CDF (California Department of Forestry, now abbreviated Cal Fire) for fire protection and paramedic services.

The Ramona Municipal Water District signed a contract with CDF in July 1993 to provide firefighters to staff Ramona Fire Department's fire apparatus. The Ramona Municipal Water District approved a $5.95 million contract with Cal Fire for 2015-16. The department has an ISO rating of 4/9.

Karl Diekman was Ramona's fire chief from 1988 to 1990. He retired in 2006 after 38 years of fire service, the last six as the chief of the Woodland Fire Department.

Captain Earl Holsapple, born in 1952, passed away on April 25, 1997, while teaching an equipment operating course at the CDF Academy. He suffered from a severe asthma attack that led to cardiac arrest. He was often seen coaching on the basketball courts of the schools. He was much loved by the people of Ramona.

Captain Robert McLaughlin was a firefighter in Ramona for 30 years. After attending Escondido High School, he became a volunteer firefighter at the age of 18. By the time he was 26 he was a captain with the Ramona Fire Department. He passed away from non-hodgkin's lymphoma on May 14, 2020, at the age of 55. Donations in his honor were made to the California Firefighters Benevolent Fund and the Burn Institute.

Also appreciated by the community is longtime Ramona resident Battalion Chief Jack Story who inspired loyalty in his firefighters. Chief Story was in charge of the fire that an arsonist set on January 28, 1995, in the Ramona Town Hall. The building was donated to Ramona by Augustus and Martha Barnett in 1894 and was in the process of being restored. Chief Story is very proud that his son Lon is now a captain with Cal Fire. Lon Story worked as an engineer at the Ramona Fire Department.

In March 2001, Michael "Mike" Vogt was appointed the department's fire battalion chief after serving as captain at the Ramona Fire Department. He had worked for Cal Fire for 18 years. Vogt has experience in dispatching procedures, truck company operations, and district and Cal Fire policies and procedures.

When Chief Saul Villagomez retired in 2013, Steve Foster took his place until 2017. Chief Foster spent 35 years in the fire service. He joined the Ramona Fire Department at the beginning of 2014, serving as battalion chief and fire marshal, and was promoted to chief January 1, 2016. When Chief Foster retired on April 7, 2017, he was replaced by Adam Lambert who left the fire service in 2018 to start a business.

On June 29, 2018, Larry Converse became the battalion chief. Chief Converse started his firefighting career as a volunteer in Alpine and Encinitas. During his 33 years in the fire service he worked in Pine Vally and Campo and for the San Miguel Fire Protection District and Cal Fire. He retired on December 28, 2019 at the age of 52.

Jeremy Snyder, 42, accepted the position of the Ramona battalion chief on March 16, 2020. He oversees a staff of 34 personnel. Chief Snyder attended Utah Valley University before becoming a dispatcher with the Riverside County Fire Department in 1998. He began working for Cal Fire in 2001. In 2015 he was promoted to Cal Fire battalion chief in Riverside. Chief Snyder implements the guidelines of the Center for Disease Control and Prevention and the San Diego County in regard fo COVID-19. He makes sure extra precautions are taken when transporting patients in the ambulances. The paramedics wear full protective gowns, masks, and eye protection.

In May 2014, the sovereign nations of Barona and Sycuan donated 75% of the $93,452 the Ramona Fire Department needed to buy three new cardiac monitor/defibrillator units for two ambulances and a medic engine. The remaining 25% came from mitigation fees.

The San Diego Regional Fire Foundation presented a $7,255 grant to the Ramona Fire Department in July 2019 for physical training workout equipment.

The department has three stations:

Station 80, located at 829 San Vicente Road, responds to about 1,800 calls a year. STK Architecture designed the two-story building, construction began in August 1995 and completion was in 1996 at a cost of $760,000. It houses a 2018 Spartan ERV Type I side control pumper that contains updated equipment for vehicle extrications and rope rescues. It has a Metro Star MFD 10" RR, Hale Qmax-XS 1,500 gpm, 500 gallon tank, and a 25 gallon tank. The engine, which cost $640,000, replaced a 2005 engine at Station 80 that was transferred to Station 82 as a reserve engine.

The station also houses a Frasier F450 ambulance. In 2017, the Ramona Water Board purchased two Frasier F450 ambulances from a factory in Texas costing $200,000 each. The liquid suspension system of the chassis allows personnel to alter the back when approaching or leaving steep driveways or roads so the tailboard will not drag. To help pay for the ambulances the Ramona Water District board voted to increase ambulance and paramedic user fees. An older ambulance is used as a reserve vehicle.

Station 81 is located at 2442 San Vicente Road in San Diego Country Estates. In 2015, an extension to the apparatus room was designed by architect Jim Nicoloff. The project included replacing the roof over the bay as there was a hole in it and adding new electrical work, lighting, and painting. The cost was about $255,000. Chief Steve Foster said closing the doors is important for security. Fire engines now are longer than they were in 1977 when the station was built. It houses a 2017 Frasier F450 ambulance and other apparatus.

Station 82 ls located at 3410 Dye Road. The 2,500-square-foot station built by Davis & Adams Construction, was opened in October 2009. The total cost of the project was $1.062 million. The district's capital improvement and replacement budget covered most of the costs for the building. The majority of the money came from San Diego County's fire mitigation fees collected from building permit applicants. Some of the additional funding for the building came out of property tax revenues. It houses a 2005 reserve engine and other apparatus.

The Ramona Fire Department is proud to serve the community.

CALLS RECALLED:

*1943: The Kenilworth Inn at the corner of Eighth and Main Streets and the Ramona Elementary School on D Street were destroyed by fire.

*1961: The volunteer firemen responded to 32 calls in 1961. Of these 32 were fire calls and four were resuscitator calls. Of the 36 alarms, 31 were in the Ramona Local Fire District and five were mutual aid calls to the California State Division of Forestry.

*1977: The department made 495 ambulance calls in 1977, including 123 vehicle accidents and transported 124 persons.

*1981: In May 1981, Robert B. Lewallen, 31, suffered second-degree burns on 60% of his body when his home on Green Valley Truck Trail was destroyed by fire. He suffered the injuries while rescuing his children from the fire and was flown by Life Flight to a hospital. Lewallen's wife, Deborah, escaped the fire. The Fernbrook Volunteer Fire Department and the Ramona Fire Department responded to the scene. When I asked him if everyone was out of the house, he said, "Yes. As long as my family is safe, that's all that matters." Sadly, he lost a home again at the same location in the 2007 fires. In 2004, he designed and constructed my home that was lost in the Cedar Fire.

*1984: An arsonist started the Bowles Fire on September 6, 1984, on the east side of Highway 67 at the Bowles Ranch, halfway between Lakeside and Ramona. The fire burned 1,500 acres in two hours. Chief Jack Story was the incident commander on the fire. CDF, U.S. Forest Service, fire departments from throughout the county, and inmates from correctional facilities fought the fire. Fernbrook was saved because a prescribed burn was planned and containment lines had already been made. A camp at Dos Picos Park was set up as command headquarters and as a place for crews to eat and sleep. S-4 air tankers dropped retardants and a U.S. Forest Service helicopter filled its bucket from San Vicente Reservoir. The fire burned 4,000 acres.

*1987: In October 1987, heavy rain soaked through the roof that was being rebuilt at the Ramona Library, causing $100,000 damage. "There was extensive damage to the building, but it could have been a lot worse," said Captain Tom MacPherson.

*1992: In October 1992, 16-year-old Karma Lee McCalister was driving home from a cross country meet with her sister and two friends when she lost control of the car on San Vicente Road near Warnock Drive. Karma McCalister died at the scene. Abba McCalister, her sister, died at a hospital. Passenger Nicole Moore was treated at the hospital and released. Luna DeYoung, also a passenger, underwent surgery for a broken leg and a broken pelvis.

*1997: There were 3,013 calls made by the department in 1997, about 75% which were for medical aid.

*2000: In May 2000, a 19-year-old woman, who was not wearing a seatbelt, died after her 1958 Volkswagon Beetle hit a tree.

*2000: In October 2000, three teenagers were injured in a rollover crash on Gunn Stage Road after the 17-year-old driver reached for the radio dial. They were flown by air ambulance to Sharp Memorial Hospital.

*2000: In October 2000, five people were involved in a crash on Highway 67 north of Mussey Grade Road. A 19-year-old woman driving a 1994 Toyota Tercel crossed over the double yellow line and hit a 1976 Chevrolet pickup.

*2000: In December 2001, a fire caused $25,000 damage in a home on Ransom Hill Lane, completely destroying the garage. Captain Brennan Blue said the fire was caused by an overheated appliance in the garage.

*2003: On October 25, 2003, the massive Cedar Fire was started in the Cleveland National Forest by a lost hunter. The fire quickly spread throughout the county. At 11:54 p.m. a command center was established consisting of chiefs from the affected areas. The fire spread to 273,246 acres and destroyed 2,820 structures. Fourteen civilians and one firefighter were killed in the fire and 113 firefighters injured. To fight the fire there were 242 engines, 32 helicopters, 42 dozers, 30 water tenders, and 2,120 personnel.

*2007: The large Witch Creek Fire started on October 21, 2007. It began on Witch Creek Road east of Ramona and merged with the Guejito Fire that started in the San Pasqual Valley. Countywide it burned 197,990 acres and cost $1.339 million. About 515,000 people were evacuated. There were 2 civilian fatalities, 36 firefighter injuries, and 1,104 homes and 414 outbuildings destroyed. Power lines of the San Diego Gas and Electric Company were blamed for the fire, bringing 2,500 lawsuits against the company.

*2018: On July 6, 2018, the temperature the National Weather Service reported at the Ramona Airport just before 1 p.m. was 115 degrees. Easterly winds were 18 mph with gusts up to 28 mph. The high temperatures throughout the county contributed to brush fires at Camp Pendleton, Dulzura, and Alpine.

*2018: On July 27 the Pasqual Fire burned 265 acres. It started near the San Diego Zoo Safari Park and moved east towards Ramona.

*2018: A large fire called the Rangeland Fire occurred on August 9 off of Rangeland Road and Highway 78, burning 250 acres of brush.

*2018: A fire that began near Hope and Main Streets burned 35 acres and threatened homes. Cal Fire, Barona Fire Department, Viejas Fire Department, and Lakeside Fire Protection District responded to the call.

*2018:   In November 2018, a home on Salida del Sol in the community of Mt. Woodson burned to the ground.

*2018:   On December 24, 2018, at 11:00 a.m. Gonzalo Rodriguez and five-year-old Christian Diaz were killed on State Route 78 near West Haverford Road when Mr. Rodriguez's Camry crossed over a double yellow line and hit a Ram pickup.

*2019:   A 73-year-old man was killed on February 26, 2019, at 9:30 a.m. when he was hit by a driver in a Ford-F150 pickup at the intersection at Seventh Street and Route 78 in Ramona.

*2019:   In March 2019, a 56-year-old man from Poway who was driving under the influence of alcohol caused a crash involving three cars on Dye Road that left him and a 74-year-old man from Ramona seriously injured. One man was airlifted to Palomar Hospital and the other to Scripps Mercy Hospital. The 53-year-old woman in the third car had only minor injuries.

*2019:   On October 25, 2019, the Sawday Fire started by an unoccupied parked travel trailer that caught fire off the Sawday Truck Trail east of Ramona. It burned 97 acres. Within 90 minutes it burned 70 acres. About 150 firefighters with 10 engines each carrying 500 gallons of water, a helicopter, and an aircraft fought the fire.

*2020:   On June 10, 2020, firefighters responded to a traffic accident on Mussey Grade Road. A 56-year-old woman from Fallbrook in a Ford Focus collided with a Subaru Impreza. She and the passenger in the Subaru died at the scene. The driver of the Subaru was transported by helicopter to Palomar Medical Center.

RAMONA AIR ATTACK BASE

The Ramona Airport at 2926 Montecito Road is one of eight county airports. It is the oldest Cal Fire air attack base in California.

In 1931 and 1932, C.T. "Red" Jensen made the first air drops on wildland fires by mounting a 30-gallon hopper on each side of the cockpit of a Hispano-Suiza biplane and dropping water near Oroville, California.

In 1943, the U.S. Navy built the Ramona airport as an emergency landing field. In 1954, the Operation Firestop program tested aerial equipment. In 1955, a Stearman biplane with a 125-gallon tank was used. By 1956, California had seven air tankers in operation and in 1957 it had twenty-six.

In 1957, Ramona was picked for the southernmost air attack base of the thirteen bases in California because of its strategic location. In 1960, the U.S. Forest Service set up an operation in Ramona. In 1966, the base became jointly owned by Cal Fire and the U.S. Forest Service. The base is operational from May to December, the longest season in California. The air traffic control tower was completed in 2003. A 4,000-foot runway was built by the U.S. Navy in 1945. In 2002 it was extended to 5,001 feet. The airport encompasses 408 acres.

The Cal Fire planes operate between 10:00 a.m. and one half hour before sunset, and the U.S. Forestry planes operate between 10:00 a.m. and 7:00 p.m. The maximum time pilots can fly is seven hours.

The "fire boss" on the ground is assisted by an air coordinator called "Airco." Chief Darrell Campbell and Captain Brian Logan planned air attack strategy at the Ramona base for Cal Fire in the 1990s. In 2014, Battalion Chief John Francois replaced long-time commander Ray Chaney as head of the Ramona Air Attack Base. From January 2016 to July 2019, Burke A. Kremensky was the air operations chief in charge of the Ramona Air Attack Base. He was promoted to Cal Fire division chief in June 2019. He has worked for Cal Fire for 33 years, beginning as a seasonal firefighter directly out of high school in Ramona. From June 2012 to December 2015, he was a Cal Fire battalion chief. He followed in the footsteps of his three brothers who also joined the fire service. His brother Mark D. Kremensky retired from Borrego Springs Fire Department. John Kremensky is a battalion chief and training officer for Cal Fire. Ken Kremensky is chief of the Barona Fire Protection District.

Chief Nick Brown was appointed Cal Fire Unit Aviation Officer of the Ramona Air Base in October 2019. He coordinates the tactical operations of airtankers and helicopters during wildfires and ensures that there is a safe environment for the pilots to fly in. Chief Brown completed the Air Tactical Group Supervisor Training (ATGS). He was head of the Deer Springs Fire Protection District from June 2015 to October 2019.

The pilots listen to air to ground dispatches, air to air, and other dispatches. Radio operators transmit information from the tower on the air base.

In the 1990s, the U.S. Forest Service contracted with ARCO in Tucson, Arizona, for the DC-4, a converted military aircraft that was used during the Berlin Airlift. The plane was piloted by Steve Holland and Chris Kniebes. It has a capacity of 4,000 gallons of fuel but normally carries about 1,000 gallons. The plane holds 2,450 gallons of chemical retardant which can be loaded into the plane in two minutes. It can be in the air in 15 minutes, then taking about 30 to 40 minutes to disperse the retardant. The DC-4 has eight doors that can open one at a time or in any combination. Sometimes lead planes (B54 Behrens) with a single pilot are sent out before the DC-4 to look for such things as power lines, water sources, and FAA air towers.

Other airtankers that dump chemical retardants are the T-70 and AA-300 which have been piloted by Billy Hoskins and Bill Miles respectively. A trail system is used for grass and sparse vegetation. A drop of 2,000 gallons covers an area of 80 by 300 feet.

The airtankers carry a red liquid called Phos-Chek which is 75 percent sulfate and 25 percent phosphate with fugitive dyes and gum thickeners added to it. The Phos-Chek (diammonium phosphate) is made by Monsanto in Ontario, California. Borate is no longer used because it sterilized the ground.

The Grumman S-2T air tankers, once used as Navy submarine trackers, come from a private company in Santa Barbara. They have two Garrett TPE331-14GR turbine engines with 1,650 hp each, cruise speed of 270 mph, rate of climb of 900 fpm, drop speed of 130 mph, gross weight of 29,150 lb., and retardant capacity of 1,200 gal. On an S-2T air tanker, the chemical is loaded hot (while the engine is running) at the loading port on the tail.

The Bell 206B helicopters have Allison 250-C 20 turbine engines with 400 horsepower, cruising speed of 135 mph, maximum rate of climb of 1,450 fpm, and retardant capacity of 75 gallons in a suspended bucket. It takes two minutes to fill the bucket that is attached to the helicopter.

Two crew members sit in the back of the helicopter and a foreman sits next to the pilot. It is not unusual for a crew to respond to two or three fires in a day. Diane Mortier, a crew member, said that the personnel are "trained in a lot of different capacities" and "have to pay attention to everything that is happening."

Now the U.S. Forest Service uses Type II Bell 205 helicopters that hold six crew members.

The helitack units are used for initial attack upon wildland fires. They are used to transport personnel, carry firefighting equipment, evacuate injured firefighters, and drop water.

Bo Donovan, who managed the Ramona Airport for six years, loved his job there and the community loved him. He died April 24, 2012, at the age of 67. The current airport manager is Meadow Chase.

Meadow Chase is the Contract Airport Manager of Ramona Airport and Fallbrook Community Airpark. She is also the owner of her own company, Chase Airport Management, Inc., which currently has the contract for these two airports through the County of San Diego. What she loves most about her job is its many diverse

responsibilities, which include doing airport inspections, customer service, emergency response, event planning, and public outreach. In addition to being a private pilot with a tailwheel endorsement and multi-engine rating, she has a Bachelor of Science in Aviation Management and Master of Business Administration from the Southern Illinois University, Carbondale.

Currently there are two S-2T fixed wing air tankers and one OV-10A tactical aircraft (also called Air Attack 330) at Ramona. The OV-10A is a turboprop light attack and observation aircraft. Cal Fire helicopters are flown by Cal Fire pilots and the airtankers are flown by contract pilots. The airtankers fly 200 to 400 hours each year. Cal Fire spends over $55 million a year on aviation activities.

The Ramona Air Attack Base responds to about 450 calls a year, pumping out about 850,000 gallons of retardant. An airtanker can drop 1,200 gallons of retardant on each drop. The base covers 1.4 million acres for Cal Fire, 380,000 acres for the U.S. Forest Service, and all of San Diego County.

LIVES RECALLED:

*Pete Fahm:

Pete Fahm wanted to be a pilot as long as he could remember. After growing up in Chile, he put himself through flying school in Tulsa, Oklahoma. He flew heavy aircraft in South America, Japan, Europe, Canada, and the United States. Fahm worked out of the Hemet Air Base and the Ramona Air Base on and off, beginning in 1970.

Over a period of five years, Pete Fahm and a crew of five men built a seaplane in Palm Springs. The men would fly aerial tankers during the fire season and work on the plane in the winter months. When the amphibious plane was finished, it flew perfectly from its first day in the air.

Fahm's life has been full of dangerous and challenging adventures. He was the first pilot in an amphibious plane to ever scoop water at Tierra del Fuego in the Strait of Magellan. He has flown through narrow passes in the Andes. He saw from his plane Mount St. Helens erupting. He fought fire at Yellowstone National Park in 1988.

This pilot has flown C-119s, DC-6s, DC-7s, and DC-42. He said, "First we fly over the fire and take into consideration the wind, the speed of the fire, its position, and how it is reacting; then we fly towards the target." Pilots like Pete Fahm provide essential help to firefighters in time of need.

*Billy Hoskins:

After 42 years at Ramona Air Attack Base, Billy Hoskins retired in 2018. He flew mostly T-70 aircraft during his years as a pilot, working the last two years of his career as a relief pilot for Ramona Air Attack Base and Hemet Ryan Air Attack Base.

On October 26, 2003, tanker pilots Billy Hoskins, Lynn McGrew, and David Gregg met with firefighter Ron Serabia who told them of the serious dangers of flying that day to fight the Cedar, Paradise, and Otay Fires. All three of the pilots knew what they were up against but were willing to help.

In October 2007, Hoskins saw smoke as he was returning from the Harris Fire to the Ramona Air Attack Base. He landed and reloaded with retardant, heading out to the Witch Creek Fire, dropping 1,000 gallons of retardant on the right shoulder of the fire and 1,000 gallons of retardant on the left side of it.

*Lynn McGrew:

McGrew is one of the first women to fly commercial aircraft and Cal Fire's first female tanker pilot. She began flying planes in 1972 at the age of 26, in Madison, Wisconsin. By the end of the year, she was teaching aerobatics at Arizona Frontier Aviation in Tucson, Arizona, In 1978, she was honored as Arizona Instructor of the Year. For 20 years she worked with commuter airlines before becoming an airtanker pilot.

During the 2007 wildfires in San Diego County, she flew the Grumman S-T Tracker. The tanker carries about 1,200 gallons of retardant and it weighs 29,000 pounds. When the fire season ended, Lynn McGrew did cloud seeding in a Piper Aztec for Atmospheric, Inc., planted trees on her Christmas tree farm, and visited with her two children.

*Ron Serabia:

Captain Serabia's father was a firefighter with the Ramona Volunteer Fire Department in the 1950s. By the age of eight, Ron knew he wanted to be a firefighter. In 1969, he began working as a seasonal firefighter for Cal Fire at the Julian Fire Station. In 1977, Serabia was promoted to fire captain and worked at the Warner Springs Fire Station. In the 1990s, Ron became air tactical group supervisor at the Ramona Air Attack Base.

While Serabia and his wife, Kathy, were driving the backroads of Barona Mesa on October 25, 2003, he saw smoke near Cedar Creek. He immediately reported it to the Monte Vista Interagency Command Center in El Cajon at 5:39 p.m. Three minutes had passed since the cut-off time for the pilots at the Ramona Air Attack Base to quit for the day. It was a very strict rule that the pilots could not fly past 5:36 p.m. They cannot fly more than seven hours a day because of safety regulations. Captain Serabia requested ten air tankers and five helicopters be available on the morning of October 26 to fight the fire. Unfortunately the aircraft at the base had been sent to San Bernardino to fight fires there. All that was available at Ramona were two Grumman S-2Ts, one helicopter, and one OV-10. Serabia, as the initial air attack commander, went into action, gathering all the information he could for the pilots. The aircraft left the base at 6:00 a.m.

In three days, tankers made 560 flights out of Ramona with ten Cal Fire tankers and two U.S. Forest Service DC-4 air tankers, including 215 aircraft on October 26. It wasn't until November 5 that the Cedar Fire was 100% contained.

In 2004, Captain Serabia became the first responder coordinator for the High Performance Wireless Research and Educational Network (HPWREN) Project. Serabia first saw how the system provided real-time imagery and real-time data during the Coyote Fire in 2003. Instead of dial-up which could take more than four hours to transmit, the HPWREN system provided high-speed wireless Internet connection. The project was developed by Hans-Werner Braum, a researcher at the San Diego Supercomputer Center, University of California, San Diego. In 2018, Captain Serabia moved from Ramona to Colorado.

RANCHO SANTA FE FIRE PROTECTION DISTRICT

The Kumeyaay Indians were the first inhabitants of Rancho Santa Fe. By 1845, Juan Maria Osuna owned the title to the land. In 1906, the Santa Fe Railway purchased the land from several land owners, including the Osunas. Ed Fletcher convinced the owners of the Santa Fe Railway to grow avocados and citrus. Walter E. Hodges, on behalf of the Santa Fe Land Development Company, promoted a dam to provide water for the orchards and the communities of Del Mar and Solana Beach.

Architects Requa Jackson and Lillian J. Rice, along with landscape architect Glenn Moore, designed an area of secluded homes among the hills of Rancho Santa Fe. According to the 2002 U.S. Census Bureau, Rancho Santa Fe is the wealthiest community in the United States.

The Rancho Santa Fe Fire Protection District covers 52 square miles and has a population of 34,000. The district serves Rancho Santa Fe, Fairbanks Ranch, The Crosby, 4S Ranch, Santa Fe Valley, Bernardo Lake Estates, Bernardo Point, Summit of Rancho Bernardo, Del Dios, Harmony Grove, Elfin Forest, and other communities. The fire department responds to about 3,000 calls a year.

Courtesy of Rancho Santa Fe Fire Protection District

In 1922, there was a California Department of Forestry (CDF) station opened seasonally. In the late 1930s, CDF opened a station at the Del Mar fairgrounds. When a devastating fire swept through Rancho Santa Fe in 1943, the residents asked CDF for help. CDF appointed Leon Janinet "Chief Fire Watcher."

The San Diego County Board of Supervisors supported the formation of a local fire department and on October 14, 1946, the board appointed local fire commissioners to the Rancho Santa Fe Fire Protection District. Leon Janinet, Paul Avery, and Barton Millard were leaders of the volunteer fire department. The fire district was comprised of one chief and 15 volunteers who protected 3,800 residents. The volunteers worked out of a shed owned by the irrigation district. In 1948, William Z. Stomski, a retired Navy chief petty officer, became the first chief. He was succeeded by Billy Jarboe and Edward Dutton who had been trained for firefighting in the State Forestry Service.

Ruby B. Duran, who was also trained by the Forestry Service, became chief in 1953. He lived at the station. One acre of land on El Fuego was sold to the fire district by the Santa Fe Irrigation District in 1953 along with a duplex for $3,500. A 300-gallon pumper was purchased with donations and district funds. A new 1948 Mack 750-gpm pumper was later purchased and used until the early 1970s. Commissioners Leon Janinet and Richard Pharr signed for a loan for $19,000, which was used to construct a station and to improve the chief's quarters.

In 1956, James A. Fox was hired as chief. He and his family lived at the station. The staff in the district designed and constructed several ambulances, brush trucks, and rescue trucks while James Fox was chief.

The first paid firefighters were hired in 1957. The district designed and constructed one of the nation's first Mobile Intensive Care Units, later called "Daisy" after the wife of Commissioner Leon Janinet.

In the 1960s, the Rancho Santa Fe Fire District had a contract with the Solana Beach Fire Protection District to share the fire chief's position. Village Park and Olivenhain were annexed to the district in the late 1960s and early 1970s.

In 1970 the first 9-1-1 emergency telephone system in Southern California was installed. Village Park and Olivenhain were annexed to the district in the late 1960s and early 1970s.

The Insurance Services Office (ISO) reduced the district's rating from 6 to 4 in 1980, saving residents as much as 30% on their insurance policies.

The first Computer Aided Dispatch (CAD) in the county was designed and installed by the district's fire personnel in 1981. This state-of-the-art dispatch system led San Marcos, Deer Springs, and Solana Beach Fire Protection Districts to join Rancho Santa Fe Fire Protection District to form the North County Dispatch/Joint Powers Agency (NCDJPA) in 1984.

When Encinitas incorporated in 1987, fire protection for Village Park and Olivenhain were transferred from the district to Encinitas. The district sold the Village Park Fire Station for $414,000 to Encinitas and transferred nine personnel to the city.

In 1987, the County Service Area was ended and the Del Dios Volunteer Fire Department became part of the Rancho Santa Fe Fire District.

In 1991, the department became the first in the area to train all firefighters to the EMT-D level, giving them advanced training in the use of cardiac defibrillation equipment.

Firefighter applicants are required to have a current State of California paramedic license and a California State Fire Marshal Firefighter I Certificate and/or have graduated from a State of California 240-hour Firefighter I Academy. Firefighters are hired on a year-long probationary basis, working as part of a shift crew while completing training and testing in all areas of the fire service and the procedures of the district. Once that year is completed they obtain regular firefighter/paramedic status.

In July 2016, the Elfin Forest/Harmony Grove Fire Department merged with the Rancho Santa Fe Protection District.

A 501(c)(3) nonprofit organization, the Rancho Santa Fe Fire District Foundation (RSFFPD), was formed in 2018 to raise funds to support the work of the firefighters, paramedics, and fire prevention personnel. An inaugural fundraiser was held May 18, 2019. The foundation has purchased a Phantom 4 Pro+ Drone Quadcopter, to allow better assessment of fire situations and get fire personnel in and out of fire situations with greater safety, and a detox sauna, which is used to help firefighters get rid of carcinogens which are absorbed through the skin while fighting fires. The foundation also gave the fire district a $15,000 grant in 2019 to purchase new tactical wildland boots for every firefighter within the district. The Rancho Santa Fe Fire District Foundation has provided over $170,000 in funding for the fire district.

In the fall of 1999, the district entered into an agreement with San Diego County to provide advanced life support. Fire personnel attended paramedic training at Palomar College and an assessment paramedic program was implemented. As new employees were hired, firefighter/paramedics were placed on all district engine companies.

Courtesy of Rancho Santa Fe Fire Protection District

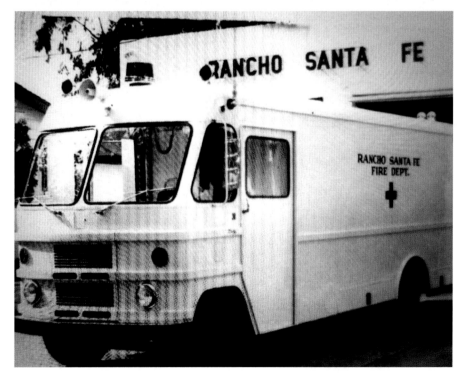

Courtesy of Rancho Santa Fe Fire Protection District

The fire district is governed by a five-person publicly elected board of directors. The current board members are James Ashcraft, John C. Tanner, Nancy C. Hillgren, Randall Malin, and Tucker Stine. The policies that the board sets are the guidelines for the administration of the department. The chief works directly with them to oversee the operations of the fire district, manage the district's finance, and create and implement strategic plans.

Chiefs of the department include: William Z. Stomski (1948), Billy Jarboe, Edward Dutton, Rudy B. Duran (1953-1956), James Arthur Fox (1956-1981), Arthur Peter Fox (1981-1987), Arden L. "Pete" Pedersen (1987-1993), Erwin Willis, (1993-2005), Nicholas Pavone (2005-2010), Tony Michel (2010-2018), and Fred Cox (2018-).

James A. Fox, who came to California from England with his wife Pat and sons John and Peter, was hired by the board in 1956. Under the leadership of Chief James Fox, the training of the volunteers was improved, the first paid firefighters were hired, and the first Mobile Intensive Care Units in the country were constructed. He is one of only three in the district to receive the Bell of Distinction.

Peter Fox, the son of Chief James Fox, was appointed chief in 1981. For several years, Fox was also chief of the Solana Beach Fire Department, but that agreement was severed by Solana Beach after the San Diego County Grand Jury examined the validity of it. The district continued constructing fire vehicles and improving facilities. He oversaw the opening of Station 3 in 1983. Reorganization took place on the eastern boundary in 1987, when the County Service Area was dissolved and Del Dios Volunteer Fire Department joined the Rancho Santa Fe district.

While Arden L. "Pete" Pedersen was chief, the size of the board was increased from a three-member to a five-member board. He was a battalion chief in Orange County before becoming the fire chief in Rancho Santa Fe on August 1, 1987.

In June 1993, Erwin Willis was hired as fire chief. He focused on fire prevention efforts. He worked with environmental agencies to allow for wildland fuel clearance around structures and roads, developed the fire wildland urban interface fire code in San Diego County, founded Fire Safe Councils in San Diego County, and developed shelter-in-place communities within the Rancho Santa Fe Fire Protection District. Willis started his career as a volunteer firefighter at the Morro Bay Fire Department in 1973 and became a full-time paid firefighter in San Luis Obispo in 1974. He went up through the ranks from firefighter, engineer, captain, battalion chief, and fire marshal. He applied for the position of fire chief in Rancho Santa Fe when his wife received a job offer at the University of San Diego as a political science professor. Chief Willis was honored as Fire Prevention Officer of the Year in 2003 by the San Diego County Fire Chiefs Association, Firefighter of the Year in 2005 by the Rancho Santa Fe Fire District employees, and Volunteer of the Year in 2008 by the Burn Institute, where he also served as a director.

In June 2019, Chief Willis, who was chief of the district for 12 years, received the Bell of Distinction for his service. A plaque bears Willis' name on the historic bell at the fire district's offices in Cielo Village. Only two others have received the district honor: Jack Mullins, a board member from 1984 to 2003 and Chief James Fox, who was chief from 1957 to 1981. The bell, originally from a Louisiana plantation, was donated by the Margaret Munsch Trust in 2000.

Nicholas Pavone was appointed chief in 2005 and retired on October 31, 2010. He served the district for almost 32 years, as firefighter, engineer, captain, training deputy chief, EMSchief, support services chief, fire marshal, and deputy chief of operations before becoming the fire chief. He began his career as a volunteer with the Pismo Beach Fire Department in 1975 and joined the Rancho Santa Fe department in 1979. Chief Pavone worked with the Del Mar, Solana Beach, and Encinitas Fire Departments to form a fire management services agreement and defended the fire district against the Witch Creek Fire in 2007. He has a Bachelor of

Science in Vocational Education from San Diego State University and an Associate of Fire Technology from Palomar College.

Tony Michel started serving as chief on November 1, 2010, and retired on December 6, 2018, after 35 years in the Rancho Santa Fe Fire Department. He began working in the district in 1983 as a 27-year-old cadet. Chief Michel was a firefighter, engineer, captain, deputy fire marshal, CERT program manager, deputy chief of training, and deputy chief of operations before becoming chief. He has a Bachelor of Science in Fire Administration from Cogswell College and a California State Chief Officer Certification.

Fred Cox, who had been promoted to deputy chief in 2015, followed Chief Michel as fire chief on December 1, 2018. Chief Fred Cox comes from a fire service family. His father, Fred Cox, Sr., served as fire chief with the Pine Valley Fire Protection District, San Diego Rural Fire District (now known as San Diego County Fire Authority), and in Del Norte County in Northern California from which he retired. He encouraged his son to become a volunteer firefighter with the Pine Valley Fire Protection District when he was in high school. Cox volunteered and worked there for 21 years, promoting through the ranks to include six years as fire chief. In 1990, while still serving Pine Valley, Cox was hired by the Rancho Santa Fe Fire Protection District. Over the past 28 years with Rancho Santa Fe Fire Protection District, he has been a firefighter, engineer, captain, battalion chief, and deputy chief, a position he held for four years. Cox has a Bachelor of Science in Fire Protection Administration and an Associate of Fire Technology. He and his wife, Karen, have been married for 14 years and have two children, Porter and Kennedy.

Chief Cox oversees a staff of one deputy chief, two division chiefs, one battalion chief/training officer, three shift battalion chiefs, 48 firefighters, and three fire prevention positions. He is in charge of three departments: suppression, managed by the deputy chief; prevention, managed by the fire marshal; and administration, managed by the administration manager.

The chief officers are: Fred Cox, chief; David "Dave" McQuead, deputy chief; Frank Twohy, volunteer recruitment and retention coordinator; Brett Davidson, battalion chief for A shift; David Livingstone, battalion chief for B shift; Brian Slattery, battalion chief for C shift; and Bruce Sherwood, battalion chief for training.

Deputy Chief David McQuead promoted through the ranks as engineer, captain, and battalion chief of Training, beginning his service with the district in 2003. As an engineer in 2008, his peers at the Rancho Santa Fe Fire Protection District honored him as Firefighter of the Year.

Frank Twohy, the volunteer recruitment and retention coordinator for the fire district, joined the Elfin Forest/Harmony Grove Fire Department in 1985, becoming its chief in 1993. In August 2002, he was picked as Firefighter of the Year by his colleagues. He worked with birds at Sea World for 18 years.

Battalion Chief Brett Davidson joined the department in 2007. From March 1989 to April 1990, he was a firefighter/EMT at General Dynamics, Convair Fire Department; from April 1990 to August 1994, a firefighter paramedic at El Centro Fire Department; from October 1986 to July 2004, a fire chief at Pine Valley Fire Protection District; and from August 1994 to August 2007, a captain at Poway Fire Department. He has an Associate of Fire Science from Miramar College and an Emergency Medical Technician-Paramedic (EMTP) degree in Pre-Hospital Emergency Medicine from Imperial Valley College.

Battalion Chief Brian Slattery has served the fire district for 17 years. Previously he was a captain with the district.

Battalion Chief Bruce Sherwood received the David B. Dewey Firefighter of the Year Award in 2018 when he was a captain. He was nominated by his fellow firefighters for his dedication, sense of duty, leadership, commitment to the fire district, and customer service.

The administrative staff are: Karlene Rannais, administrative manager; Burgen Havens, accounting specialist; Vanessa Schrandt, accounting technician; and Sandra Reyes, office support coordinator.

The fire prevention staff are: Marlene Donner, fire marshal; Conor Lenehan, deputy fire marshal; Nicole Berry and Brandon Closs, fire prevention specialists; Dan Schaffer, defensible space inspector; Julie Taber, public education coordinator; and Sarah Montagne, office support coordinator.

The captains are: Luke Bennett, Nick Brandow, Joe Carter, Nick Chapin, Correy Cooper, Chris Danner, Marshall Jordan, Trever Krueger, Ray Ligtenberg, Paul Lorenzo, Craig McVey, Chris Mertz, Paul Roman, Brian Salameh, Cole Thompson, and Tanner Worley. Sadly, Captain Dale E. Mosby died on November 16, 2020.

The engineers are: Curtis Benz, John Carey, Kyle Carranza, Brian Ciuchta, Troy Duncan, Jake Elkins, Nate Fritchle, Lee Haskin, Mike Hernandez, Abel Martinez, Scott Schieber, Brian Schmid, Stephen Sepich, Matthew Sivba, Alex Trottier, Tim Wood, and Scott Young.

The firefighter/paramedics are: Jake Barkhimer, Sean Canfield, Chase Cantrell, Justin Cloyd, Alec Connelly, Manny Fernandez, Josh Guzman, Richard LaFluer, Chris Pane, Robert Scott, Haydne Shimer, Samuel Stamy, Michael Weeks, and Derek Wheeler.

The personnel are being vigilant about following the CDC COVID-19 protocols for first responders. The department continues to operate and to respond to all emergencies.

Each station has three shifts, A, B, and C, working 24 hours at a time. Training is required for two hours during each shift. The types of training include emergency medical scenarios, rescue drills, breathing apparatus skills, wildland and structure operations, vehicle operations, and hazardous materials.

Firefighter/paramedic salaries start at $78,211 and go up to $95,066. Captains earn $97,242 their first year and by their fifth year they make $118,198. The range of the fire chief's salary is from $178,056 to $223,196.

The administrative office, located at 18027 Calle Ambiente, Rancho Santa Fe, across the street from Station 4, was built in June 1992. Services include plan submissions, plan checks, car seat installations, and other business or prevention matters. The second floor of the building houses the NCDJPA Dispatch Center, which serves Rancho Santa Fe, Solana Beach, San Marcos, Encinitas, Vista, Elfin Forest, and Harmony Grove.

Each of the six fire stations is located to ensure that Rancho Santa Fe, 4S Ranch, Fairbanks Ranch, The Crosby, Del Dios, Elfin Forest, Harmony Grove, and surrounding communities have adequate protection.

Station 1 at 16936 El Fuego, Rancho Santa Fe, serves downtown Rancho Santa Fe, Sun Valley, Bridges, Rancho La Cima, Rancho Del Lago, Groves, Stone Bridge, and South Pointe Farms. It was originally built in 1949 and renovated in August 1999. Besides being staffed with one paramedic engine company and one paramedic ambulance, this station has wildland firefighting and rescue apparatus.

Station 2 is located at 16930 Four Glee Road, San Diego, and serves 4S Ranch, Santa Fe Valley, and Bernardo Lakes Estates. It also protects a business park and Bernardo Point and the Summit of Rancho Bernardo. The station has wildland firefighting and rescue apparatus. The original station, consisting of a mobile home and a metal apparatus building, was opened in August 1990 with nine firefighters. A new station was dedicated in 2003. It houses one paramedic engine company and one paramedic ambulance.

Station 2 houses the district's Firefighter Training Facility. Construction for the facility began in November 2003 and was completed in July 2004. It has a 4-story training tower with three burn rooms, three underground vaults simulating confined-space rescue incidents, an extrication area where firefighters practice cutting cars apart to free victims of traffic collisions, three roof props to simulate ventilation techniques, a 33,000-gallon drafting pit, and a splash wall. The facility also has an on-site classroom.

Station 3 is located at 16936 El Apaio, Rancho Santa Fe. It serves Fairbanks Ranch, Whispering Palms, Del Mar Country Club, Rancho Santa Fe Farms, Rancho Santa Fe Lakes, Santa Fe Sur, Rancho Farms Estates, Del Rayo Estates, Montecito, Rancho Santa Fe, and other surrounding communities. The original 3,000-square-foot Station 3 was built in 1983 in Fairbanks Ranch across from the Helen Woodward Animal Center. It was demolished in 2010 and replaced with a 10,500-square-foot station in 2012 that was designed by JKA Architecture and cost $5 million to build.

In 1986, the Essential Services Buildings Seismic Act required that public safety buildings be 125% stronger than non-safety buildings. Because the station is in a flood zone, special construction techniques were implemented. The station was designed as a two-story structure so that fire trucks and ambulances can enter and exit safely. The old station had only one driveway to enter and exit so firefighters had to stop traffic on El Apajo and back their trucks into the station. The facility has an emergency generator and diesel tanks. The station can house up to six firefighters. It has an apparatus room with two bays, bunk rooms, fitness area, kitchen, day room, study, and workshop. Surprisingly, the station has a brass pole which allows firefighters to drop down from their living quarters to the fire trucks. The station houses one paramedic engine company and one paramedic ambulance.

Station 4, which opened in 2004 at 18040 Calle Ambiente, Rancho Santa Fe, serves Cielo, The Crosby, Santa Fe Valley, Del Dios, Mount Israel, The Summit of Rancho Santa Fe, Hacienda Santa Fe, Rancho Del Rio, and other surrounding communities. It houses one paramedic engine company and one paramedic ambulance. The station also has wildland firefighting and rescue apparatus.

Station 5 at 2604 Overlook Point Road is in the Harmony Grove Village in Escondido. Construction began on a station in August 2019 and opened on October 8, 2020. The Rancho Santa Fe Fire Protection District personnel had been using two single-wide trailers as the station for over four and half years. The 9,000-square-foot station includes five dorm rooms, gym, kitchen and dining room, recreation room, training room, and a three-wide apparatus bay. The station cost was $7 million.

Station 5 houses one paramedic engine company and one paramedic ambulance.

Station 6 is at 20223 Elfin Forest Road, Elfin Forest . The Rancho Santa Fe Fire District Foundation donated a new septic system and living quarters to the station in 2019. It houses one paramedic engine company and one paramedic ambulance.

In 2018, the department purchased a Spartan side-control pumper with a Gladiator MFD 10" RR, Hale RME 1,500 gpm, 500-gallon tank, and a 30-gallon foam tank.

In 2020, a Spartan rear-mount pumper was acquired with a Spartan Gladiator, MFD cab with 10" raised roof, Cummins X15 565 hp, Hale RME 1,500-gpm pump, 500 U.S. gallon tank, and 30 U.S. gallon foam cell.

The department has acquired six frontline Type I pumpers, one for each station. Each engine pumps 1,500 gallons per minute, holds 500 gallons of water in a tank, carries 2,600 feet of hose, contains class A and B foam systems, and stores advanced life support medical supplies and tools.

It also has three frontline Type III brush engines housed at three stations, each pumping 500 gpm, and carrying 2,600 feet of hose. The engine seats up to four firefighters.

Two water tenders are housed at Station 4 and Station 6 for use throughout the district. Each water tender pumps 500 gpm, holds 2,100 gallons of water, and carries its own portable water tank and portable pump.

There are four command vehicles, each assigned to a chief officer. Each vehicle has multiple radios, mapping displays, and turnouts.

The district participates in an agreement with the California Governor's Office of Emergency Services (Cal OES) for a Type I apparatus. Cal OES assigns engines for use in local fire departments. The vehicles are equipped and maintained by the state. The districts agree to staff the engines anywhere in the state. When the units are called into service, Cal OES pays the wages of personnel.

More than 75% of the calls are medical emergencies. Besides the residences, there is a large urban wildland area to protect. The district has fire safety codes for homeowners. Trees and bushes must be a certain distance from a house and cannot exceed a certain height. Roofs must be nonflammable, and shrubs near a house must always be watered. Indoor sprinklers are required. Columns must be masonry, stucco, or precast concrete; windows must be dual-paned or tempered glass; wood fences cannot touch the house.

All the activity of the personnel—fostering teamwork, taking part in training, operating strategically located fire stations, purchasing up-to-date apparatus, and ensuring people in the community meet residential and landscaping requirements—keeps the department alert and ready to provide help to anyone in need.

CALLS RECALLED:

*1943: In November 1943, a wildfire destroyed homes, brush, and farmlands as Santa Ana winds pushed the fire from Rancho Bernardo, through Rancho Santa Fe, to Del Mar and Solana Beach.

*1979: A wildland fire started near Black Mountain Road burned into the district in the Fairbanks Ranch area. Six structures were destroyed.

*1990: Target shooters started a wildland fire in Aliso Canyon that spread to Del Dios. One home was lost and 3,200 acres burned.

*2007: The Witch Creek Fire started east of Ramona on October 21, 2007, from a downed power line. It reached the Rancho Fe Fire District at 1:30 a.m. on October 22 and 21,000 residents in the district was evacuated at 10:30 a.m. Strike teams from Northern California helped the Rancho Santa Fe firefighters fight the fire. In the Rancho Santa Fe district 61 homes and outbuildings burned, 23 homes and outbuildings damaged, and 6,000 acres destroyed. In the county, 1,265 homes and 587 outbuildings were destroyed and 247,800 acres burned.

*2014: Rancho Santa Fe Fire Department was the initial response on the Bernardo Fire in 4S Ranch on May 13, 2014, which was caused by sparks from construction crew equipment. The incident command was expanded to include Cal Fire and San Diego Fire-Rescue Department with many other agencies arriving to assist. By the time the fire was extinguished on May 17, over 200 firefighters had fought the fire. The fire threatened 50 homes and burned 1,548 acres.

*2014: On May 14, 2014, the Cocos Fire was set in San Marcos at 5:38 p.m. by a thirteen-year-old juvenile. It was close to the Rancho Santa Fe district and residents in Mt. Israel and Del Dios were evacuated. The fire was contained on May 22 at 6:30 p.m. It burned 1,995 acres.

*2017: On August 8, 2017, firefighters, paramedics, and EMTs from Rancho Santa Fe, Encinitas, Escondido, and San Marcos fire departments responded to a traffic collision at the intersection of Elfin Forest Road and Harmony Grove Road in Elfin Forest. Seven teenagers in a SUV and a woman and two children in a second SUV were transported to hospitals.

*2018: On March 9, 2018, a pickup truck rolled over the side of the road near Suerte Del Este and Canyon De Oro in Elfin Forest. One person in the truck with critical injuries was transported to Palomar Medical Center.

*2018: On October 9, 2018, firefighters from Rancho Santa Fe, Cal Fire, San Diego, and Encinitas responded to a fire in a field of dry grass near Artesian Road and Rio Vista Road in Rancho Santa Fe. A helicopter and a hand crew also assisted. The fire, caused by a riding lawnmower striking a rock, was extinguished in 30 minutes.

*2019: On April 26, 2019, firefighters found a home in flames in the 4000 block of Camino Privado. They were able to keep the fire from spreading to other structures and had it extinguished in one hour. In addition to the Rancho Santa Fe crew, there were firefighters from Carlsbad, Encinitas, San Diego, and Solana Beach.

*2019: On November 27, 2019, a $10.8 million mansion was destroyed by fire. Four members of a cleaning crew were inside the 20,000-square-foot home on Spyglass Lane but were able to escape. Rancho Santa Fe, Del Mar, Encinitas, Solana Beach, and San Diego fire departments responded to the two-alarm fire.

*2020: On June 10, 2020, BR265 was deployed to the India Fire on Camp Pendleton as part of a Type III strike team.

*2020: In October 2020, the OES engine was assigned to the Glass Fire in the Howell Mountain area.

RINCON FIRE DEPARTMENT

The Rincon Indian Reservation is northeast of Escondido, in Valley Center, covering an area of 4,275 acres with 535 members. The Band of Luiseño Indians was established in 1875 and has a sovereign tribal government.

The Band of Luiseño Indians dates back over 10,000 years. The tribe first had contact with the Spanish in the sixteenth century. Native Americans still have strong spiritual ties to the land.

The diversion of the San Luis Rey River to Lake Wohlford had a major effect on the Rincon Reservation and four other tribes which depended on the water. The U.S. Government promised the reservations rights to the river but then gave the water to Escondido and Vista. After 50 years of litigation, a settlement was made in 2017 giving Rincon, La Jolla, Pauma, Pala, and San Pasqual tribes equal access to more than five billion gallons annually of Colorado River water to compensate them for the lost San Luis Rey River water.

1993

1993

Bo Mazzetti, who has been chairman of the five-member tribal council of the Rincon Band for five years, was reelected in December 2018 for a two-year term. The vice-chairwoman, Tishall Turner, was also reelected in December. The three other council members are John Constantino, Laurie E. Gonzales, and Alfonso Kolb Sr. The tribal council has legislative, administrative, and legal governing responsibilities for the Rincon Band.

Bo Mazzetti served as a council member for six years before being elected vice-chairman. Mazzetti then assumed the role of acting chairman due to the death of Chairman Vernon Wright who was in charge of the tribal council from 2006 to 2008. In 2005 and 2006 the chairman was John Currier.

Mazzetti is a member of the executive team for the Reservation Transportation Authority (RTA) which improves reservation roads. He has owned Mazzetti and Company, a building, engineering, and well drilling company since 1979. He graduated from California Polytechnic University with a Bachelor of Science in Behavioral Science.

Harrah's Resort Southern California, owned by the Rincon Band, was built on the reservation in 2001 for $300 million. The resort is operated under contract by Harrah's

Entertainment, Inc. The 59,000-square-foot casino has 1,087 rooms, 1,075 gaming machines, and 68 gaming tables. The profits from the resort go to the Rincon tribal government. It allows them to provide government services, cultural programs, and economic development resources for their members and surrounding communities.

The Rincon Band of Luiseno Indians support many non-profit organizations. In December 2012, the Rincon Band of Luiseno Indians donated $100,000 to the Palomar Health Foundation, which supports Palomar Medical Center and Pomerado Hospital. In 2013, they donated two school buses to the Warner Unified School District. In 2016, they helped over 100 non-profit causes. In 2019, Harrah's Resort made nearly $250,000 charitable donations.

Before 2006, the reservation contracted with the San Pasqual Volunteer Fire Department at a cost of $400,000 per year.

The Rincon Fire Department opened April 3, 2006. The first chief of the department was Gerad Rodriguez. The tribal member continued as a firefighter for the San Diego Fire-Rescue Department where he had worked for 20 years. He assisted with administration and writing grants for the Rincon Fire Department on his days off. A rotating duty chief from the Pala reservation supervised fire operations from day to day. Rodriguez said that a benefit of establishing the Rincon Fire Department is that it could train firefighters specifically for high-rise buildings. The 21-story hotel tower was designed with ventilation and sprinkler systems that reduce fire risk.

Edward "Ed" Hadfield was appointed chief in 2015. During his 30 years in the fire service, he has served as a division chief in Coronado from 2007 to 2012 and chief officer, fire marshal, and operations deputy chief with the Santa Maria Fire Department from 2013 to 2015. Previously, he worked for the Vista Fire Department and Rancho Santa Fe Fire Protection District and other agencies. He also was a captain in the Huntington Beach Fire Department. In the early 1990s, Chief Hadfield was one of the graduates of Palomar College Fire Academy's first class. He holds a Bachelor of Science in Organizational Leadership from Azusa Pacific University and an Associate of Fire Protection Administration from Santa Ana College. In 2017, he received a Master of Organizational Leadership from California Coast University. He is also a certified chief officer, fire marshal, and safety officer with the state. Hadfield has been an instructor at statewide and national fire service conferences focusing on leadership and fire command operations.

Chief Hadfield established regional fire command programs, mentoring models and health and safety programs, which upgraded and professionalized his agencies. Hadfield further applied data-based management of risk models at the regional level

1993

to achieve continual improvement and data tracking of specific objectives. He participated in Underwriter Laboratories and NIST (National Institute of Standards and Technology) studies aimed at improving firefighter safety nationwide, which has led to firefighters using risk management models far greater than ever before.

On January 19, 2018, Chief Ed Hadfield was awarded the California Fire Chief Certification and Designation by California State Fire Training (SFT). Hadfield was the 37th fire chief in California to receive the award. In June 2018, Chief Ed Hadfield received the leadership award given by North San Diego Business Chamber for his excellent work in running the department. In July 2018, Governor Jerry Brown appointed Chief Hadfield to the State 9-1-1 Advisory Board. Hadfield serves as Area 4 South director for the California Fire Chiefs Association Board of Directors and director-at-large of the International Association of Fire Chiefs Board of Directors and chairman of the California Department of Forestry and Fire Protection Native American Advisory Council.

Besides Chief Hadfield, the members of the department from the A shift are: John Feess and Chip Duncan, captains; James Wrather and Scott Semer engineers; Jordan Lehr and Colin Carson, firefighter/paramedics; and Aaron Hayre, Chad Jeremiah, Jarred Solomon, and Tyler Ross, firefighter/EMTs; from the B shift are: Mark Richards and Mark Cook, captains; Larry Hogueisson and David Clark, engineers; Brandon Hardina and Brian Boulware, firefighter/paramedics; and Samuel Listoe, Andrew Johnson, and Justin Hopkins, firefighter/EMTs; and from the C shift are: Jeff Robeck and Larry Roberts, captains; Matt Moore and Levi Annon, engineers; Gabe Morettini and Deryck Beveridge, firefighter/paramedics; and Adam Kirk, David Ly, James McPherson, and Matthew Molitor, firefighter/EMTs.

The annual operating budget is about $1.5 million. In 2016, the yearly salary for captains was $98,040 and engineers $82,248.

The department has a four-person paramedic engine company, a four-person paramedic truck company, and two-person paramedic ambulance.

The department has a 75-foot extension ladder truck that was purchased in 2002. It also has another aerial ladder truck, Type 1 structure engine, and a Type III brush engine.

Station 64 is located at 33485 Valley Center Road just south of Harrah's Rincon casino. It houses Engine 6411 (Type I); Brush 6461 (Type III International 4 x 4); Truck 6471 (Pierce 105' rear-mount); and Tanker (2016 International).

A 13,872-square-foot station was designed by architect James Nicoloff and built in 2006 with tribal funds at a cost of $4 million. The station was blessed in a Luiseño Indian ceremony before opening on April 8, 2006. It has an administrative office at one end, a four-bay apparatus room in the center, and living quarters at the other end. The apparatus room has doors at each end so that vehicles can drive forward to access Valley Center Road and, when returning, circle back into the station. This area also includes two workbenches.

The living quarters include 11 bedrooms with desks and individual storage lockers, six bathrooms, and a kitchen with stainless steel appliances, including one refrigerator for each shift. The kitchen has a service counter to the open dining and lounge area with a television and recliner chairs for personnel.

There is a laundry storage room, an exercise room, two locker rooms to store protective gear, medical room to store equipment and supplies, and a room to store breathing apparatus.

Hydrants have been upgraded and maps show where each home on the reservation is.

The department has an ISO rating of class 2! Of the 58,000 fire departments in the United States, only 586 departments have received this rating. The department is now in the top two percent nationwide. In 2016 it had a rating of class 3. Previously it had a rating of class 5. This new rating means the residents have lower insurance premiums.

The Rincon Band broke ground on a $20 million 43,000-square-foot tribal administration building north of the fire department on Valley Center Road in July 2017.

Paramedics James Banister and Scott Ferguson, who provide advanced life saving measures to the Rincon community, saved four lives within seven months, from June to December 2016. They were honored at the North San Diego Business Chamber's fifth annual Heroes Award event held in Escondido in January 2017.

The Rincon Fire Department received the 2018 Wildfire Mitigation Award during the International Association of Fire Chiefs Wildland-Interface Conference in Reno, Nevada, on February 28, 2018.

The department has partnered with Palomar College Fire Academy to provide personnel at the fire station college credit and training requirements while on duty.

The firefighters and paramedics take great pride in the work they do for the Native American community and surrounding areas. They respond to calls 24 hours a day, 7 days a week, 365 days a year.

1993

CALLS RECALLED:

*1988: More than 350 firefighters from Cal Fire and departments in San Diego, Escondido, Santee, Lakeside, El Cajon, La Mesa, and Lemon Grove fought a wildfire in December 1988. The fire burned 300 acres of brush.

*2003: In September 2003, seventy-five percent of Rincon Reservation burned in a wildfire.

*2003: The Paradise Fire began on a hill called Snake Mountain near where the fire station is located on October 26, 2003, and was fully contained on November 6. It is believed that the fire was started by an arsonist. Seventeen homes on the reservation were destroyed in the fire. The fire killed 17 people, burned 330,000 acres, and destroyed 2,400 homes in the county.

*2007: The Rincon and La Jolla Band of Luiseño Indians suffered loss of homes and businesses in the Poomacha and Witch Creek fires in October 2007, including the loss of Rincon's chapel, which was built in the late 1800s. The Poomacha Fire destroyed 65 homes and buildings on the Rincon reservation.

*2016: In 2016, the department responded to 1,123 medical emergencies, 38 fires, 19 traffic collisions, 19 fire alarms, 16 hazardous conditions, and 20 public service calls.

*2017: In July 2017, a person was killed and three others were hospitalized after getting in a crash in the 33400 block of Valley Center Road, south of Harrah's Casino.

*2019: The responses in 2019 were: alarms, 31; fires, 78; rescues, 10; medical, 1,854; and other, 99.

SAN DIEGO FIRE-RESCUE DEPARTMENT

The San Diego Fire-Rescue Department was established in 1889. It provides fire and emergency medical services to a population of 1,419,845 in an area of 343 square miles. It has 52 stations, nine permanent lifeguard stations and 31 seasonal stations, 892 uniformed fire personnel, 98 permanent uniformed lifeguard personnel, and 246 civilian personnel.

On May 17, 1869, the Pioneer Hook & Ladder Company was founded with a budget of $250 and 50 volunteer men. The citizens chose the following officers: W. S. McCormick, foreman; John N. Young, first assistant; William P. Henderson, second assistant; B. C. Brown, secretary; and A. H. Julian, treasurer. In 1870, the firemen added these officers: Chalmers Scott, president; John M. Heidelberg, steward; and A. H. Julian, E. W. Nottage, and George W. Hazzard, trustees.

On October 9, 1872, the Pioneer Hook & Ladder Company was replaced by the San Diego Fire Engine Company No. 1. In the same year, the company purchased a horse-drawn wagon with twelve buckets for bucket brigades for $900.

In January 1878, a fire bell weighing 550 pounds was purchased for $95. In July 1880, the bell was broken, and a new alarm bell weighing 1,000 pounds was bought

San Diego Fire Department, 1887. Courtesy of San Diego Historical Center.

for $300. On July 23, 1885, an additional bell was purchased for $500. It was inscribed "Presented to San Diego Engine Company No. 1 by Bryant Howard, Cashier, Consolidated National Bank, San Diego."

In 1886, the Board of Fire Delegates of the City of San Diego was established by the trustees of the city. On January 6, 1887, the trustees elected James Rooney, president, Frank J. Higgins, secretary, Bryant Howard treasurer, S. McDowell, chief engineer, and John Moffitt and C. F Murphy, assistant engineers.

In November 1887, a La France steam fire engine was acquired at a cost of $4,000. In 1887, the volunteer fire company had 2 horse-drawn steam fire engines, 1 hose wagon, 3,500 feet of hose, 11 horses, 6 chemical fire extinguishers, and 2 fire bells. The expenses for the year was about $12,500.

Prompted by fires in 1888, a change was made from a volunteer company to a full-time paid fire department on August 5, 1889. A board of fire commissioners was appointed by the mayor. Firemen received $12.50 a month, engine drivers and hose carriage drivers made $75 a month, and engineers made $100 a month.

Firemen were required to work 24 days straight, for 24-hour shifts. They received one hour off for meals per day and one day off per month. The families of the firemen lived in the fire station.

At a public auction in 1914 at a horse broker's stable located on G Street behind City Hall,, fifteen horses were advertised. Five two-horse teams found buyers for a combined price of $2,040. Some of the horses were retired to pasture on city-owned land. In 1917, horses were no longer used by the department as it had become mechanized.

On June 30, 1919, the first gasoline-powered fireboat in the United States was christened by the department. It could pump ten hose streams and had two deck guns. It took the mechanics in the shop about six years to build it. The fireboat, 65 by 18 feet, was named Bill Kettner to honor the congressman. Walter Forward designed the pumps.

Fog nozzles started being used about 1920. A demonstration for 55 chiefs was given by Chief Scott in Los Angeles. Oil was put on the bottom of a tank and put on fire.

The physical requirements for being a fireman were to be at least 5 feet 8 inches tall and weigh between 155 and 160 pounds. The younger men were encouraged to be athletic. The firemen had handball, basketball, and baseball teams. Three of the men who went on to join professional baseball teams were Frank Davis, short stop

San Diego Fire Department Engine No. 2, 1910.
Courtesy of San Diego Historical Center.

for the Chicago White Sox, Benny Hoven for the St. Louis Nationals, Tom Downey for the Coast League, and Latheat Hanyon for the Brooklyn Dodgers.

San Diego Fire Department hired African Americans Tim Williams, Sandy Baker, and James Cross in 1919. In 1920, Joe Smith joined them at Station 3 near Balboa Park. In 1930, the four African Americans were transferred to Logan Heights, then a white neighborhood. The residents complained about what kind of role models the four firefighters were for the people in the neighborhood. The men were sent to Station 19 on Oceanview Boulevard in southeast San Diego. Joe Bowdan began working at Station 19 in 1945.

By 1956, the department had 26 engine companies, 2 truck companies, 1 fire boat, 1 patrol boat, 25 stations, and 416 firefighters.

In 1957, Battalion Chief Robert Ely invented the National Standard Hose Thread. Previously fire departments across the country used different hose threads and could not connect their hoses. Eventually the National Standard Hose Thread was used by every department in the United States.

In 1969, the 56-hour work week and the three-platoon schedule was implemented.

In August 1974 the San Diego Fire Department hired five female firefighters. They failed to meet the physical requirements and were fired. In 1977, Lonnie Kitch successfully passed her training and probationary period and served the department for 31 years.

As the population grew, the number of medical aid calls increased. In 1979, paramedic service was added to the department. In 1980, all personnel were trained as EMTs.

In 1998, lifeguard service became part of the San Diego Fire Department.

The department is organized into Emergency Operations headed by an assistant chief and Support Services that is also led by an assistant chief. Deputy chiefs oversee Operations, Emergency Medical Services, Community Risk Reduction Division, the Emergency Command and Data Center, Special Operations, and Logistics.

Fire chiefs of the department are: A. B. Cairns (1889-1905), Ray Shute (1905-1907), Eugene Donnelly (1907-1909), Louis Almgren (1909-1935), John Parrish (1935-1947), George Courser (1947-1960), Ray Shukraft (1960-1968), Leonard T. Bell (1968-1975), Dee J. Rogers (1975-1979), Earle G. Roberts (1979-1984), Roger Phillips (1984-1985), John Delotch (1985-1992), Robert Osby (1992-2002), Jeff Bowman (2002-2006), Tracy Jarman (2006-2009), Javier Mainar (2009-2015), Brian Fennessy (2015-2018), and Colin Stowell (2018-).

A. B. Cairns was the first chief of the San Diego Fire Department. Before becoming San Diego Fire Department's first chief engineer in 1889, A. B. Cairns was a member of the New York Fire Department for several years and foreman of Washington Engine Company No. 20 from May 1862 until 1866. He initiated the first fire alarm system that was installed by the Gamewell Company. In 1894, Chief A. B. Cairns invented and patented the first aerial ladder in the United States. He used the profits he received from this invention to purchase equipment for the San Diego Fire Department. He retired on November 29, 1905, because of poor health.

Ray Shute was chosen to succeed Chief Cairns as chief engineer. Previously, he was a member of the San Francisco Fire Department.

Louis Almgren was born in Peoria, Illinois, and came to San Diego when he was 10 years old. His Swedish parents came to the United States in 1871. His father had a contract building the Ballast Point and Point Loma Lighthouse. Louis Almgren worked there for 50 cents a day, then worked at different occupations in the building trade in San Diego until 1900. George R. Harrison, who owned the Union Ice Company, was a commissioner of the fire department, along with Al Edwoods and John P. Burt. Almgren, as well as Ellis Frishey, were assigned to the truck company on the Plaza in 1901. Harry Cook was driving the truck and riding the horses.

There were eight stations when Almgren joined the fire department in 1903. The firehouse was located on the west side of 3rd Street between Broadway and E Street (Station No. 1). Station No. 2 was on 5th Street between A and B Streets. One station was on 6th Street between I and J Streets and later three stations were established: one on University Avenue, one on 4th and Laurel, the other on the east end by the East End School.

When Almgren started working for the fire department, there was only horse-drawn equipment, then a year later a converted Rambler touring car was converted into a hose and chemical combination wagon. He became a steam engineer on the horse-drawn vehicles. In 1911, the firemen got their first aerial truck, then, until 1916, the department was motorized but they still had horses that belonged to the city that were later given to the street department. Chief Almgren passed away on May 15, 1961.

George Courser integrated the department in 1951. He said, "You will work side by side each other as one. If there is any man not willing to abide by this order, then he should quit." Previously, the African American firefighters were only allowed to work at Station 19 at 36th Street and Ocean View Boulevard. Chief Courser decided to not send all the African American firefighters to Station 19. He hired Ben Holman and assigned him to the all-white Station 14 in North Park. Courser made San Diego the first city in America to integrate its fire department.

Ray Shukraft joined the department as a probationary fireman in 1937 and was promoted to engineer in 1943, lieutenant in 1947, captain in 1951, and battalion chief in 1955. He took a leave of absence in 1960 to serve as state fire marshal, rejoining the department in 1960 to become its chief.

Leonard T. Bell was deputy chief of San Diego Fire Department for four years before being appointed chief on July 1, 1968. He had been a member of the department for 26 years, more than 13 years in the fire prevention bureau, where for many years he headed the arson investigation detail with the rank of fire marshal and later battalion chief.

Dee J. Rogers was the ninth fire chief of the San Diego Fire Department. He served in the U.S. Navy in World War II and then worked his way from probationary fireman to chief. He loved his work, his city, and the brave men with whom he served. He was a president of the Fire Chiefs Department of the League of California Cities. He passed away on January 9. 2006.

Roger Phillip worked for the San Diego Fire Department for 31 years. He was appointed chief in 1984 and retired on October 31, 1985, at the age of 54. Chief Phillip graduated from Hoover High School and served in the Korean War. He was born on October 5, 1932, and died on August 19, 2018.

John Deloth became the first African American chief of San Diego Fire Department in November 1985. Delotch joined the department in 1963. He was promoted to engineer in 1970 and became a captain in 1974, then was promoted to battalion chief, shift commander, and deputy chief. His son, Randall, joined the department in 1992. Chief Deloth died in March 2009 from pneumonia at the age of 72.

Robert Osby served the fire service for 46 years. He was appointed chief in 1992. Chief Osby helped form Brothers United in 1972 to bring more African Americans into the fire department and to help those already in the department move up. He is a graduate of the University of Redlands and John F. Kennedy School of State and Local Government at Harvard.

Jeff Bowman was appointed chief on May 6, 2002. Chief Bowman joined the Anaheim Fire Department in 1973 as a firefighter. He graduated paramedic training in 1976 and was promoted to captain in 1979. In 1983, he was promoted to battalion chief, followed by a move to division chief two years later. On December 9, 1986, he was appointed chief of the Anaheim Fire Department. In

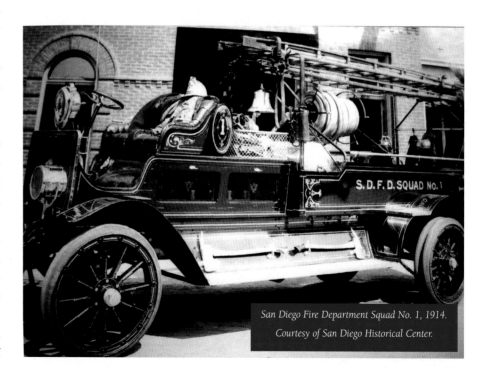

San Diego Fire Department Squad No. 1, 1914.
Courtesy of San Diego Historical Center.

2002, Chief Jeff Bowman changed the name of the department to the San Diego Fire-Rescue Department. He instituted a merit-based promotion system. Chief Bowman was president of both the California Fire Chiefs Association and the Orange County Fire Chiefs Association. When he retired from San Diego Fire-Rescue Department, he became a vintner in Escondido, naming his wine "Screaming Chief." The name, "Screaming Chief," is an homage to firefighting in the 19th century. Without the luxury of modern electronics, a fire ground commander of the period would shout his orders through a "speaking trumpet," so he was referred to as a "Screaming Chief."

Tracy Jarman joined San Diego's fire department in 1984, moved up to assistant chief in 2003, and was appointed chief in 2006. Chief Jarman administered a staff of 928 firefighters, 124 lifeguards, 85 uniformed positions in Emergency Medical Services, 121 civilian personnel, and oversaw a budget of $160 million. She helped increase the number of fire stations from 44 to 47, spearheaded the effort to get a second firefighting helicopter, and helped replace the department's aging fleet. Jarman was named the 2008 "Fire Chief of the Year" by the California Fire Chiefs Association.

San Diego Fire Station No. 9, 1922. Courtesy of San Diego Historical Center.

Javier Mainar was appointed chief on October 13, 2009, and he retired in November 2015 after being in the fire service for 35 years. During the October 2007 wildfires, he was the city's incident commander. He improved the response time in economically disadvantaged neighborhoods. Chief Mainar joined the department as a firefighter in 1980 and progressed through the ranks, becoming a battalion chief in Operations and then assistant chief for Support Services in 2006, overseeing Logistics, Fire Communications, Fire Prevention, and Fiscal and Administrative Services. He was also a supervising fire and bomb investigator with the Metro Arson Strike Team (MAST), human resources officer, and plans officer for the Urban Search and Rescue (US&R). Chief Mainar has an Associate of Fire Science from Miramar College and a Bachelor of Arts in Public Administration from San Diego State University. He has a son who is a firefighter in the department.

Brian Fennessy's career as a firefighter began in 1978 when he was hired by the U.S. Forest Service and Bureau of Land Management on hotshot and helishot crews. In 1990 began working for the San Diego Fire-Rescue Department, working his way up the ranks to assistant chief and chief in 2015. Two and one half years later, at the age of 58, he was appointed chief of the Orange County Fire Authority, which covers more than 70 stations 1.7 million residents in 23 cities, and the unincorporated areas of the county. While in the City of San Diego, he changed the communications center to a command center with 24-hour supervision by battalion chiefs. He encouraged the department to adopt the peak-hour engine concept to reduce response time, creating roving fire crews for 12 hours a day to cover outages when engines are out of service because they have to do training.

Kevin Ester, who has been in the fire service for 42 and one half years, served as interim chief from April 2018 to August 2018. From June 1978 to June 1982, he was a fire explorer and from June 1982 to June 1985 a firefighter for Orange County Fire Authority. Since then, he has served the San Diego Fire-Rescue Department as a firefighter (June 1985 to June 1995); fire engineer (June 1995 to February 1997); fire captain (February 1997 to June 2007); motive fleet officer, Logistics Division (July 2000 to January 2013); battalion chief (June 2007 to January 2013); deputy fire chief, Logistics Division (January 2013 to June 2016); assistant fire chief, Business Operations (June 2016 to April 2018); interim chief (April 2018 to August 2018); and assistant chief (August 2018 to December 2020).

Colin Stowell, a 30-year veteran of the fire service, was appointed chief by Mayor Kevin Faulconer on August 13, 2018. He joined the San Diego Fire-Rescue Department in 1988, promoted to captain in 2002, battalion chief in 2007, deputy chief in 2012, and assistant chief in 2015. In 2016, he became chief for Heartland Fire & Rescue which serves El Cajon, La Mesa, and Lemon Grove. He earned an Associate of Fire Science from Miramar College, a Bachelor of Science in Public Administration from San Diego State University, and completed the Executive Fire Officer Program at the National Fire Academy. At his new position, he oversees a workforce of 1,235 personnel and a budget of $269,732,985.

The department has 52 stations.

Station 1, located at 1222 First Avenue, opened in 1971. It was originally opened at 865 Second Avenue in 1904. It serves downtown and the surrounding areas. Engine 1's district is 0.78 square miles. Engine 201's district is 0.54 square miles.

It houses Engine 1 (2020 Pierce Arrow XT); Engine 201 (2020 Pierce Arrow XT); Truck 1 (2020 Pierce Arrow XT); Air/light Unit 1 (2020 Freightliner M2 106); X-ray Unit 1 (2007 Pierce Arrow XT); Chemical Unit 1 (2009 Ford F-550); Mobile Canteen Unit (2013 Mercedes Sprinter); Utility Unit 81 (2011 Ford F-250); Medic 1 (paramedic unit and medic rescue rig); and Battalion 1 (2009 Chevrolet Suburban).

Station 2 is located at 875 W. Cedar Street. The original station at 1171 10th Avenue was closed in 1971 and combined with Station 1. In March 2016, construction of Station 2 began and opened in June 2018. The station was designed by Rob Wellington Quigley Architects. It is a 25,000-square-foot, three-story building with three transparent apparatus bays, solar panels, rooftop greenery, and public art. It cost $13 million to build.

The station serves Little Italy and the downtown area west of the train and trolley tracks. It houses Engine 2 (2017 Pierce Arrow XT 6710); US&R Unit 2 (2015 Pierce Arrow XT walk-around heavy rescue); and US&R Utility Unit 2 (2012 Ford F-550).

Station 3 is located at 725 West Kalmia Street. It began operation on 4th Avenue and Laurel Street in 1900. In 1909, it moved to 5th and Palm Streets. That building was closed temporarily from 1933 to 1937 and then relocated to 725 West Kalmia Street in December 1977. It serves midtown as well as Balboa Park and its surrounding areas. The station's district is 2.24 square miles. It houses Engine 3 (2018 Pierce Arrow XT 6710).

Station 4 at 404 8th Street is the oldest operating fire station in San Diego. The building was placed in service in February 1938. It serves East Village and its surrounding areas. The station's district is 0.66 square miles. It houses Engine 4 (2015 Pierce Arrow XT 6710) and Heavy Rescue 4 (1992 Pierce Lance II powered by a 400 hp, 552 cubic inch, V6 Detroit Diesel motor).

Station 5, located at 3902 Ninth Street, opened in August 1951. The station's district is 4.12 square miles, serving Hillcrest and its surrounding areas. It houses Engine 5 (2009 Pierce Arrow XT 6710); Battalion 2 (2009 Chevrolet Suburban), and Utility Unit 82 (2011 Ford F-250).

Station 6, located at 693 Twining Avenue, opened in March 1978. The station's district is 4.89 square miles. It houses Engine 6 (2017 Pierce Arrow XT 6710).

Station 7, located at 944 Cesar E. Chavez Parkway, originally opened in December 1913. The station's district is 1.71 square miles, serving downtown and its surrounding areas. It houses Engine 7 (2013 Pierce Arrow XT).

Station 8, located at 3974 Goldfinch Street, originally opened in May 1912. The staton's district is 2.66 square miles, serving Mission Hills and its surrounding areas. It houses Engine 8 (2016 Pierce Arrow XT).

Station 9, located at 870 Ardath Lane, opened in November 1979. The station's district is 4.72 square miles, serving La Jolla and its surrounding areas. It houses Engine 9 (2018 Pierce Arrow XT 6710) ; Paramedic Unit; Medic Rescue Rig; and Mobile Operations Detail (MOD) Squad 1.

Station 10, located at 4605 62nd Street, opened in March 1977. It first opened at 4470 Park Boulevard at 4605 62nd Street in 1913 and closed in 1933. Then it opened at 4704 College Way in 1934 at a cost of $4,700. (The address was changed to College Avenue in 1960). The station's district is 4.37 square miles, serving San Diego State University and its surrounding areas. It houses Engine 10 (2017 Pierce Arrow XT); Truck 10 (2012 Pierce Arrow XT); Brush Unit 10 (2020 Freightliner M2 106 / Pierce Type 3 wildland); and Chem. 10 (2009 Ford F-5500).

Station 11, located at 945 25th Street, opened in October 1997. It was originally opened in 1913 at a cost of $4,700. The building was remodeled to add a truck company in 1975. The station's district is 2.85 square miles, serving Golden Hill and its surrounding areas. It houses Engine 11 (2013 Pierce Arrow XT 6710); Truck 11 (2016 Pierce Arrow XT 6700) and Medic 11 (paramedic unit and medic rescue rig).

Station 12, located at 4964 Imperial Avenue, opened in December 2005. It was originally opened at 2284 Kearney Avenue in 1914. That station was closed in 1933. The station was opened at 4964 Imperial Avenue in March 1948 at a cost of $41,000. A new building was opened in December 2005. The station's district is 7.04 square miles, serving Lincoln Park/Valencia Park and its surrounding areas. It houses Engine 12 (2017 Pierce Arrow XT 6710); Truck 12 (2012 Pierce Arrow XT (500/500/105' rear-mount aerial); Battalion 6 (2009 Chevrolet Suburban); Brush Unit 12 (International / Pierce); and Utility Unit 86 (2011 Ford F-250 4x4); and Medic 12 (paramedic unit and medic rescue rig).

Station 13, located at 809 Nautilis Street, opened in March 2007. It was originally opened in 1913 at 7877 Herschel Avenue. The building was rebuilt at the same location in 1937. It was moved to 809 Nautilis Street in March 1976 at a cost of $75,000 and was remodeled and reopened in 2007. The station's district is 2.48 square miles, serving La Jolla and its surrounding areas. It houses Engine 13 (2018 Pierce Arrow XT 6710).

Station 14, located at 4011 32nd Street, opened in July 1992. It was originally built in 1913 on Zoo Drive for the Panama-California Exposition in Balboa Park then relocated to 3035 University Avenue in 1917 when the Exposition closed. Since 1943, the station has been located at 4011 32nd Street, and the current building opened in July 1992. The station's district is 3.19 square miles, serving North Park and its surrounding areas. It houses Engine 14 (2019 Pierce Arrow XT 6710); Truck 14 (2017 Pierce Arrow XT 6700 (105' rear-mount); Shift Commander 1; and Brush Unit 14 (2017 Freightliner / Pierce).

Station 15, located at 4711 Voltaire Street, opened in August 1949. It was originally opened in 1915 at 4926 Newport Avenue and then was relocated to 4711 Voltaire Street in August 1949 at a cost of $37,000. The station's district is 2.32 square miles, serving Ocean Beach and its surrounding areas. It houses Engine 15 (2020 Pierce Arrow XT 6710) and Utility Unit 83 (2011 Ford F-250 4x4).

Station 16, located at 2110 Via Casa Alta, opened in September 1982. It was originally opened at the Santa Fe Wharf at the foot of Market Street then was relocated to 402 Harbor Lane in 1946 and to 1100 West Broadway in 1962. There was no station house there; the crew lived on the fireboat. The Harbor Department took over the fireboats in 1966. The station's district is 3.45 square miles, serving La Jolla and its surrounding areas. It houses Engine 16 (2019 Pierce Arrow XT 6710).

Station 17, located at 4206 Chamoune Avenue, opened in June 2016. It was originally opened at 4108 University Avenue in 1924, then it was relocated to 4206 Chamoune Avenue in October 1950 at a cost of $29,400. In June 2016, the building was demolished and replaced with a three-story, 10,000-square-foot station. The station's district is 4 square miles, serving City Heights and its surrounding areas. It houses Engine 17 (2013 Pierce Arrow XT 6710).

Station 18, located at 4676 Felton Street, opened in March 1989. It was originally opened in 1927 at a cost of $10,800. The station's district is 2.98 square miles, serving Kensington/Normal Heights and its surrounding areas. It houses Engine 18 (2013 Pierce Arrow XT 6710); Medic 18 (paramedic unit and medic rescue rig); and OES Unit 34.

Station 19, located at 3601 Ocean View Boulevard, opened in March 1986. It was originally opened in 1927 at 3601 Woolman Avenue. The address changed the next year to 3601 Ocean View Boulevard. The station's district is 3.96 square miles, serving Southcrest and its surrounding areas. The station houses Engine 19 (2017 Pierce Arrow XT 6710) and Water Tender 19.

Station 20, located at 3305 Kemper Street, opened in November 1962. It was originally opened at 3575 Kettner in 1928. It is responsible for repair, maintenance, and testing of fire hose. There are 3,000 feet of hose on each of the San Diego Fire-Rescue Department's 48 fire engines. The cost ranges from $70.00 for a small diameter hose to $400.00 for a large 4-inch hose. The station's district is 4.60 square miles, serving Loma Portal/Sports Arena and its surrounding areas. It houses Engine 20 (2016 Pierce Arrow XT 6710); Truck 20 (2012 Pierce Arrow XT 500/500/105' rear-mount); and Medic 20 (paramedic unit and medic rescue rig).

Station 21, located at 750 Grand Avenue, opened in October 1979. It was originally opened at 4202 Mission Boulevard in 1934 at a cost of $5,000. The station's district is 4.07 square miles, serving Mission Beach/Pacific Beach and its surrounding areas. It houses Engine 21 (2019 Pierce Arrow XT 6710); Truck 21 (2016 Pierce Arrow XT 6700 105' rear-mount aerial); and Medic 21 (paramedic unit and medic rescue rig).

Station 22, located at 1055 Catalina Boulevard, opened in December 1942 at a cost of $7,800. The station's district is 5.97 square miles, serving Point Loma and its surrounding areas. The station repairs all small equipment such as rescue saws, cutters, spreaders, blowers, and nozzles. It also does yearly maintenance on all truck and engine company small engine equipment. The station houses Engine 22 (2017 Pierce Arrow XT 6710).

Station 23, located at 2190 Comstock Street, opened in December 1964. It was originally opened at Colon (now Village Place) and Park Boulevard for the 1935 Exposition. It was opened at 2190 Comstock Street in 1943 and rebuilt in December 1964 at a cost of $83,200. The station covers 4 square miles, serving Linda Vista and its surrounding areas. It houses Engine 23 (2016 Pierce Arrow XT).

Station 24, located at 13077 Hartfield Avenue, opened in July 1993. It was originally opened at Midway Drive in 1945. That site was abandoned, and the station was moved to 5064 Clairemont Drive and became Station 27 in 1959. In 1973, Station 24 opened on Mango Drive at Del Mar Heights Road, and it was moved to 13077 Hartfield Avenue in July 1993. The station's district is 16.32 square miles, serving Carmel Valley/Del Mar Heights and its surrounding areas. It houses Engine

24 (2010 Pierce Arrow XT), Brush Engine (Type III 2018 Freightliner / Pierce), and Medic 24 (paramedic unit and medic rescue rig).

Station 25, located at 1972 Chicago Street, was opened in December 1953. It was temporarily opened at Camp Callan in 1946. It serves Bay Park and its surrounding areas. The station's district is 5.40 square miles, serving Bay Park and its surrounding areas. It houses Engine 25 (2009 Pierce Arrow XT 6710) and Battalion 3 (2009 Chevrolet Suburban).

Station 26, located at 2850 54th Street, opened in August 1959. It was originally opened at 3880 Kearny Villa road in 1958, and this older station became Station 28. The station's district is 3.39 square miles, serving Chollas/Redwood Village and its surrounding areas. The personnel are responsible for orientation and continued training of field paramedics and maintenance of emergency medical equipment. The paramedic bike team is also located at Fire Station 26. The station houses Engine 26 (2012 Pierce Arrow XT), Medic 26 (paramedic unit and medic rescue rig), and Medic 62.

Station 27, located at 5064 Clairemont Drive, opened in 1959. It was originally opened at 179 West San Ysidro Boulevard in 1958. In 1959, the station at 5064 Clairemont Drive was built as Station 24 at a cost of $51,400. It became Station 27 in 1959 and the San Ysidro station became Station 29. The station's district is 5.80 square miles, serving West Clairemont and its surrounding areas. It houses Engine 27 (2020 Pierce Arrow XT 6710).

Station 28, located at 3880 Kearny Villa Road, was opened in July 1958. It was originally built in 1958 as Station 26 at a cost of $68,100. It covers 7.76 square miles, serving Kearny Mesa/Montgomery Field and its surrounding areas. The personnel are responsible for testing the pumping capacity of each new fire engine before it is placed into a station. They ensure the engines actually pump the amount of water the manufacturer specifies. The station houses Engine 28 (2013 Pierce Arrow XT 6710); Truck 28 (2012 Pierce Arrow XT 6700 500/500/105' rear-mount aerial); Water Tender 28 (2010 International 7600 / KME); Crash 28 (1985 Oshkosh P-19 4x4 ARFF); and Foam Unit 28 (2012 International 7600 / Pierce).

Station 29, located at 198 San Ysidro Boulevard, opened in December 2005. It was originally built in 1958 as Station 27. It became Station 29 in 1959. The station was rebuilt on the same location in March 1963, and the current station was opened in December 2005. The station's district is 6.21 square miles, serving San Ysidro and its surrounding areas. It houses Engine 29, Truck 29 (2017 Pierce Arrow XT); Brush Unit 29 (International/Pierce 500/500/30F); and Medic 29 (paramedic unit and a medic rescue rig).

Station 30, located at 2265 Coronado Avenue, opened in August 1959 at a cost of $84,800. The station's district is 9.76 square miles, serving Nestor/South San Diego and its surrounding areas. It houses Engine 30 (2012 Pierce Arrow) and Medic 30 (paramedic unit and a medic rescue rig).

Station 31, located at 6002 Camino Rico, opened in December 2005. It was originally opened in 1960 at a cost of $71,700. The station's district is 6.30 square miles, serving Grantville/Del Cerro and its surrounding areas. It houses Engine 31 (2012 Pierce Arrow XT); Utility Unit 84; and Canteen Unit 2.

Station 32, located at 484 Briarwood Road, was opened in May 1961 at a cost of $49,000. The station's district is 7.40 square miles, serving Paradise Hills and its surrounding areas. It houses Engine 32 (2013 Pierce Arrow XT) and Medic 32 (paramedic unit and medic rescue rig).

Station 33, located at 16966 Bernardo Center Drive, opened in January 2010. It was originally on Shelter Island in 1961. The harbor department took over that building in 1965, and Station 33 moved to Rancho Bernardo in December 1969. The community raised funds and worked with the city to help pay for an extensive remodel of the station, reopening in January 2010. The station's district is 25.44 square miles, serving Rancho Bernardo and its surrounding areas. It houses Engine

33 (2015 Pierce Arrow XT); Brush Unit 33 (Type III 2008 International / Pierce); and Medic 33 (paramedic unit and medic rescue rig).

Station 34, located at 6565 Cowles Mountain Boulevard, was opened in November 1963 at a cost of $71,900. The station's district is 12.74 square miles, serving San Carlos and its surrounding areas. It houses an Engine 34 (2012 Pierce Arrow XT and Brush Engine 34 (2020 Freightliner M2 106 / Pierce Type III wildland).

Station 35, located at 4285 Eastgate Mall, was opened in December 1971. It was originally opened on the UCSD campus. It serves University City and its surrounding areas. The station's district is 11.32 square miles, serving University City and its surrounding areas. It houses Engine 35 (2015 Pierce Arrow XT 6710); Truck 35 (2020 Pierce Arrow XT 6710 102' Ascendant tractor-drawn aerial); Brush Unit 35 (Type III 2017 Freightliner / Pierce); Battalion 5 (2009 Chevrolet Suburban); and Utility Unit 85 (2011 Ford F-250 4x4).

Station 36, located at 5855 Chateau Drive, was opened in August 1969 at a cost of $101,000. The station's district is 5.32 square miles, serving East Clairemont and its surrounding areas. It is responsible for repairing and maintaining approximately 450 self-contained breathing apparatus (SCBA) and approximately 1,400 air cylinders used by San Diego and Poway firefighters. It houses Engine 36 (2012 Pierce Arrow XT) and Medic 36 (paramedic unit and a medic rescue rig).

Station 37, located at 11640 Spring Canyon Road, opened in October 2001. The station's district is 11.28 square miles, serving Scripps Ranch and its surrounding areas. It houses Engine 37 (2017 Pierce Arrow XT), Brush Unit 37 (Type III 2018 Freightliner / Pierce); and Medic 37 (paramedic unit and a medic rescue rig).

Station 38, located at 8441 New Salem Street, opened in August 1980. It serves Mira Mesa and the surrounding areas. The station's district is 7.55 square miles, serving Mira Mesa and the surrounding areas. It houses Engine 38 (2012 Pierce Arrow XT); Brush Unit 37 (Type III 2018 Freightliner / Pierce; and Medic 37 (paramedic unit and medic rescue rig).

Station 39, located at 4949 La Cuenta Drive, opened in June 1976. The station's district is 10.65 square miles, serving Tierrasanta and the surrounding areas. It houses Engine 39 (2012 Pierce Arrow XT) and Medic 39 (paramedic unit and medic rescue rig).

Station 40, located at 13993 Salmon River Road, was opened in June 1981. The station's district is 13.87 square miles, serving Rancho Peñasquitos and its surrounding areas. The personnel are responsible for the repair, maintenance, annual inspection, and testing of all ground ladders. The firefighters look for loose rivets or nuts, cracks, or other faults. There are three ladders on each engine and ten ladders on each truck. The crews also repair small tools with wooden handles such as axes. It houses Engine 40 (2019 Pierce Arrow XT 6710); Truck 40 (2017 Pierce Arrow XT 105' rear-mount); Brush Unit 40 (Type III 2008 International / Pierce); Water Tender 40 (2010 International 7600/KME; Air/Light Unit 40 (2020 Freightliner M2 106 / Pierce walk-around rescue body); and Medic 40 (paramedic unit and medic rescue rig).

Station 41, located at 4941 Carroll Canyon Road, was opened in March 1990. The station's district is 10.20 square miles, serving Sorrento Valley and its surrounding areas. It houses Engine 41 (2018 Pierce Arrow XT 6710); USAR Unit 41 (2009 Pierce Arrow XT heavy rescue); USAR Utility Unit 1 (2012 Ford F-550); and Medic 41 (paramedic unit and medic rescue).

Station 42, located at 12119 World Trade Drive, opened in September 1988. The station's district is 6.50 square miles, serving Carmel Mountain Ranch and its surrounding areas. It houses Engine. 42 (2017 Pierce Arrow XT).

Station 43, located at 1590 La Media Road, opened in October 1996. The station's district is 10.51 square miles, serving Otay Mesa and its surrounding areas. It houses Engine 43 (2017 Pierce Arrow XT); Brush Unit 43 (Type III 2016 Freightliner / Pierce); and Crash 43 (Oshkosh P-19 4x4 ARFF).

Station 44, located at 10011 Black Mountain Road, was opened in 2000. The station's district is 6.58 square miles, serving eastern Mira Mesa and its surrounding areas. It houses Engine 44 (2017 Pierce Arrow XT); Truck 44 (2017 Pierce Arrow XT 105' rear-mount aerial); Brush Unit 44 (International / Pierce); Battalion 7 (2009 Chevrolet Suburban); and Utility Unit 87 (- 2011 Ford F-250 4x4).

Station 45, located at 9366 Friars Road, opened in November 2015 at a cost of $11.1 million. It was originally placed in service in March 2006. The station's district is 4.28 square miles, serving west Mission Valley and its surrounding areas. The personnel are responsible for identifying, containing, and removing hazardous materials. It houses Engine 45 (2012 Pierce Arrow XT); Truck 45 (2016 Pierce Arrow XT 6700 105' rear-mount aerial); Battalion 4 (2009 Chevrolet Suburban); Hazmat Unit 1 (2016 Pierce Arrow XT walk-in heavy rescue); Hazmat Unit 2 (2015 Pierce Arrow XT walk-in heavy rescue); Hazmat Unit 61; OES (2017 HME 1871/HME Ahrens-Fox).

Station 46, located at 14556 Lazanja Drive, was opened in February 2004. The station's district is 7.35 square miles, serving Santaluz and its surrounding areas. It houses Engine 46 (2017 Pierce Arrow XT).

The 10,00-square-foot station houses up to 10 firefighters. Areas included an apparatus room with three drive-thru bays, bunk rooms, fitness area, kitchen, dayroom, shop, dispatch and administration spaces. The site design includes space for public and private vehicle parking, hose drying facilities, fueling facilities, and an emergency generator. It was designed by JKA Architeture. The cost of the station was $2.15 million.

Station 47, located at 6041 Edgewood Bend Court, opened in February 2008. The station's district is 2.95 square miles, serving Pacific Highlands Ranch and its surrounding areas. It houses Engine 47 (2015 Pierce Arrow XT 6710).

Station 50, located at 7177 Shoreline Drive, was dedicated on November 24, 2020. It houses Engine 50.

The 12,347-square-foot station includes a new emergency traffic signal, public lobby access off Nobel Drive, efficient storm water design, solar panels, screened parking areas, drought tolerant landscaping, habitat revegetation, and brush management zones. The three-story station has three apparatus bays located on the first floor, with fire trucks entering the station from Shoreline Drive and exiting onto Nobel Drive. It also houses a communal living space, including a kitchen, dining area, and ready room located on the top floor, training room, and a large outdoor terrace. This area will serve as a highly functional space for the firefighters, who are part-time residents. It houses 10 firefighters. The San Diego City Council approved the building of the station in January 2019 and construction began in April 2019. It was designed by Safdie Rabines Architects.

Station 51, located at 7180 Skyline Drive, opened in August 2015. It serves Skyline Hills and its surrounding area. It houses Engine 51 (2015 Pierce Arrow XT).

Lifeguard Division's Mission Bay Lifeguard Headquarters is located at 2581 Quivira Court. It houses Lifeguard Rescue 44 (2015 Pierce Saber AWD).

1913 "Auction Sale". Auction of the fire horse. Courtesy of Title Insurance and Trust Company, San Diego.

Air Operations Division's base is located at 3750 John J. Montgomery Drive. It houses Copter 1 (1980 Bell 212 Twin-Two-Twelve N800D); Copter 2 (2008 Bell 412EP N807JS), Copter 3 (2017 Sikorsky S-70i Firehawk N283SD); Air Ops 1; and Air Ops 2.

In June 2018, the department purchased a S-70 Black Hawk helicopter from Sikorsky Aircraft Corporation at a cost of $19.8 million. It was modified as a Firehawk helicopter with a 1,000-gallon tank, retractable snorkel, and extended landing gear.

Battalion 1 includes Stations 1, 2, 3, 4, 7, 11, and the San Diego Airport Station. Battalion 2 includes Stations 5, 8, 14, 18, 23, 28, and 36. Battalion 3 includes Stations

15, 20, 21, 22, 25, and 27. Battalion 4 includes Stations 10, 17, 26, 31, 34, 39, and 45. Battalion 5 includes Stations 9, 13, 16, 24, 35, 41, and 47. Battalion 6 includes Stations 6, 12, 19, 29, 30, 32, 43, and 51. Battalion 7 includes Stations 33, 37, 38, 40, 42, 44, and 46.

The apparatus of San Diego Fire-Rescue Department includes 13 trucks, five reserve aerial trucks, two aircraft crash trucks, seven battalion chief vehicles, 11 brush engines Type III, one Cal EMA (California Emergency Management Agency) Type I engine, one Cal EMA Type III engine, two chem pickup rigs, one communications and command van, one environmental response team, two explosive device teams and x-ray units, two fast response squads, 48 fire engines, 32 reserve fire engines, one foam tender, two hazmat units, one reserve hazmat response, 28 lifeguard vehicles, two light and air rigs, one mobile canteen, one shift commander's vehicle, two US&R (Urban Search and Rescue) rigs, and two water tenders.

Each brush rig has off-road tires, a 600-gallon tank, and specialized tools like backfire canisters, burn-over protection, and triple hose backpack. Sometimes the rig is a mobile home for the crew.

In March 2020, the city officials approved a $58.5 million contract to buy 16 engines, nine ladder trucks, four brush rigs, two heavy rescue vehicles, two water tenders, two aircraft rescue vehicles, one bomb unit, one cliff rescue unit, and one hazardous materials unit. The goal is to have all the fire vehicles made by Pierce Manufacturing to simplify service and parts replacement.

Lorraine Hutchinson, who retired as deputy chief for the department in June 2015, worked her way up through the ranks and is the first African American woman in the history of the department to be promoted to engineer, captain, battalion chief, and deputy chief. Her last assignment was in Fire Operations as the B Division deputy chief/shift commander. She supervised seven battalion chiefs who oversee the seven geographical areas that make up the City of San Diego. She was responsible for the day-to-day operations of the department when she was on duty. She has an Associate of Fire Technology from Miramar College and a Bachelor of Science in Organizational Leadership from National University. Chief Hutchinson has been honored with the City of San Diego's Diversity Distinction Award, San Diego Metropolitan Magazine's 40 Under Forty Award, San Diego Business Journal's 2011 Women who Mean Business Award, a nomination for the 2014 San Diego Magazine's Woman of the Year award, the Susan G. Komen's 2014 Honorary Breast Cancer Survivor, and in 2014 as the San Diego Padres Honorary Bat Girl. Her husband, Steve, is a lieutenant in the San Diego Police Department.

David Picone, a battalion chief who has worked for the department for 21 years, received the Chief Sandy Davis Safety Officer of the Year award from the International Association of Fire Chiefs on September 1, 2020. During the three years Chief Picone has been the health and safety officer, he has implemented peer support programs for the fire personnel.

From April 10 through April 28, personnel from the Diego Firefighters Association, Local 145, donated $57,000 to local community organizations that help San Diegans through the COVID-19 pandemic. Each day they virtually visited one organization and provided a $3,000 donation. Local 145 President Jesse Connor said, "Firefighters live and work in the communities. We go into people's homes and see the financial impacts of COVID-19 on a daily basis. Like so many others, we are compelled to do more to help our community through this difficult time."

The personnel of the San Diego Fire-Rescue Department have been, and continue to be, dedicated to providing the best possible fire protection and emergency medical services to the city.

CALLS RECALLED:

*1884: On December 12, 1884, a fire destroyed the planing mill and beehive factory of George M. Wetherbee on the corner of G and Arctic Streets at a loss of $12,000.

*1888: On May 3, 1888, a fire burned over half a block downtown. The building belonging to Hamilton & Co. was destroyed. The loss from the fire was $150,000.

*1888: On May 26, 1888, the San Diego Printing Company building was destroyed. The loss was about $40,000.

*1888: On June 1, 1888, the Foreman & Stone building on Seventh Street was destroyed at a lost of about $40,000.

*1888: On August 29, 1888, a building on H Street, between State and Union Streets, burned at a lost of $6,000.

*1888: On September 5, 1888, the Backesto Block at the corner of Fifth and H Streets burned. The Klauber & Levi building was destroyed. The loss was about $300,000.

*1910: On June 17, 1910, the American-Hawaiian Company's freighter S.S. Alaskan was on fire while tied up at the wharf. When longshoremen took the tarp off the number 4 hatch, they saw a blast of smoke and hot gas. Since there was 500 tons of calcium carbide on board, the firefighters could not use water on the fire. The only way to fight the fire was with chemical tanks and hand extinguishers. Chief Louis Almgren ordered that liquid carbonic acid be introduced through holes in the ship plate to extinguish the fire. It took three weeks to put out the fire. It was the first fire in history to be extinguished using carbon dioxide gas. The insurance company, Liverpool Headquarters of the Lloyds of London, presented the fire department with a $10,000 present for putting the fire out.

*1913: On October 5, 1918, a fire started at the Standard Oil Company tank yard on the waterfront. A spark from a locomotive caused a fire in a 250,000-gallon tank of distillate oil. Several other tanks nearby caught fire. A tank holding 1,500,000 gallons of black oil erupted. Firefighters were only able to spray water on the other tanks. A third tank, holding 250,000 gallons of gasoline, exploded. The burning oil caused fires on adjoining lumber yards. The pier caught fire. It took three days to put out the fire.

*1913: One motor driven chemical engine answered 328 alarms during 1913 at an average monthly cost for gasoline and oil of $6.07.

*1918: Ray Gundlach was killed by the collapse of a structure while fighting a fire at the Steele Packing Company. He had only been working as a firefighter for 20 days.

*1925: A fire started in the alcohol storage area of the Brunswig Drug Company. Five firefighters suffered severe lung irritation battling the fire. The three-alarm fire took three hours to contain and cost $100,000.

*1925: In November 1925, a fire occurred at the San Diego Civic Auditorium in Balboa Park while the annual firemen's ball was being held. Five hundred feet of 2-1/2 inch hose that was being used at the ball for decoration was destroyed.

*1936: On October 21, 1936, the Whitney Department Store on 5th and 6th Avenues burned. Thirty-five hose lines, totaling three miles of hose, was used to control the fire.

*1942: In July 1942, nine buildings on the rim of Mission Valley were damaged by fire.

*1944: In September 1944, 40 buildings along the rim of the 30th Street canyon were damaged by fire.

*1948: On September 8, 1948, ten firefighters were injured fighting a fire that started in the basement of the Goodrich Surplus Store at 6th and Market Streets. The store was on the ground floor of the Victory Hotel with guests staying on the second and third floors. After all residents were evacuated, firefighters began going into the basement. A backdraft occurred and the men were blown out into the street. One firefighter's helmet was blown across the street. The fire loss was $200,000.

*1953: Lt. Willard H. Tomkins died of a heart attack while fighting a three-alarm fire at the Arts and Crafts Press Company on 3rd and Ash Streets.

*1955: On January 3, 1955, a fire at the Burnett Furniture Company at 7th Street and University Avenue was fought by more than 100 firefighters. Chief George Courser ordered three crews off the southwest corner of the roof. He was the last to leave and the roof partially collapsed as he jumped off. The fire loss was over $1 million.

*1956: On September 14, 1956, firefighters responded to a brush fire that was moving through a canyon in the Kensington Park area. It took 6 hours and 27 minutes to put out the fire. Twenty-five homes were damaged and 19 firefighters were injured.

*1957: On September 27,1957, a five-alarm canyon fire swept through the Hillcrest area. Nineteen fire companies responded to the fire. Two homes were destroyed and seven homes were damaged.

*1960: On June 28, 1960, Lt. Burton Rogers suffered a heart attack while loading equipment after a grass fire.

*1966: Engineer Roger Saum died of a heart attack while fighting a fire in Logan Heights.

*1978: On February 22, 1978, the 62-year-old Electric Building which housed the Aerospace Museum burned in a three-alarm fire caused by arson. The building had been built for the 1915 Exposition and had been renovated. Almost 60 original and replica aircraft, many artifacts and books, and rare engines were lost. The building was made of wood and had no sprinkler system. The loss in the destruction of the 62-year-old building was $10 million. In February 1980 the Aerospace Museum reopened in the Ford Building.

*1978: On March 8, 1978, an arsonist set fire to the Old Globe Theatre. The loss in the destruction of the 43-year-old building was $4 million. It was originally built in 1935 for the California Pacific International Exposition. The Old Globe Theatre was replaced in 1982.

*1978: On March 21, 1978, Engineer Charles Kinnel was killed by a hit-and-run driver on Texas Street while performing emergency service at a traffic accident.

*1978: On September 25, 1978, a Cessna 172 and a Pacific Southwest Airlines (PSA) Boeing 727 collided and crashed into North Park near Dwight and Nile Streets. One hundred and forty-four people died, including seven people on the ground. More than 20 structures were destroyed or damaged.

*1981: In 1981 a La Jolla condominium building under construction burned. An overturned tar pot ignited the fire. Twenty-one engine and seven truck companies responded to the six-alarm incident. The fire resulted in a $5 million loss.

*1985: On June 30, 1985, a fire burned into Normal Heights from the Mission Valley canyons. The fire destroyed 76 homes and damaged 57 other homes. Over 400 firefighters from San Diego and other agencies fought the fire.

*1997: In August 1997, Engineer Joseph Estavillo contracted Strep A through cuts on his hands through his gloves while fighting a brush fire in the northern part of San Diego County. He died three days later at the age of 44.

*1999: On December 25, 1999, a fire started at the 15-story Cathedral Arms Apartments in North Park. The fire killed one person and injured three others.

*2001: San Diego Urban Search & Rescue Task Force 8 responded to the September 2001 World Trade Center terrorist attack in New York City. There were 2,973 people who were killed, including 343 firefighters, police officers and rescue workers.

*2003: On October 25, 2003, a large wildfire, called the Cedar Fire, was started by a hunter in the Cleveland National Forest near Ramona. At 5:30 p.m. it was reported as a 20-acre fire, by midnight it was 5,500 acres, and by 3:00 a.m. it was 62,000 acres. The San Diego Fire-Rescue Department responded with 50 engine companies, 11 brush rigs, nine truck companies, and 2 airport firefighting rigs. In San Diego, 28,676 acres burned and 335 structures were destroyed. In the county, the Cedar Fire killed 15 people, burned 2,820 structures, and destroyed 280,278 acres. Losses were estimated at $204 million.

*2003: On August 1, 2003, a condominium under construction at University Town Center was set on fire by the Earth Liberation Front. Over 100 firefighters fought the fire. It cost $50 million in damages.

*2007: On October 21, 2007, Santa Ana winds started a fire east of Ramona in the Witch Creek area. By 4:00 a.m. the next morning, the Witch Creek Fire had made its way to the San Diego City limits. The Guejito Fire started in the San Pasqual Valley at 2:00 a.m. on October 22. The two fires merged. Three hundred and sixty-five homes were destroyed in Rancho Bernardo and 9,250 acres burned in the City of San Diego. Countywide, 1,141 homes were destroyed and two people died. More than 500,000 people were evacuated, 200,000 of them within the city. The San Diego Fire-Rescue Department had 73 engines, seven trucks, and 420 firefighters deployed.

The Harris Fire in southern San Diego County also started on October 21. It burned 90,440 acres but did not enter the City of San Diego. Five people died in the Harris Fire.

*2010: On April 1, 2010, EMT Esteban Bahena was killed while on the scene of a car accident.

*2010: The department responded to 113,982 calls.

*2018: In 2018, crews within Battalion 5 responded to 998 fires, 585 rescues, nearly 11,000 medical aid calls and more than 2,800 hazard calls.

*2018: In November 2018, thirty-seven firefighters from the San Diego Urban Search and Rescue Task Force 8 searched over 1,500 structures for victims of the Camp Fire in Paradise, California. The task force included personnel from San Diego, Carlsbad, Chula Vista, San Marcos, Santee, and Heartland fire departments.

*2019: The department responded to the following calls in 2019: fire, 4,505; rescue, 1,427; emergency medical response, 112,838; urgent medical response, 15,650; non-emergency medical response, 14,513; hazard, 12,008; and service, 552.

*2020: In September and October 2020, fire personnel assisted at the Valley Fire and other incidents throughout the state. Firefighters worked extra shifts to cover all stations and deployments.

SAN DIEGO FIREHOUSE MUSEUM

There are nearly 300 museums which preserve the heritage of firefighting in America. The San Diego Firehouse Museum stands out in its early history of firefighting in the West.

Located at 1572 Columbia Street in the Little Italy section of downtown San Diego, uniquely, the museum is housed in what was once San Diego's Fire Station No. 6. Joseph Cook leased the property to the City of San Diego in 1913 and by 1915 Station No. 6 was constructed and included a maintenance facility and machine shop for the other five fire stations as well. Today, historic No. 6 is located in Otay Mesa.

The nonprofit Pioneer Hook and Ladder Company (PH&L), founded in 1966 with 22 members, established the museum in 1972. The museum's operations are overseen by PH&L board members: president, Kevin McWalters, SDFRD fire captain; vice president, Jack Gosney, retired Del Mar fire chief; secretary, John Fisher, SDFRD battalion chief; and treasurer, Mark Adler. Other board members are: Stu Sprung, retired from San Francisco Fire; Kevin Ester, SDFRD deputy chief; Dave Duea, owner of Fire Etc.; Bill Black; and Dale Wineteer, Road One Towing.

"Old La Jolla" hand drawn 1886 fire engine.
Courtesy of the San Diego Firehouse Museum.

Captain Mike Colafrancesco is the executive director of the museum. Among his duties with the San Diego Fire-Rescue Department (SDFRD), he has served as the coordinator for the Cadet Program which helps young people between the ages of 16 to 21 learn about fire and emergency medical services careers and as treasurer of the San Diego Fire-Rescue Department Sports Club. He and Captain John Brubaker compiled the history of the San Diego Fire-Rescue Department for the 125th anniversary (1889-2014) book of the department.

Board member Stu Spring has written a book about the museum titled "The 6 House: the history of the San Diego Firehouse Museum." After he graduated from the University of San Diego, he was a firefighter for 20 years in Oceanside and San Francisco. Stu Spring is currently a commercial pilot, fire training consultant, and writer.

In 1914 under the leadership of Chief Louis Almgren, the crew at Station No. 6 began building a wood-hulled fireboat powered by gas. On November 19, 1919, the fireboat was christened the Bill Kettner in honor of Congressman William "Bill" Kettner who influenced the development of San Diego Harbor and brought the U.S. Navy facilities to San Diego. It was the first gasoline-powered fireboat in the United States.

After 1915, as more fire stations were built, Station No. 6 was renovated to meet the demands of maintenance of fire engines. Additional bay doors, a battalion chief's office, a storage room, a paint shop, and a carpenter shop were added.

Robert Ely joined the San Diego Fire-Rescue Department in 1941, promoting to a battalion chief nine years later. While on the Bill Kettner Fireboat, he devised educators, suction devices to pump out flooded compartments on ships. The educator fittings became standard equipment on all U.S. naval ships. In 1944 Chief Ely was assigned to Fire Station 6, where he became concerned about compatibility of hose threads and hookup fittings used in the fire service. He created the National Standard Thread (NST) which was adopted by fire departments throughout the United States. After 33 years working at the San Diego Fire-Rescue Department, he continued to be active in state, national, and international fire safety organizations. Also, he helped restore fire apparatus at the San Diego Firehouse Museum, including a Seagrave pumper in use during the 1915 Exposition in Balboa Park.

Photo taken around 1915 at San Diego Fire Station No. 6.
Courtesy of the San Diego Firehouse Museum.

The apparatus displayed includes San Diego's 1886 horse-drawn steam engine. In 1832 the New York Mutual Hook and Ladder Company first used a fire horse. Fire horses were used to pull hose and chemical wagons, steamers, and hook and ladder trucks until 1921. Only about one out of 100 of the horses considered were selected. They had to be strong, calm, and fearless. The firefighters and communities had a strong bond with the fire horses.

The museum has seven antique fire apparatus, including San Diego's only remaining hand-drawn fire engine, an 1841 Ramsey hand pumper, whose only source of water was a bucket brigade. Besides apparatus, the museum has collections of uniforms, badges, patches, extinguishers, helmets, fire alarm boxes, hydrants, wrenches, documents, and historical photographs.

A collection of fire marks (also known as house plates and badges) is part of the memorabilia. Fire marks were first used by insurance companies after the Great Fire of London in 1666. The marks were placed on the exteriors of homes and businesses to alert fire brigades that a building was insured against damage by fire and to discourage arson. Fire marks carried the symbol or the name of the insurer and were made of cast iron, lead, brass, tinned sheet iron, copper or zinc. They were used from 1752 to about 1900.

A memorial hall honors the 343 firefighters who lost their lives on September 11, 2001, at the World Trade Center. A piece of structural steel from the site is on display.

The museum preserves the heritage of over 100 years of firefighting in the San Diego area.

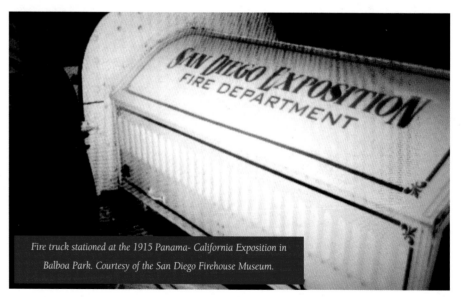

Fire truck stationed at the 1915 Panama-California Exposition in Balboa Park. Courtesy of the San Diego Firehouse Museum.

Many people have contributed to the collection of the museum, including Vic Venburg (businessman), Tom Sefton (San Diego Trust and Savings), Winter family (ABC Towing), Roscoe Elwood "Pappy" Hazard (Hazard Construction), Chief Leonard Bell (SDFRD), Dave Duea (Fire, Etc.), and the Navarro family (Jerome's Furniture). Volunteers, mostly retired firefighters, relate stories to visitors about the artifacts and apparatus which date back to 1841. They also operate a mobile canteen, delivering refreshments to fire personnel in times of large incidents.

The museum has a Children's Safety Room, an interactive room created for children to learn about fire safety and prevention.

SAN MARCOS FIRE DEPARTMENT

San Marcos is bordered on the east by Escondido, south by Del Dios, north by Deer Springs, and west by Vista. It is 30 miles north of San Diego at an elevation of 570 feet. The district has a population of 96,198 and consists of 33 square miles (26 square miles within the city limits and seven square miles surrounding the city).

Mt. Whitney, south of San Marcos, was a sacred mountain to the Native Americans. Spanish soldiers who discovered the valley on St. Mark's Day on April 25, 1795, named it "Los Vallecitos de San Marcos."

Major Gustavus French Merriam, a Union Army Civil War veteran, bought 160 acres in 1875 and named it Twin Oaks Valley. The town was laid out in 1883 by James F. Barham and his son John. Originally called San Marcos-Twin Oaks Valley, the name was later changed to San Marcos-Richland-Twin Oaks, then to San Marcos.

Other early settlers to San Marcos were the Godwins, Uhlands, Huchtings, Mahrs, and Buchers. Children were sent to the Richland School at the corner of Richland Road and Mission Avenue which was built in 1889 at a cost of $2,000. The school had a

San Marcos Volunteer Fire Department. Courtesy of San Marcos Historical Society.

belfry with a 400-pound bell. The Old Richland School House, also known as the Green Gables Estate, is now at 134 Woodland Parkway and used as a banquet hall.

For many years San Marcos was a farming and ranching community. One of the more notable farms was the large and productive Hollandia Dairy which was founded by Dutch businessman Arie de Jong.

The farmhands and ranchmen were interested in forming a fire department. On February 6, 1936, the San Marcos Volunteer Fire Department was established. Charter members were Fred Williams, Fred Carpenter, Ray Robles, H. O. Bishop, Glen Hayden, Bill Karminsky, Art Taylor, Norman Bucher, Bill Uhland, Walter Jensen, Ben Katheisen, Ray Livernois, and Nevin Willbanks. William "Bill" Uhland became a captain in the volunteer department. He was later on the San Marcos School Board, San Marcos Cemetery Board, and member and twice the president of the San Marcos Rotary Club. He died on April 1, 2019, at the age of 88.

Fred Willimas was elected fire chief in 1936 and served in that position until 1948, He worked as an auto mechanic at Fred "Pappy" Carpenter's Flying A Service Station from 1928 until 1972. Chief Williams recalls, "There was only one truck and there weren't any fire hydrants. We would suck the water out of ponds, streams, or anything that was around. It was a lot tougher fighting fires then."

The minutes of a firemen's meeting was held on November 27, 1936. The regular firemen's meeting was held at the San Marcos garage.

Roll call was taken. Minutes were read and approved. Treasurer's report shows a balance of $9.44 in the personal fund and the firemen's fund empty. E. M. Marvel donated a fine pair of bulldog gogglers for general purpose.

Jack Peterson reported for the dance committee, stating he had contacted ranch hands and figured they may consider a 50-50 proposition.

Company 'B" reported that wood had been secured and ladder securely strapped to truck during their two week working period on truck and clubhouse.

Dennis Mahr and Willie James were appointed cooks for the following meeting.

By motion the meeting adjourned.

Homer Huchting, sec.

The only fire truck at that time was a 1926 Diamond Reo that they kept next to Williams' garage on Mission Road. There were a total of 25 volunteers. Officers were elected to positions of chief, assistant chief, captains, and lieutenants.

At the firemen's meeting on August 4, 1937, the treasure's report showed a balance of $27.71 in the personal fund and $19.50 in the firemen's fund. It was decided to have a firemen's ball on August 21, 1937. No action was taken on a general discussion in regard to burning brush at practice drills.

The Depression was still on and the seeds of war were forming in Europe and Asia. However, the volunteers, as demonstrated in their minutes, continued to count every penny and to give as much time and effort to sustain the fire department financially. Tamale dinners and firemen's balls were but a few of the duties that were so much a part of volunteerism in the fire service.

San Marcos was fortunate in always having a list of people waiting to join the volunteer fire department. The only time personnel got thin was during World War II. It was during the war that a young 16-year-old, Norm Bucher, joined the department. He had to get permission from his parents. Norm Bucher joined his brothers, Walt and Bill, and their father, Ed, in serving as San Marcos volunteers for many, many years. Bill Bucher joined the department when he turned 18 in 1952.

Also, during World War II, sections of a relocation camp building were donated to the department as a firehouse in 1943.

Charles A. Carpenter became San Marcos's first paid firefighter in 1946. He would later be promoted to fire chief in 1956. Carpenter had moved to San Marcos in 1944 after fighting brush fires in the early 1930s in the Horseshoe Bend area of Idaho and Cuyamaca State Park in California.

San Marcos became a fire protection district in 1945 and, therefore, a tax-supported organization. The minutes of the February 1, 1950, firemen's meeting showed a roster of 17 volunteers and a treasure's report of $153.35 in the firemen's fund. It was moved and seconded that H. O. Bishop be reimbursed 101 pounds of sugar for his past years of service serving refreshments. The motion carried.

Wayne Fulton and Duane Hartman were hired full-time in 1965. Bob Kuenzi replaced Duane Hartman a year later. In 1972, two additional firefighters were hired.

The San Marcos-Richland-Twin Oaks Fire District signed a contract with American La France Ford in December 1959 to construct a fire engine. It specified a 750-gpm pump with a 500-gallon booster tank with a commercial cab.

In 1963 the San Marcos-Richmond-Twin Oaks designation was changed and simplified to San Marcos to meet state codes regarding reorganization of fire districts.

George W. "Kurly" Benedom dispatched alarms every hour, every day for many years from the Texaco station on days he worked there and from his house across the street from the gas station on evenings. When Kurly Benedom had to go to the hospital for surgery in 1966 at the age of 87, Bob Jeans, who was a volunteer fireman as well as a plumber, had a radio and telephone installed in his house to dispatch calls. Jane Jeans, his wife, became the dispatcher on a 24-hour basis.

By 1968 San Marcos had a fire chief, seven firemen, 25 volunteers, three pumpers, and two trucks.

San Marcos built a 5,200-square-foot fire station at 333 Firebird Lane in 1970 for $98,890. It was built on the same site as the relocation camp building which had been used as a firehouse since 1943. William Merritt Townsend, who was on the board of directors of the fire department from 1955 to 1968, designed the station. At that time, there were four paid firefighters with Chief Charles Carpenter and, of course, a wealth of volunteer firefighters.

In October 1976, the San Marcos Fire Department, in an act of generosity and compassion, donated a 1940 Van Pelt fire engine to the newly formed and fledging Fernbrook Volunteer Fire Company located south of Ramona. The fire truck had been purchased for $900 by San Marcos in June 1948. At a formal ceremony on October 14, 1976, Charles Carpenter, fire chief, and Charles Hahne, chairman of the board of directors, handed title of the fire engine over to Lucille and Franklin Ingham of the Fernbrook volunteers. Fernbrook was one of over 30 volunteer departments that were being formed with the termination of the San Diego County/California Department of Forestry contract. The engine was originally used by the San Marcos Volunteer Fire Department and by the California Department of Forestry and Fire Protection and housed in a garage on Pico Drive. When San Diego County Office of Fire Services delivered a 1956 engine to the Fernbrook Volunteer Fire Company in Ramona, the county sold the engine. Bill Carroll, a San Marcos volunteer firefighter, located the fire truck and refurbished it. He later donated it to the San Marcos Historical Society. For many years it was used at public events and then it was stored in the back lot of Heritage Park. In August 2019, the San Marcos Historical Society voted to pledge $5,000 as seed money to restore the engine and to reach out to the community to raise $20,000 to restore the fire truck. The project is called "SOFiE" (Save our fire engine).

The fire personnel used a new $18,000 rescue truck received in 1984 two and half hours after it was received to handle a car fire. The department's 10-year-old rescue vehicle was retired several months earlier.

In 1987 the fire protection district came under the jurisdiction of the San Marcos City Council. This reduced costs by eliminating duplication of some administrative duties and facilities.

Paramedic service was added to the department in 1988. Now every engine and ambulance has a paramedic. Engine companies are staffed with three people. The department responds to each medical assistance with a fire apparatus and an ambulance. This means two paramedics are able to help a patient and there is personnel to assist. Paramedics are usually able to reach a patient within five minutes. Seventy percent of the calls are medical aids.

Volunteers assist the department with such services as fire prevention education, office support, delivery of food supplies at fires, inspection of fire hydrants, and citizen assistance.

In November 1997, the department received a new brush engine to be housed at Station 3 that cost $185,000. The brush engine built in 1986 was switched to reserve status.

The San Marcos Regional Emergency Services Training Center at 184 Santar Place was built with a fire and rescue drill tower that includes a sprinkler and standpipe system. The five-story tower opened in April 2001. It is part of the $7.5 million public safety center that includes a 31,000-square-foot sheriff's station, a firefighting training center, and classroom buildings for Palomar College's programs. Each day begins with an apparatus and equipment check followed by at least two hours of training.

Today the San Marcos Fire Department is a modern, progressive, and professional organization. San Marcos itself is a vibrant, sprawling city with Highway 78 running

San Marcos 2017 Pierce 100' Heavy-duty Aerial Ladder.

through it between Interstate 15 and Interstate 5. It has a large community of light industrial parks, Palomar College, and California State University, San Marcos. A railroad runs directly through the community and there is an abundance of restaurants, modern shops, and malls.

The chiefs of the department are: Fred Williams (1936-1948), Stanley Mahr (1949-1950), Lee A. Garner (1951-1955), Charles Carpenter (1956-1978), Stanley Mourning (1978-1984), Harry "Hal" Townsend (1984-2005), Todd Newman (2005-2013), Brett Van Wey (2014-2019), and Dan Baron (2019-).

Lee Garner was selected as chief in 1951. That year the department had only $60.95 and was entirely volunteer.

Charles Carpenter was the first paid chief of the department. He had a chicken ranch on San Marcos Boulevard.

Stanley "Stan" Mourning retired in February 1984 after six years as the San Marcos Fire Department's chief. His first year as chief, there were seven employees and more than 35 volunteers. "The volunteers had so much spirit, and no matter what you asked them to do, they did it," Mourning said. His salary as chief was $42,000 a year. He pushed to have a computerized dispatch system that flashed the address, location, and type of fire in progress. He started his career as a volunteer fireman with the Spring Valley Fire Department in 1954 and became the department's assistant chief.

Harry Townsend was appointed chief on July 1, 1984, at the age of 38. He joined the San Marcos Fire Department after spending eight years as a deputy sheriff assigned primarily to North County. In August 1978, he became Chief Mourning's administrative assistant, then on July 1981, Townsend became his deputy chief. Chief Townsend became a volunteer fireman in San Marcos immediately after he was discharged from the Air Force where he was a military policeman. He became a full-time fireman on April 4, 1977. He was a 1963 graduate of San Marcos High School and then attended Palomar College.

The department in 1982 consisted of 16 full-time personnel and about 30 volunteers. Cliff Hunter, who was with fire department since June 1971, was promoted from fire marshal to deputy chief on July 1, 1984. The five captains in 1984 were Duane Hartman, Bob Kuenzi, Steve Parker, Larry Bryson, and Greg Woolf. The volunteers trained every two weeks and often came in to train with the paid firemen at other times. Chief Townsend said, "The volunteers are the backbone of our district. They always have been. As long as I'm chief we'll have a volunteer force." Norman Bucher, a 39-year veteran of the volunteers, was the first assistant chief of the force, and Ed Fredendall was second assistant chief. The department had three

structure engines, three brush engines, three staff cars, two Jaws of Life, one rescue squad unit, an Office of Emergency Services structure pick-up and utility pick-up. It had a resuscitation unit that cost $12,000.

A parade and festival in 1986 marked the 50th anniversary of the San Marcos Fire Department. In 2006, a ceremony celebrated the 70th anniversary of the department. At the event, Betty Ferguson, who served on the fire district's board of directors in the 1970s, said, "They were a proud bunch of men just willing to serve their community. The men left their farms, businesses, and places of work to put their lives on the line."

In 1998, Larry Webb was promoted from division chief to deputy chief.

Todd Newman was picked as chief in 2005. He spent 30 years with the department, including eight as chief.

Brett Van Wey was named chief in 2014. He began his career in the fire service as a reserve firefighter. He was promoted from firefighter to engineer in 1994 and became a battalion chief in San Marcos in 2001. Chief Van Wey has an Associate in Fire Science from Palomar College and a Bachelor of Arts in Public Administration from San Diego State University. For almost 19 years he was the fire technology coordinator at Palomar College.

Dan Baron was appointed chief on June 27, 2019. He has worked in the fire service for 22 years, including 19 years with the San Marcos Fire Department, working his way up from firefighter to engineer, captain, battalion chief, and division chief. He plans to continue increasing coordination with Escondido Fire Department, Cal Fire, law enforcement, SDG&E, and other agencies. Chief Baron aims to enhance customer service to the community through programs including drowning prevention and wildfire preparedness. Barron's wife and three children joined him for his pinning as chief.

The division chief for the Emergency Services Division is Bill Frederick. Chief Frederick was a battalion chief for the San Marcos Fire Department from February 2014 to May 2019. He has a Bachelor of Science from Columbia Southern University. The division is responsible for training, emergency medical services, communications, fleet management, facilities, and special operations.

The battalion chief and fire marshal for the Fire Prevention Division is Jason N. Nailon. Chief Nailon has served the San Marcos Fire Department since February 2018. He is a part-time adjunct faculty instructor for fire technology at Palomar College. He is an executive board member of SoCal FPO (Fire Prevention Officers), California Fire Chiefs Association. He worked for the Apple Valley Protection Fire District for almost

28 years. Chief Nailon has an Associate of Science in Fire Technology from Victor Valley College and a Bachelor of Applied Science in Public Safety Administration from Grand Canyon University. The division is responsible for plan reviews, business inspections, public education, vegetation management, fire investigation, community programs, water supply, pre-fire planning, and underground fire services.

In April 2020, the San Marcos Fire Department received a Class 1 Public Protection Classification from the Insurance Service Organization (ISO)! There are only 37 fire departments in California and 348 fire departments in the United States which have a ISO 1 rating. Departments are evaluated by the fire department's response capabilities, apparatus, location of fire stations, training, emergency communications, water supply, and community fire risk reductions. The ISO ratings reflect the effectiveness of the fire protection and insurance companies use it when establishing premiums for fire insurance. (In 1983, the department had an ISO rating of 6.)

San Marcos currently has 80 employees staffing four fire stations under the leadership of Chief Dan Baron. The department has a budget of about $18 million. It has four paramedic engine companies, three brush engines, one primary truck, one water tender, four ambulances, one trail rescue vehicle, three reserve fire engines, five command vehicles, one reserve truck, three reserve ambulances, and one mobile emergency operation center.

Station 1 is located at 180 W. Mission Road. The station was dedicated in October 2000. The 15,000 square-foot-station cost $3.3 million. It is south of the old station, which was demolished. The old station had pink walls, but the newer station has mint green and white. The San Marcos Professional Firefighters Association donated leather recliners and a large-screen television for the recreation room. A battalion chief is assigned to the station. It houses Engine 141, a 2017 Pierce Velocity PUC, and Brush 141, a 2020 Pierce Type III Freightliner M2 106, 500-gpm pump, foam and water tank, and 500 gal. tank. A Pierce aerial ladder fire truck was delivered on October 25, 2017. It has a 100-foot heavy-duty tiller, 525 hp, and 1,000-gpm flow capacity.

Station 2, located at 1250 S. Rancho Santa Fe Road, was built in 1980 at a cost of $200,000. In 2005, the department spent $4 million to expand and remodel the station. It houses Engine 142, a 1979 Crown Firecoach.

Station 3, located at 404 Woodland Parkway, was dedicated in May 1991 to the Bucher family. Joseph E. "Ed" Bucher, who moved to San Marcos in 1896, spent 28 years with the San Marcos Fire Department while his three sons, Walter, Norman, and William, also retired from the department. Their combined service was 101 years. The station, which serves the Richmond community, cost $694,055 to construct. It houses Engine 143, a 2020 Pierce Velocity 7010 rescue pumper that was delivered on April 30, 2020. It has a Detroit Diesel DD13 engine, 505 hp, foam and water tank, 1,500-gpm pump, and 500-gallon tank.

Station 4, located at 204 Elijo Road, was built in 2008. It was designed by RJM Design Group and WLC Architects. A battalion chief is assigned to this station. It houses a 2005 Pierce Dash engine and a 2005 Ford Type 111 ambulance.

A long, proud history of independent, self-sustaining Americans caring for their neighbors with sacrifice and determination.

CALLS RECALLED:

*1937:   On October 15, 1937, the volunteer firefighters put out a rubbish fire in chicken pens at Ed Welch's ranch.

*1964:   The firemen responded to a fire at the home of Mrs. Frances Fox, a pet lover who had 300 dogs and many cats and birds at her residence. Twenty-nine dogs and 75 birds died in the fire, and there was $6,000 damage to the home. Several of the firemen were bitten by dogs.

*1964:   Assistant Fire Chief Norman Bucher responded with nine firemen to a fire at the home of Phillip Moran. The house was destroyed.

*1966:   Chief Charles Carpenter led a crew of 16 in fighting a brush fire that burned 40 acres and threatened three homes.

*1970:   On one day in April 1970 the firemen removed a doe from the freeway, doused a blaze which burned a corral that housed 12 pigs, and removed a calf on Mulberry Street.

*1972:   Loretta Dickey suffered a serious fall from her horse in a canyon west of Twin Oaks Valley Road. It took the rescue crew nearly an hour to carry her through the rough terrain to an ambulance.

*1976: Firefighter Michael Brown entered a burning house to save the life of 69-year-old Glen Brockway. The victim had second-degree burns over 25% of his body and would have died without being saved by the firefighter.

*1976 Guadalupe Lopez suffered third-degree burns over 30% of his body when his van exploded. He was trapped in the van for 12 minutes. When the San Marcos firefighters arrived, the van was totally involved in flames.

*1977: A truck was hit by a freight train at a railroad crossing on Richland Road. The train dragged the truck about 570 feet. The three men in the truck were injured.

*1979: A 400-acre fire burned behind Palomar College in the Twin Oaks Valley. More than 200 firefighters from North County fought the blaze.

*1981: A fire in Palomar College's audiovisual workshop caused $200,000 damage.

*1983: While the firefighters were fighting a house fire they found the body of Gerald Ricke in the house, dead from a gunshot wound.

*1985: The firefighters responded to about 1,700 calls.

*1998: In August 1998, firefighters battled a 40-acre mulch fire in a landfill. Airtankers, helicopters, are bulldozers were used to help the fire crews.

*2005: The department responded to about 6,300 calls.

*2014: On May 14, 2014, a brush fire known as the Cocos Fire started near California State University, San Marcos. The university was evacuated on May 14. All schools in San Marcos were closed on May 15 and 16. The fire was set by a 13-year-old girl. The fire burned 1,995 acres, destroyed 40 buildings, and cost $5.7 million.

*2014: In August 2014 the San Marcos Fire Department sent firefighters to Mendocino County for 14 days to help fight the Lodge Lightning Complex Fire which burned 12,536 acres.

*2015: The department had 21 structure fires in 2015.

*2019: In October 2019, a 3-acre brush fire near Plateau Avenue and Twin Oaks Valley Road was extinguished within 30 minutes. About 100 people were evacuated and 3,000 residents were without power.

*2020: On August 16, 2020, a 84-year-old driver and a 77-year-old passenger were involved in a rollover collision at San Elijo Road and Schoolhouse Way. The fire personnel extricated them from the car and they were taken to Palomar Medical Center with serious injuries.

*2020: In September 2020, Battalion Chief Jason Nailon was assigned to the SCU Lightning Complex Fire for two weeks assisting Cal Fire Incident Management Team 6 as a Field Public Information Officer. He said it was a rewarding and humbling experience. The SCU Lightning Complex Fire started on August 18, covering five counties, burning 396,624 acres, destroying 222 structures, damaging 26 structures, and injuring 6 people. SCU stands for Cal Fire's Santa Clara Unit.

SAN MIGUEL CONSOLIDATED FIRE PROTECTION DISTRICT

The district covers a 47-square-mile area northeast of San Diego, serving about 134,000 residents of Bostonia, Casa de Oro, Crest, Grossmont/Mt. Helix, La Presa, Rancho San Diego, Spring Valley, and unincorporated areas of El Cajon and La Mesa.

San Miguel Consolidated Fire Protection District (San Miguel Fire & Rescue) was formed on July 1, 1988, through a merger of the Spring Valley and Grossmont/Mt Heliz Fire Protection Districts, and on July 3, 2008, with the East County Fire Protection District.

In 2012, the district signed a $68 million five-year contract with Cal Fire to provide services. At that time, the district had a deficit of over $2 million. In 2016 the fire board decided it would save $1.5 million in just one year by serving the area itself. The total budget for 2017-2018 was $22,479,925. The projected budget for 2020-2021 is $21,512,800.

In 2017 the San Miguel Consolidated Fire Protection District Board voted four to three to return to a stand-alone fire department. It has a seven-member board of directors: Jim Ek, William A. Kiel, Theresa McKenna, Jeff Nelson, Kim Raddatz, Dave Rickards, and Mike Vacio.

Bostonia

Chris Brainard was appointed chief on March 22, 2017. After attending Paramedic School at University of California, San Diego, in 1978, he began working for San Diego Fire & Rescue in 1981, retiring as a deputy chief in June 2014. From 2014 to 2016, he provided emergency system consulting. San Miguel Consolidated Fire Protection District hired him in August 2016 as a transition consultant to bring the department back to local control. He has taught fire behavior and fire investigation at numerous colleges and written many articles for fire and EMS journals.

Chief Brainard leads a staff of 82 personnel, including 2 division chiefs, 3 battalion chiefs, 25 captains, 20 engineers, and 23 firefighter/paramedics.

Gehrig Browning was promoted to operations division chief in 2019. He oversees fire/EMS operations, fleet management, and facilities. Chief Browning began his fire career with the San Miguel Fire & Rescue in 1990 as a reserve firefighter. He was hired as a full-time firefighter in October 1991, promoted to engineer in 1997, and became a paramedic in 1998. In 2002, he was promoted to captain, working out of Station 16 and serving La Presa. He became a battalion chief in 2017. Chief Browning has served as a a training officer, reserve program coordinator, EMS coordinator, and the liaison officer to the CHP's Dignitary Protection Division. He has also worked with the CERT program and the Burn Institute.

Jim Marugg, the division chief for administration, began working for the San Miguel Fire & Rescue in 2000 after working for 17 years as a transport paramedic. He has represented the district on state, regional, and local committees related to EMS. These committees have written the plans for medical disaster response in San Diego County and provided a framework for the FIRESCOPE Field Operations Guide which is used nationally and internationally. Chief Marugg has worked his way up through the ranks, from firefighter/paramedic, fire captain, training captain, safety officer, and battalion chief. He has a Bachelor of Science in Biology and Life Sciences, a Master of Science in Emergency Service Administration, and a California State Certificate as a Fire Officer, Chief Officer, and Fire Instructor.

Leah Harris, the head of the Administrative Services Division, started her career in public service in 2008 in the Finance Office of Cal Fire. In 2012, she received her Bachelor of Science in Business Administration from National University and is currently working on her Master of Public Administration from National University. She oversees budgetary, fiscal, personnel/payroll, human resources, and contract management.

Diana Herron, the Administrative Analyst, joined San Miguel Fire & Rescue in 2018. She received her Bachelor of Science in Business Administration from National University.

Liz Dibb, the Accounting Specialist, has been working with the district for more than 10 years. She began working in the fire service in 2007 with East County Fire Protection District as the Finance Officer until the consolidation with San Miguel Fire & Rescue. At San Miguel Fire she started as an Administrative Finance Specialist until December 2012 when San Miguel contracted with Cal Fire where she worked as a Senior Personnel Specialist. In July 2017, she became the Accounting Specialist for San Miguel Fire & Rescue.

Shayna Rians, Administrative Assistant, joined San Miguel Fire & Rescue in late 2017 and serves as the Board Recording Secretary. She also manages website updates, social media posts, and public education requests. She began her career in public service in 2005, working for the County Library and then Health & Human Services for over 11 years before becoming a police and EMS dispatcher.

William "Brent" Napier, Deputy Fire Marshal, worked for 20 years in construction and building materials for an overseas company both domestically and abroad before entering the field of fire prevention. He has a Bachelor of Science and a Master of Science in Business.

Colton Israels, Fire Inspector, began his career in fire service in 2017 as a firefighter with the Elfin Forest Fire Department. In 2019, he became a Fire Prevention Specialist with the Rancho Santa Fe Fire District. He has completed CA OSFM Inspector 1 & 2 courses along with FEMA courses in both community risk reduction, disaster mitigation, and damage assessment.

Jonathan Newman, Fire Inspector, has worked in the public safety field since graduating from college. He has a Bachelor of Arts in Public Administration from San Diego State University and has completed state fire marshal and fire protection courses from Miramar College.

Art Camarena has served as the Logistics Officer for San Miguel Fire & Rescue since 2014. He has been in the fire service since 1980, working his way up to the rank of captain before moving to logistics in 2010. He has been an active Reserve Company Officer with the Orange County Fire Authority since 1983 and has worked for Disney Fire Department and San Diego County Fire. Camarena has state certifications as a FF I and FF II, Driver Operator 1-A, 1-B, 1-C, and EMT-1 along with Fire Officer and Water Group Manager, and has attended Palomar, Rancho Santiago, and Miramar Colleges.

The battalion chiefs are Rich Durrell, Justin Fuller, and Andrew Lawler.

Richard "Rick" Durrell, Training Battalion Chief, joined San Miguel Fire Department in February 2002 as a firefighter/paramedic. He is a CSFM instructor and has performed as lead instructor in both regional and local Firefighter 1 academies. He oversees all training for the district, ensuring all department mandates are met, while building and implementing training curriculum and programs, and tracking employees' certifications and licenses. Chief Durrell started his career in 1996 at the age of 16 as a reserve firefighter with San Diego Rural Fire District. He attended Heartland's 15th Fire Academy in 1990 where he obtained his Firefighter 1. Durrell worked for 12 years with Sycuan Fire Department, promoting through the ranks to finish his last five years as a captain. He grew up in Harbison Canyon and graduated from Granite Hills High School in 1988 where he played volleyball and wrestled for four years.

The current captains include Brian Bayne, Roddey Blunt, Michael Christiansen, Richard Chvilicek, Kevin Clark, Read Clark, John Fiehler, Kurt Fryling, Michael Good, Jack Grogger, Mike Hays, Brian Komp, Brian Lieberman, Robert Lundstrom, Nick Nava, Ronald Quinlan, Thomas Paden, Ronald Quinlan, Tobin Riley, Bradley Rodeheaver, Kyle Root, Jeff Shinn, Ray Trussell, and Glenn Williams.

The engineers and firefighter/paramedics include Damian Arruda, Joe Bartucca, Eric Benton, Jacob Burkard, Patrick Carroll, Christopher Ciampi, Andrew Delgadillo, Taylor Diehl, Gavin Doudna, Kevin Doyle, Travis Embleton, Ryan Ferguson, Matt Foster, Ronnie Gilman, Ryan Graff, Jonathan Hamblin, Brian Hamel, Eric Hille, Jeffrey Hofmann, Brad Hurley, Glen Jones, Brian Kuklinski, Tim Lewis, Chris Lobaugh, C.J. Marin, Kyle McKee, Mike McKinley, Scott Medinger, Steven Michel, Stanley Milewski, Kari Moore, Gerardo Padilla, Nick Parra, Corey Powell, Robert Pumphrey, Brian Rhodes Jr., Matt Richards, Todd Romenesko, Bobby Ruth, Michael Shandley, Cameron Smith, Matthew Thompson, Nick Williams, and Bill Zapeda.

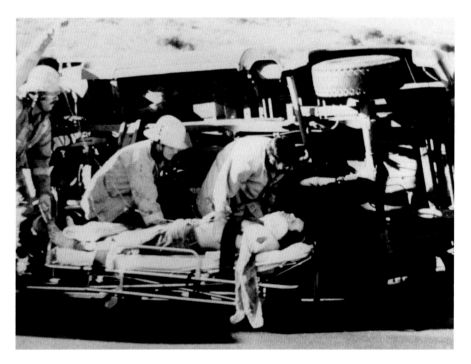

Damian Arruda has been a firefighter/paramedic with the district since November 2003.

Joseph "Joe" Bartucca became a firefighter/paramedic with the district in July 2018. Previously he worked for the Sycuan Fire Department for 18 years, serving as the wellness coordinator from May 2007 to July 2018. He attended Santa Ana College and University of California, Los Angeles, for Prehospital Care. He graduated from Damien High School.

Matt Foster joined San Miguel Fire & Rescue as a firefighter/paramedic in June 2017. From 2014 to 2015 he worked for American Medical Response and from 2015 to 2017 for Mercy Ambulance.

Firefighter/paramedic Michael "Mike" McKinley began his career in the fire service in July 1998 in Spring Valley.

Engineer Richard "Rick" Pascall died of job-related melanoma on October 1, 2010, at the age of 49. He was hired by the San Miguel Consolidated Fire Protection District in October 1993, after briefly serving with the U.S. Forest Service. He called driving Engine 23 the best job in the world. Engineer Pascall had a Bachelor of Science in Fire Science from San Diego State University. Firefighters transported him from his home with full honors, accompanied by personnel of San Miguel, Lakeside, Viejas, and Alpine Fire Departments. Flags were flown at half staff in his honor.

In the Operations Division there are three platoons consisting of three firefighters per unit, per station, and one battalion chief on duty, totaling 25 positions per 24-hour day. All three platoons rotate duty coverage throughout the year resulting in 24-hour shifts calculated into a 56-hour work week. Each fire unit consists of a firefighter/paramedic, engineer, and captain.

The district has eight fire stations.

Station 14 is located at 3255 Helix Street in Spring Valley.

Station 15 and the administrative headquarters is located at 2850 Via Orange Way in Spring Valley. It houses Truck 15, a 2020 Pierce Arrow XT.

Station 16 is located at 905 Gillespie Drive in Spring Valley.

On March 1, 2020, San Miguel Fire and Rescue received a 107-foot heavy-duty aerial ladder named Truck 15..

Truck 15 has 107-feet of vetical and 100-feet of horizonal reach.

Firefighter/Paramedic Grotke on top of San Miguel's Truck 15 107- foot ladder.

Station 18 is located at 1811 Suncrest Boulevard in El Cajon.

Station 19 is located at 727 East Bradley Avenue in El Cajon.

Station 21 is located at 10105 Vivera Drive in La Mesa.

Station 22 is located at 11501 Via Rancho Santa Fe in El Cajon.

Station 23 is located at 2140 Dehesa Road in El Cajon.

Chief Brainard said: "It is my hope that you never need our emergency services, but know that we stand ready to respond, 24 hours per day."

San Miguel's Brush 14 was assigned to the Valley Fire, September 2020.

CALLS RECALLED:

*2018:   The Green Fire burned 10 acres in Rancho San Diego before being extinguished by San Miguel Fire & Rescue, Cal Fire, and one helicopter. Several residents were evacuated.

*2019:   The department responded to over 13,000 fire and medical aid emergencies in 2019. Crews respond to calls covering commercial and industrial operations, single-family residences, large apartment buildings and condominium projects, and urban/wildland interface area.

*2020:   On July 30, 2020, a wildfire near the reservoir in Spring Valley burned 3 acres.

*2020:   On August 1, 2020, firefighters were part of the Central Zone Strike Team assigned to the Apple Fire in Riverside. Crews were dispatched at 3:30 a.m.

*2020:   On August 5, 2020, a San Miguel crew was at the Apple Fire, providing structure defense in the Oak Glen area. The Apple Fire started on July 31 and burned 33,424 acres.

*2020: On August 7, 2020, the personnel assisted Chula Vista Fire Department with a vegetation fire near Main Street and Heritage Road.

*2020: On August 6, 2020, firefighters rescued a kitten from the top of a power pole. No one knew who the owner was so the kitten was taken back to the station for shelter and food. He was then handed over to the Humane Society the next day.

*2020: On August 8, 2020, a vehicle fire spread into vegetation along Highway 94.

*2020: On August 12, 2020, firefighters were sent to the Lake Fire in the Angeles National Forest. The Lake Fire started on August 12 and burned 31,089 acres.

*2020: On August 19, 2020, personnel were assigned to the Jones Fire in Northern California near Nevada.

*2020; On August 20, 2020, there was a fire in the 1400 block of N, Magnolia.

*2020: On August 21, 2020, 11 personnel were sent to the Lightning Complex Fires in Northern California.

*2020: On August 21, 2020, firefighters responded to a homeless encampment fire in the vegetation off of Jamacha Road.

*2020: On August 26, 2020, Chief Rich Durrell was assigned as Strike Team Leader for OES Strike Team 6841A at the CZU Lightning Complex Fire, and Captain Ronald Quinlan was assigned as a trainee for the team. The team performed "firing out" operations, burning vegetation ahead of the wildfire to create a buffer to stop it from jumping the road. The fire started on August 17 in the Santa Cruz Mountains and burned 86,509 acres, destroyed 1,490 structures, and killed 1 person.

*2020: On September 6, crews begin assisting with the Valley Fire. The Valley Fire started on September 5 at Japatul Road and Carveacre Road in the Japatul Valley. The fire burned 17,665 acres, destroyed 30 homes and 31 other structures, and damaged 11 structures.

SAN PASQUAL FIRE DEPARTMENT

Twenty-six miles north of San Diego and five miles east of Escondido is San Pasqual Valley, a 17-square-mile area with a population of 28,123.

Eighty-one Kumeyaay Indians lived in the fertile valley in 1835. Four years after the death of Chief Jose Pedro Panto in 1874, the Kumeyaay were evicted from the valley by the San Diego government. The Kumeyaay joined other tribes or moved up into the canyons. A park and a school in Escondido are named after Chief Panto's daughter, Felicita.

The only battle of the Mexican War fought in California took place in San Pasqual on December 6, 1846. Captain Andres Pico's Mexican lancers defeated Brigadier General Stephen W Kearney's American soldiers. While there was only one unconfirmed Mexican death, 22 Americans died in the battle. The two-acre site of the San Pasqual Battlefield Monument was dedicated in 1925 and the 50-acre San Pasqual State Historic Park was dedicated on December 6, 1986.

The Clevengers settled in the valley in 1872. By 1890 the Judsons, Fentons, Rockwoods, and Trussells had moved to San Pasqual.

When San Diego City built Sutherland Dam above the agricultural community in 1954, it cut off the water to San Pasqual. The farmers and dairymen won a suit against the city. Most of San Pasqual was bought by San Diego City in 1957.

The 1,800-acre San Diego Zoo Safari Park in San Pasqual opened on May 9, 1972. The wildlife preserve, showing animals in their natural habitats, attracts over three million visitors a year.

At the east end of the valley is the 238-acre Seventh-day Adventist Church's San Pasqual Academy, the oldest parochial school in California.

The San Pasqual Volunteer Fire Department located at 17701 San Pasqual Valley Road was formed in 1975. It was supported by a benefit fee and augmentation funds. The department had an automatic aid agreement with Ramona Fire Department and San Diego Fire Department.

Past chiefs of the department included Gary Paterson (1975), Hunter (1980), Ben Duncan (1982), Dan Cleveland (1983), Gil Turrentine (1984-2009), David Davis (2009-2014), and Chris Kisslinger (2014). Gilbert Turrentine said, "It's been fun to take a failing fire department and make something out of it." He added that "everybody worked at creating a viable agency that functioned quite well." Chief Turrentine's 55 years of experience as a volunteer firefighter helped to take the department a long way. His grandfather was the first paid chief of the Coronado Fire Department. As a sixteen-year-old boy Gil Turrentine drove one of the two ambulances in all of North County. A first aid card was the only requirement for the job and the ambulance had no radio, It was not unusual for him to drive over an hour to a call. Before joining San Pasqual's department, he was a firefighter for Rincon del Diablo Fire Department. Chief Turrentine's goal was to "mold something for the future." Chief Turrentine died August 13, 2010, at the age of 74.

Chief Turrentine's crew consisted of Assistant Chief Bob Hall, Division Chief Bob Trahan, four captains, eight engineers, and 20 firefighters. They trained every other Sunday, the Wednesday before the Sunday drill, and the Tuesday after the Sunday drill. The firefighters responded to about one call a day.

The first station was a converted chicken coop. The firefighters took the tin off the roof and put tile on it. Later the building was used to store equipment. In 1989 the department built a new station to which sleeping quarters and a kitchen were added in 1992.

A 1945 Federal engine located at the San Pasqual Academy was the first fire engine in the valley. Later there were two 1974 1,000-gpm International triple-combination engines, a 1980 300-gpm Pierce mini pumper, a 1967 brush rig, a 1972 CDF Model 1 with a 500-gallon pump, a 1980 4,400-gallon water tender, a 1984 Chevy rescue rig, a 1958 Ford heavy rescue truck, a 1984 Chevy Stakeside with lift-gate, a 1978 Plymouth Valerie, a 1973 Ford pickup, a 1973 staff car, a 1964 750-gpm Ford triple combination engine, a 1968 Willy jeep, and a 1924 Seagrave. When Captain John Loop's mother died in 1991, he donated a 1974 International engine cab-forward to the department in her honor.

Oftentimes the firefighters of San Pasqual Volunteer Fire Department took rejects from other departments in California and other states and made something usable out of them or they traded with other agencies for what they needed. For instance, when the city off Elsinore wanted to get rid of a hose tower, Chief Turrentine hauled the 4,000-pound tower to San Pasqual. The city of Elsinore paid for the crane to put it on the truck bed.

Chevron Oil Company donated a 1980 4,400-gallon water tender to the department. A driver for the company drove it from Albuquerque, stopping at Phoenix along the way to have the tender decontaminated and serviced before delivering it to the San Pasqual department.

After Rub and Blanche Nelson died, their daughter Carol donated their 1924 Seagrave to the department in December 1991. Eighty-five percent of the fire truck was in its original state and it still ran! The Seagrave was in the 1991 Escondido Christmas parade.

The San Diego County Board of Supervisors ended its contract with the San Pasqual Volunteer Fire Department on September 17, 2014. The San Diego County Fire Authority now purchases and maintains the equipment for Station 84 and Cal Fire and volunteer reserves staff the station.

Calls recalled:

*1898:   John Judson's creamery was destroyed by fire.

*1970s: Years ago, Assistant Chief Bob Hall took a strike team out of Zone 9 during a fire on Dye Road in Ramona. When the San Pasqual firefighters got their engine as far as Ramona, it ran out of gas! Another time, a wheel came off their jeep and hit a car.

Once a man climbed an 80-foot palm tree to rescue a pet falcon. Near the top of the tree, the man dropped his climbing rope. The San Pasqual firefighters requested an aerial ladder from San Diego Fire-Rescue Department to assist in the rescue. When the man was safely on the ground, the first thing he wanted to do was go back up the tree to rescue the bird!

*1974:   In August 1974, a 96-acre blaze three miles northeast of the San Diego Safari Park burned near six homes and destroyed 150 avocado trees.

*1975:   Twenty families were evacuated from San Pasqual in September 1975. A fire that started in the valley spread over 3,000 acres of North County.

*1975:   A brush fire in August 1975 near the San Diego Zoo Safari Park burned 500 acres.

*2014:   The San Pasqual Volunteer Fire Department was fined $1,000 in September 2014 for stealing water from a fire hydrant in Poway on four occasions and delivering the water to a friend of the vice president of the volunteer department's board of directors.

*2018:   In July 2018, a 365-acre wildfire near the San Diego Zoo Safari Park caused evacuation of homes and the closures of roads along Highway 78.

*2018:   In August 2018, a 100-acre brush fire, known as the Cloverdale Fire, east of the San Diego Zoo Safari Park was caused by sparks from a tire rim hitting brush. Firefighters from Cal Fire, San Diego, Escondido, and other departments fought the fire, assisted by three helicopters and two air tankers.

SAN PASQUAL RESERVATION FIRE ACADEMY

The San Pasqual Reservation Fire Academy was established in 2006. It is accredited by the Office of the California State Marshall (CSFM) and the International Fire Service Accreditation Congress (IFSAC). It is the only fire academy in California to provide IFSAC accreditation. With this accreditation, students can compete for positions in the United States and overseas.

The academy is a department of the San Pasqual Band of Mission Indians and is located at 16460 Kumeyaay Way in Valley Center. Battalion Chief John Ghiotto is the director of the academy.

The fourteen-week course, totaling 664 hours, provides for 34 individual certifications and 15.5 college units. The certifications are:

1. IFSAC Firefighter I
2. IFSAC Firefighter 2
3. IFSAC Rope Rescue Level 1
4. IFSAC Vehicle Extrication 1
5. IFSAC Technical Rescue Core
6. IFSAC Hazmat First Responder Operations
7. IFSAC Hazmat First Responder Awareness
8. IFSAC Hazmat Product Control
9. IFSAC Hazmat Personal Protective Equipment
10. IFSAC Wildland Firefighter 1
11. CSFM Auto Extrication
12. CSFM Basic Incident Command System
13. CSFM Firefighter Survival
14. CSFM Confined Space Rescue Awareness
15. CSFM Rapid Intervention Crew Operations
16. CSFM Low Angle Rope Rescue Operation
17. CSFM Fire Control 1, Basic Fire Chemistry
18. CSFM Fire Control 2, Basic Operations, Structural
19. CSFM Hazmat First Responder Operational Level
20. CSFM Fire Control 3B, Structural Firefighting
21. CSFM Accredited Firefighter
22. NWCG (National Wildfire Coordinating Group) Introduction to ICS (Incident Command System)
23. NWCG Basic ICS
24. NWCG Basic Fire Suppression Orientation
25. NWCG Firefighter Training
26. NWCG Firefighter Type 1 Training
27. NWCG Introduction to Wildland Fire Behavior
28. NWCG Human Factors in the Wildland Fire
29. CSTI (California Specialized Training Institute) Hazmat First Responder Awareness
30. CSTI Hazmat First Responder Operations
31. Truck Operation Awareness
32. Swiftwater Rescue Awareness

SAN PASQUAL RESERVATION FIRE DEPARTMENT

The San Pasqual Reservation is on 1,379 acres near Woods Valley, Lower Hellhole, and Bear Valley. In 1910, the U.S. government patented land for a reservation for the San Pasqual Indians in the hills above Lake Wohlford. Most of the tribal members lived off the reservation because they needed to find work near cities. In the 1950s, a tribal hall was built at 16460 Kumeyaay Way in Valley Center and descendants of the original band of Indians began living on the reservation because they did not want to lose the land. The band is led by a five-member council. The reservation has over 1,500 residents.

The Valley View Casino & Hotel opened in 2001 at a cost of $180 million. In March 2018, the casino began a $50 million expansion that added 43,000 square feet to the casino and renovated the existing casino, hotel, and restaurants. The facility has helped tremendously to improve the lives of the San Pasqual Band of Mission Indians.

The current tribal council members are Stephen W. Cope, Justin Quis Quis, Tilda Green, David Toler, Jr., and Joe Chavez.

The San Pasqual Reservation Fire Department was established in 1998. Howard Masy, who retired from Cal Fire, led a crew of volunteer firefighters from 1998 to 2001.

Firefighters Javier Ramirez and Gabriel Vallez with visitor Gloria Warren.

The department now has 20 full-time paid firefighters. The personnel include Harold L. Rodriguez, fire chief; Kenneth Yarger, part-time fire chief; Julian Clay, Richard Vance, Paul Martinez, Nick Alvarado, and Daniel Martinez, captains; Julian Alvarado, Gene Jose, and Adelaide Campoverde, engineers; and firefighters Matthew Alvarado, Johnny Perez, Andy Quintanilla, Todd Baham, Javier Ramirez, Joseph Morales, Bryan Stiver, Elizabeth Scott, Ruby Zwicker, and Gabriel Vallez.

Harold Rodriquez was appointed chief in 2014. From September 1, 2013, to November 21, 2014, Chief Rodriguez oversaw the Valley Center Fire Department. He was the chief of the San Pasqual Reservation Fire Department from February 2001 to August 2013. Previously Chief Rodriquez was a captain at the Barona Fire Department. He attended Moreno Valley Community College, Palomar College, and Fallbrook Union High School.

The station is located at 16460 Kumeyaay Way.

The department has a contract with North County Dispatch JPA (Joint Powers Authority) for dispatch service.

Apparatus includes a 2004 Type 1 HME engine with 1,000-gallon capacity and two command vehicles. A 1998 Type 2 International with a 500-gallon capacity was moved to the San Pasqual Fire Academy to use for training.

On September 24, 2009, the fire department acquired a Spartan tractor driven aerial truck built by Smeal Fire Apparatus Company. It was put into service in November 2010. The truck has a 100-foot aerial ladder as well as a tiller, an axel that is used to steer the truck from the rear. In addition to using the truck on the reservation, it is used for mutual aid calls to Pauma, Pala, Rincon, and Valley Center.

In July 2018, a HME Type III engine was purchased. It has an International 7400 chassis and a Cummins ISL9, 330-hp engine.

The San Pasqual Reservation Fire Department is proud to provide fire, rescue, and emergency medical services to the community. The fire personnel respect the ways and traditions of all the people they care for.

CALLS RECALLED:

*2003: Sixty-seven homes were destroyed and 1,400 acres burned on the San Pasqual Reservation in the Cedar Fire. Most of the homes were not insured. The home of Francis Jones, 94, the oldest resident of the reservation, burned within 15 minutes. San Pasqual Kumeyaay Audrey Toler, 76, survived the fire standing shoeless in an open field. Pasqual member Steven Lovett, a U.S. Navy corpsman who returned from Iraq in August 2003, was severely burned when he helped a woman to safety. Her sister died in a car nearby. "Fire doesn't know city limits or reservation boundaries," said Allen E. Lawson, the San Pasqual tribal chairman in 2003. "It doesn't discriminate on the basis of skin color or wealth."

*2003: The fire personnel had 716 calls in 2003.

*2007: The Witch Creek Fire burned 17,200 acres on the San Pasqual, Pauma-Yuima, Rincon, La Jolla, and Pala reservations.

*2016: On October 11, 2016, emergency personnel from San Pasqual Reservation Fire Department, Valley Center Fire Department, Mercy Ambulance, and Reach 16 helicopter worked as a team to save the life of Jacob Bennett, a San Diego Gas & Electric lineman. While Bennett was working on a metal pole that was replacing a wooden one, a high voltage line came in contact with a grounded line. For almost ten minutes Bennett hung suspended in cardiac arrest. The San Pasqual Reservation Fire Department was first on the incident and used a defibrillator to start Bennett's heart.

*2020: In April 2020, a crash on State Route 76 at Rincon Ranch Road in Pauma Valley killed one driver.

SANTA YSABEL RESERVATION FIRE DEPARTMENT

Firefighter Matthew Molitor with visitor Lori Vouros at Santa Ysabel Reservation Fire Department.

Since 2011, the FEMA Industrial Fire and Safety Association (I.F.S.A.) has provided funds for expenses such as apparatus and salaries. Previously, the department was run by the reservation.

The tribal fire station, located at 1 School House Canyon Road, is manned by a captain and one to two firefighters 24 hours a day, 7 days a week. It is home to a 2006 HME engine and a 2005 Pierce engine, as well as a water tender and a brush rig.

The department has a mutual aid agreement with Cal Fire and Mesa Grande Reservation Fire Department.

The Iipay Nation of Santa Ysabel, formerly known as Santa Ysabel Band of Diegueno Mission Indians, live on a 15,270-acre reservation in the northeastern part of San Diego County near Mesa Grande and Black Mountain to the west and Volcan Mountain and Julian to the east. The band has 700 members.

The reservation was founded in 1893. The Iipay Nation of Santa Ysabel is governed by an elected tribal council. In 2007, the tribe established a constitution to protect their culture and land.

The tribe owned the Santa Ysabel Casino on State Route 79 for seven years. They went out of business on February 3, 2014, after being denied chapter 11 bankruptcy. In January 2019, the Iipay Nation of Santa Ysabel opened a marijuana dispensary at the closed casino.

SANTEE FIRE DEPARTMENT

Santee, located twenty miles northeast of San Diego, was founded by George Cowles. His widow, Jennie Cowles, married real estate developer Milton Santee and convinced the voters in Cowleston to rename the city Santee in 1893.

Besides having residential and commercial buildings, the city has a large wildland-urban interface. It is bordered by the 5,800-acre Mission Trails Regional Park and State Routes 52, 67, and 125.

The Santee Fire Department serves a population of 58,000. Personnel respond from two fire stations in a 16.5 square-mile area.

The first fire engine was a 1933 Dodge government surplus truck which was housed in the back of Floyd's Shell Station on Mission Avenue. Shortly afterwards, the volunteer firemen got a 1942 Dodge fire engine for the protection of Edgemoor Hospital.

The department was established in 1956 as a County Fire Protection District. In March 1957, the district leased land from the county to build a fire station at 10130 Mission Gorge Road at a cost of $13,000. It also bought a 1957 International Harvester chassis with a 750-gpm Hale pump and a Peter Pirsch & Sons body.

In August 1959, two firemen were hired and paid $350 a month. In October 1959, J. J. Kavanaugh was appointed as the first paid fire chief. He resigned in July 1960. Assistant Chief Carl Sullan acted as interim chief until he was promoted to chief.

During the time Carl Sullan was chief from January 1961 to May 1962, two more firemen were hired so that a two-platoon system could be implemented. A 1954 GMC pumper was purchased from the El Cajon Fire Department.

John Clarke was picked in May 1962 to be in charge of ten paid firemen. He had previously served for 22 years with the New York Fire Department. A Peter Wheat Bread was converted into the department's first ambulance.

A house at 9312 Carlton Hills Boulevard was purchased in 1963 for $12,700 and converted into Fire Station 2 at a cost of $30,000. It housed a 1964 Seagrave 1,000-gpm pumper and a two-men crew.

In April 1964, Chief George Wilder replaced Chief John Clarke. Chief Wilder served 43 years in the United States Navy with tours in World War I and World War II. He worked for 14 years with the Santa Barbara Fire Department between the wars. While in the U.S. Navy, he ran firefighting schools in San Pedro, Roosevelt Naval Base, and Philadelphia.

Santee fire chief car 1954 Ford

Santee 1960: 1942 Dodge and 1947 Chevrolet

By July 1965, the Santee Fire Department had 15 firemen. The annual budget was $269,250 ($192,000 for wages, $21,000 for capital, $25,000 for maintenance, $20,000 as a reserve, and $11,250 in a bond). An Air Force tanker was converted into the district's first brush rig.

After Chief Wilder retired on June 30, 1965, Elmer Snelson was hired as chief in January 1966. In 1967, the Heartland Mutual Aid Agreement was signed by Santee, El Cajon, La Mesa, Lakeside, Lemon Grove, and Spring Valley.

In 1970, the annual budget was $625,000, and there were 23 firefighters and one dispatcher. In February 1972, a new fire station at 8950 Cottonwood Avenue was dedicated. It replaced the station at 10130 Mission Gorge Road.

Chief Snelson retired in November 1973. Ron Berry served as chief from November 1973 to January 1988. In 1975, the Santee Fire Department operated the first paramedic ambulance in San Diego County. At this time, the department adopted a three-platoon schedule. The year 1977 marked the end of volunteer firefighters because of liability issues.

In 1980, Proposition K, a Benefit Assessment Fee, passed with a 78% approval. The proposition supplemented the tax revenue lost when Proposition 13 passed in 1978 limiting property taxation.

The city incorporated in 1980. In 1985, the fire department became a municipal city department. It had a Class 2 ISO rating in 1986. The department continues to have an ISO Rating 2.

In 1983, an Emergency One truck with a 95-foot aerial platform was purchased at a cost of $365,000.

In 1996, Proposition 218 ensured that taxes on property owners were subject to voter approval. This affected the paramedic benefit fee that was increased without a two-thirds voter approval. In 1997, Proposition F required that a charter amendment require more than a simple majority vote of the electorate. Santee firefighters campaigned for continued paramedic service to the residents of Santee, Lakeside, and Bostonia. The proposition passed with 91.23% of the residents voting in favor of the fee! The Santee Fire Department was the first department in Heartland to place paramedics on engine and truck companies.

In 2011, Santee had 17 firefighters.

In May 2015, Santee hosted a regional wildland training exercises for 300 firefighters from the Santee, El Cajon, La Mesa, Lemon Grove, Alpine, Barona and Viejas fire departments. The firefighters performed live training, including mock evacuations, laying out fire hoses, and structure defense.

Santee 1964 Seagrave, 1st new pumper in chrome yellow, now red is the standard color on Santee rigs.

1971 Ford, Santee's first tall squirt pumper.

2nd ambulance

The men who have served as Santee Fire Department's chiefs are: Claar Teitsort (1955-1956), Arlin Van Atta (1959), J.J. Kavanaugh (1959-1960), Carl Sullen (1961-1962), John Clarke (1962-1964), George Wilder (1964-1965), Elmer Snelson (1966-1973), Ron Berry (1973-1988), George E. Tockstein, Jr. (1988-1996), Edd Long (1996-1997), Bob Pfohl (1997-2006), Mike Rottenberg (2006-2010), Bob Leigh (2011-2014), Richard Mattick (2014-2015), Richard Smith (2015-2018), and John Garlow (2019-).

Bob Leigh was appointed chief in 2011 and retired in April 2014. His salary was $145,000. Leigh formalized maintenance procedures for critical fire apparatus, initiated a reorganization plan calling for a chief, deputy chief, and three battalion chiefs, and made a plan to ensure continuation of city functions in a major disaster.

Richard Smith served as fire chief from December 16, 2015, to December 12, 2018. He was with the Santee Fire Department for 28 years and was appointed division chief in 2012. Previously, for seven years, he was the training officer. In the 1990s he was an arson investigator. He has been a volunteer instructor training firefighters in Tecate, Mexico, for the Firefighters Crossing Borders. Chief Smith has a Bachelor of Arts in Psychology from San Diego State University.

Public education van

Cab and chassis from 1992, rest built by firemen

John Garlow was appointed Santee's chief in February 2019. He was promoted through the ranks, including captain in 2009, division chief in 2016, and acting chief in January 2019. Chief Garlow worked for the Alpine Fire Protection District as a cadet firefighter early in his career. Also in February 2019, Battalion Chief Tim Stuber was promoted to deputy chief.

Those serving as Santee's fire chiefs currently are: Fire Chief John Garlow; Deputy Chief Tim Stuber; Division Chief Richard "Rich" Smith, who handles operations and acts as the city's fire marshal; Battalion Chief Brad Peterson, who oversees B-division as well as public education and EMS; and Battalion Chief Jeff Hernandez, who oversees C-division as well as fleet, facilities, and fire department safety.

The department has 48 firefighters. The Santee Firefighters Association became a chartered local of the IAFF on May 17, 2004. The association joined the California Professional Firefighters (CPF) in May 2007. The board members are Jesse Fournier, president; Eddie Adame, vice-president; Tony Romero, secretary; Matt Brown, treasurer; and Jeremy Carroll, board member.

The fire administration offices are located at 10601 Magnolia Avenue.

Haz Mat/rescue rig at Station 4

Station 4, located at 8950 Cottonwood Avenue, houses Engine 4 (2016 Pierce Arrow XT with 500 gallons of water); Truck 4 (2016 Pierce Arrow XT 100; tractor-drawn aerial); Brush 4 (2019 Freightliner 4 x 4 / Pierce FX3 Type III woodland); and 2009 Ford F450 Super Duty ambulance.

Station 5, located at 9130 Carlton Oaks Drive opened in 2000. It houses Engine 5 (2014 Pierce Arrow XT); 2000 Pierce Saber rescue pumper; and Ford F450 Super Duty ambulance.

The history of Santee's fire apparatus includes: 1933 Dodge, 1942 Dodge, 1957 International Harvester, 1960 brush rigs, 1964 Seagrave, 1970 Crown, 1971 Ford telesqurt, 1974 Clark, 1980 brush rigs, 1983 E-One aerial platform, 1984 E-One hurricane, 1986 Pierce Arrow telesqurt, 1990 E-One Hush, 1996 Model 15 brush rig, 1996 Pierce Dash, 1999 Pierce Saber telesqurt, 2000 Pierce Saber rescue, and 2004 Pierce Arrow XT.

Beginning in the 1960s, fire engines were painted yellow instead of red. Research showed that yellow fire engines were less likely to be involved in accidents. However, the engine delivered to Santee in September 2016 was red! The department decided to change from yellow to red as red is a tradition dating back to the early days of fire service. Battalion Chief Stuber, chairperson of the apparatus committee, went to the Pierce Manufacturing plant in Appleton, Wisconsin, three times to review pre-construction and meet with the engineers to see if the engine was built to specifications, and to make a final inspection. The engine has up-to-date electronics, including Panasonic Toughbook, which includes a camera, backlit keyboard, GPS receiver, and a broadband.

In 2016, the Firehouse Subs Safety Foundation provided the Santee Fire Department with grant funds for life-saving equipment. A thermal imaging camera and a vehicle stabilization kit were purchased with $20,000 from the foundation. The thermal imaging camera helps in detecting fires behind walls and ceilings and helps to rescue victims who are obscured by lack of visibility. The stabilization kit is used to hold a vehicle in place during an accident. The foundation has granted over $40 million to provide equipment, training, and support to first responders.

Division Chief Johnny L. Terry served the department for nearly 30 years. He joined the department as a volunteer. Terry died on May 2, 2010.

Six firefighters who have lost their lives during their years in service with the Santee Fire Department are memorialized with engraved granite stones at the front of Station 4.

Thomas J. Whelchel, who served with the Santee Fire Department from September 1960 to October 1968, died of a heart attack in his home on October 23, 1963, at the age of 33. He graduated from Brown Military Academy and joined the Air Force in 1947. He served in the military during the Korean War until 1959 and attained the rank of staff sergeant. His badge was retired and still hangs on the wall at Station 4 in a shadowbox. The flagpole at Station 5 (formerly Station 2) was dedicated in his memory.

Michael R. Kiehl, who joined the Santee Fire Department in October 1962, was killed in Vietnam on April 19, 1966, at the age of 21. The Santee Firefighters Association has maintained a perpetual scholarship in his name ever since. A plaque hangs in a shadowbox at Station 4 in his memory.

Gary J. Block, who served with the Santee Fire Department from August 1966 to August 1969, suffered burns to 65% of his body at a training fire in a condemned two-bedroom house. He passed away from his injuries on August 21, 1969, at the age of 28. He was a first-aid instructor and a reserve and rescue squad leader for the Sheriff's Department. A Heroism Award was created in his name for extraordinary acts of heroism under life-threatening conditions.

Jack D. Stephenson, who was with the department from May 1966 to July 1977, died on July 25, 1977, at the age of 37. He was a veteran of the U.S. Air Force. Stephenson was hired on May 1, 1966, and was known as "Stovepipe" by his co-workers due to his wiry figure. Over the next 11 years, he worked his way through the ranks to become a fire captain. Captain Stephenson was the driving force behind what led to the Santee Fire Department's paramedic program in 1975, the first fire department paramedic program in San Diego County. He was one of eight firefighters to graduate from the first paramedic class at the UCSD School of Medicine. He was posthumously awarded the Gary J. Block Memorial Firefighter of the Year Award.

Louis R. Ortiz proudly served the department from September 1978 to April 1994. He joined the Santee Fire Protection District on September 21, 1978. He was a CPR instructor and served on several department committees. He was also in the Army National Guard. Ortiz spent nearly 40 straight hours assisting victims of the Northridge earthquake a year prior to his passing. At the age of 50, he was struck and killed by a drunk driver while walking along a street in Ramona on April 4, 1994.

Howard Rayon, who was a member of the department from January 1977 to December 2006, graduated from the Heartland Fire Academy. He was promoted to captain after just six years on the job, then became division chief in 1997 and oversaw operations and training. He was promoted to deputy chief shortly before his

1987 Pierce tele-squirt

retirement in 2005. Chief Rayon was responsible for critical department projects, including the Heartland CAD (Computer-assisted Dispatch) and 800 MHz projects. He continued to teach fire service courses. He was a safety officer on one of the California Type 1 Incident Management Teams. He became a lawyer and specialized in labor law and firefighter litigation. Rayon was a charter member of the Laguna Hot Shots in the Cleveland National Forest in 1974. The California State Firefighters' Association annual conference in 2009 was named in his honor. He passed away on October 18, 2009, from a job-related illness.

Victor, a rescued lab/bulldog/hound dog, became a member of the department in June 2018. His owner was sent to prison in 2017 without the possibility of parole. The dog was placed in protective custody and then taken to the Haven Humane Society in Redding. While at the shelter, the staff noticed his outgoing personality and intense drive for a ball and contacted the National Disaster Dog Foundation in Santa Paula. The foundation trained Victor and he was partnered with Firefighter/paramedic Billy Walkenhorst, a member of the San Diego Urban Search and Rescue Task Force 8. Walkenhorst takes care of the dog both at work and at his home. He is the only one who feeds him! When Walkenhorst goes on an emergency call in Santee, Victor stays in a kennel at the station.

Day or night, the firefighters and paramedics are available to help the people in the community and surrounding areas.

CALLS RECALLED:

*1950:   The Conejos Fire burned 64,000 acres.

*1956:   The Inaja Fire killed 11 firefighters, destroyed five homes, and burned 43,904 acres.

*1966:   There was a 300-acre brush fire in Santee that started at Conjeo Road and Mast Boulevard.

*1967:   The Woodson Fire destroyed 26 homes and burned 55,000 acres.

*1977:   At the Cajon Speedway, a vehicle became airborne and landed in the pit area. One person was killed and 18 injured.

*1982:   At Cuyamaca Street and Prospect Avenue in Santee, an ambulance was struck broadside by a station wagon. The ambulance flipped onto the passenger side and burst into flames. The driver, Bill Garland, suffered second- and third-degree burns.

*1988:   In September 1988, the Cowles Mountain Fire burned 600 acres and damaged 20 homes. Chief George Tockstein said about 250 firefighters responded to the brush fire.

*1998:   In November 1988, the Old Topanga Fire killed 3 people, burned 18,000 acres, and destroyed 359 homes. More than 7,000 firefighters fought the fire.

*2001:   On March 5, 2001, a 15-year-old boy opened fire on students at Santana High School, killing two students and wounding 13 others.

*2003:   On October 25, 2003, the massive Cedar Fire was started in the Cleveland National Forest by a lost hunter.

*2010:   Firefighters fought a 50-acre brush fire north of Santee Lakes.

*2010:   In September 2010, forty acres of brush threatened homes near Carlton Hills Boulevard and Lake Canyon Road. Four helicopters and two Cal Fire airtankers were used to assist firefighters on the ground.

*2011:   Crews put out a 12-acre brush fire behind homes off Carlton Oaks.

*2012:   A fire at a home on Santana Street caused $100,000 in damage.

*2013:   On January 15, 2013, firefighters responded to a two-alarm fire that damaged a four-bedroom 3,000-square-foot home. It took about an hour to extinguish the fire.

*2014:   In April 2014, a brush fire burned along Carlton Oaks Drive. Santee and Lakeside firefighters are joined by a strike team of five Cal Fire engines.

*2015:   In September 2015, flight instructor Robert C. Sarrisin, 59, of Rancho Penasquitos and student pilot, Jeffrey Michael Johnson, 50 of El Cajon were killed when their plane crashed into a roof of a Santee house.

*2016:   In March 2016, a bicyclist was killed after she strayed from the curb and into the path of a Toyota Avalon on Cuyamaca Avenue.

*2018:   In February 2018, a small plane crashed into a storage yard in Santee shortly after taking off from Gillespie Field, killing two people and one of two dogs who were onboard.

*2018:   When a young girl saw that two trees were on fire in the front yard of her home on Avanti Avenue at about 3:40 a.m., she woke up her family. There was no serious damage to the house.

*2018:   In November 2018, a man in his 70s was killed when a fire destroyed his home. A sheriff's deputy who was first on the scene tried to rescue him, but the smoke was too intense, Santee Battalion

Chief John Sengebusch said. Firefighters then attempted a rescue but were unable to reach him.

*2019:   A car exploded in January 2019 on Carlton Hills Boulevard. Crews quickly put out the fire.

*2019:   In February, a large construction truck came down a steep road and plowed into a Santee home. No one was hurt.

*2019:   In March 2019, a woman was killed when her home at the Mission Del Magnolia Mobile Home Park caught fire. "Within seconds, literally seconds, the entire home was on fire, and you saw fire blowing out the front windows," Battalion Chief Justin Matsushita said.

*2019:   On May 7, 2019, at Magnolia Avenue and Riverview Parkway, a 32-year-old man walking on Magnolia Avenue was hit by a hit-and-run driver and taken to the hospital with serious head injuries.

*2019:   In May 2019, a mobile home at the Cameron Mobile Estates on Magnolia Avenue was destroyed by a fire. Firefighters from Santee, Lakeside, San Miguel, and Heartland Fire & Rescue responded to the blaze, with the first crews arriving within 5 minutes of the initial call.

*2020:   In January 2020, a 46-year-old Santee man was killed when his 2016 Dodge Ram rolled 50 feet down an embankment east of Forester Creek Road.

*2020:   In September 2020, a brush fire broke out along Forester Creek, north of State Route 52 near the junction with State Route 125 close to homes. It burned about five acres. Four strike teams were assigned to the fire and two helicopters dropped water on it.

SHELTER VALLEY FIRE DEPARTMENT

In 1846 General Stephen W. Kearney and his troops along with Kit Carson traveled the Great Southern Overland Stage Trail to reach San Pasqual Valley for a battle between the Americans and the Mexicans.

In that same year of 1846 a Mormon caravan traveling through nearby Box Canyon became trapped in a ravine. The Mormons took their covered wagons apart piece by piece, board by board, to get over the ravine, then used axes to cut the remaining walls of the ravine to carve out a path for the wagons. They rebuilt each wagon to pass through what is known as Box Canyon in Shelter Valley. The now famous Butterfield Stagecoach traveled this same route, taking passengers, mail, and freight along the desert floor from 1861 to 1865. Along this historic route traveled by the pioneers is the isolated community of Shelter Valley with its volunteer fire department.

This desert community is surrounded on the east, south, and west by desert state parks. To the north is found the 7,000-acre Starr-Rutherford cattle ranch.

The temperature in this community can reach 116 degrees in the summer. The low has been recorded at 8 degrees in the winter. The daily temperature variances sometimes reach 65 degrees.

The desert chaparral in this area consists of creosote bushes, mesquite, wild apricots, and cactus. While the Santa Ana winds may wreck havoc on many fire departments fighting wildland fires, winds affect this particular community very little. The Santa Anas blow high above the town, hence the name "Shelter."

Today approximately 320 people live in Shelter Valley. When Fire Chief Tom McBride helped pave the way in 1982 for the department to continue operating after the County of San Diego stopped funding it, the fire department had about 16 volunteers. Although the desert area is enormous, the Shelter Valley Volunteer Fire Department only responded to a 6 square-mile area when the County of San Diego ceased to fund the department. The department received its revenue entirely from donations and fundraisers.

The fire station at 7260 Great Southern Overland Stage Trail housed two vehicles, a 1953 1,000-gpm GMC with a 1,000-gallon tank and a 1976 International tender that held 750 gallons of water.

The Shelter Valley firefighters had no ties to the County of San Diego or any other agencies, even for dispatch. The townspeople developed their own dispatch system.

Residents in the community took turns monitoring a specific phone line 24 hours a day, seven days a week. No matter who was on duty or where a home was, the call forwarding system relayed the emergency number to the resident who was on call.

John N, Taylor, who retired from the Julian Union School District, became the fire chief in 1987. Like many of the residents of Shelter Valley, Chief Taylor, a fiercely independent man, has a character to match the harsh landscape. He spent three years building his retirement home. He was followed by Chief Kevin Bennett, who had been with the department since 1999.

The Shelter Valley Volunteer Fire Department was originally formed in 1976. The order of chiefs were J.C. Carlyle, George Ewing, Tom McBride, George Polk, Mike Trendly, John N. Taylor, and Kevin Bennett.

Now the San Diego County Fire Authority contracts with Cal Fire (Station 53) to staff the station. Cal Fire responds to fire and medical emergencies from Anza Borrego State Park to the Imperial County and Highway 78. It is staffed with two firefighters

on each shift, one who is a paramedic. Station 53 houses Engine 53 (2017 International 7400), Patrol 53 (2016 Ford F-550), Water Tender, and Rescue 53 (2004 Ford F-350).

In 2012 the San Diego County Fire Authority spent $686,000 remodeling the fire station with a 1,200-square-foot bay for apparatus, a reception area, three bedrooms, and a new kitchen. The water supply was increased from 10,000 gallons to 30,000 gallons.

CALLS RECALLED:

*1981:   On May 23, 1981, the volunteer firefighters assisted the California Division of Forestry on a 3-acre brush fire near Little Blair Valley. The fire was started from the spark of a pick used by a camper.

*2003:   After the Cedar Fire, 80 evacuees from Julian and Ramona went to Shelter Valley. Susan Pugh, a registered nurse who lost her home in the Cedar Fire, helped the department's nurse, Valerie Rogers, set up a triage center to help the evacuees.

*2011:   The Great Fire started October 1, 2011, at 12:53 p.m. on the south side of Highway 78 and Scissors Crossing near Shelter Valley. It burned 2,135 acres. There were 379 fire personnel, 15 fire engines, one helicopter, three dozers, and five water tenders on the wildfire.

*2012:   The Vallecitos Fire burned 350 acres southeast of Julian.

*2012:   About 100 residents were evacuated from Shelter Valley as a 1,000-acre fire, named the Banner Fire, moved toward Granite Mountain in May 2012. Fire crews with 30 engines, four helicopters, six air tankers, and one bulldozer fought the blaze.

*2016:   A woman was burned when she went into her home on Lost Dollar Trail to rescue her dogs from a fire. She was taken to the UCSD Burn Center by helicopter.

SOLANA BEACH FIRE DEPARTMENT

Solana Beach covers 3.4 square miles and has a population of 13,494 (2017). It is 17 miles north of San Diego, the Pacific Ocean is to west, Encinitas to the north, and Del Mar to the south. Many of the restaurants and shops in Solana Beach are along the historic Route 101 coast highway. Since there is rising sea levels and coastal erosion, much of Solana Beach's coastline is protected by a sea wall, which is partly funded by a fee levied on oceanfront property owners.

The area was originally settled by Native Americans known as La Jollans in 7,000 B.C. Then the Kumeyaay-Ipai were in the region until the mid-1700s when the Spanish invaded. In 1821, Spain gave the land to Mexico. It became part of the United States in 1851, after the Mexican-American War.

The city began to grow when Lake Hodges Dam was built in 1918. The same year, the Santa Fe Irrigation District was created. Colonel Ed Fletcher purchased 201 acres from a farmer in 1922 to develop Solana Beach. During the Great Depression and World War II there was a downturn. In the 1950s, economic growth resumed. Solana Beach incorporated in 1986. In 1995 the Santa Fe train station, serving both Amtrak and the Coaster was moved from Del Mar to Solana Beach.

In the 1960s, the Rancho Santa Fe Board of Directors shared the chief's position with the Solana Beach Fire Department. The San Dieguito Ambulance District, known as CSA-17, was formed by the San Diego County Board of Supervisors in 1969 to provide ambulance services to the cities of Encinitas, Del Mar, Solana Beach, and Rancho Santa Fe.

Fire chiefs of the Solana Beach Fire Department include: Elmo Taylor (1949-1953), Philip Wiswell (1953-1954), A. W. Crosswaite (1954-1955), H. H. Beck (1955-1956), Lee Wilson (1956-1963), R. W. Stephenson (1963-1964), James A. Fox (1964-1981), Arthur Peter Fox (1981-1987), Fred Irwin (1987-1993), William Robuck (1994-1994), David Holmerud, interim chief (1995-1995), George K. George (1995-2003), David Ott (2003-2009), Mark Muir (2009-2011), Scott Henry (2011-2013), Mike Daigle (2013-2015), and Mike Stein (2016-).

James A. Fox, who came to California from England with his wife Pat and sons John and Peter, was hired by the Rancho Santa Fe Fire Protection District board in 1956. He was the chief also of Solana Beach Fire Department. Under the leadership of Chief Fox, the training of the volunteers was improved, the first paid firefighters were hired, and the first Mobile Intensive Care Units in the country was constructed.

He is one of only three in the Rancho Santa Fe Fire Protection District to receive the Bell of Distinction.

Peter Fox, the son of Chief James Fox, was appointed chief of Rancho Santa Fe Fire Protection District in 1981. Fox was also chief of the Solana Beach Fire Department but that agreement was severed by Solana Beach after the San Diego County Grand Jury examined the validity of it.

Chief David Holmerud was with the Solana Beach Fire Department for 32 years. He was the interim chief of the department in 1995 and assisted Chief David Ott as deputy chief. He graduated from the National Fire Academy Executive Fire Officer Certification in 1993.

David Ott was chief of Del Mar and Solana Beach from July 2003 to October 2009. In 2005 Chief Ott also became deputy city manager for Solana Beach and city

manager in 2006. Ott was a firefighter and engineer with the U.S. Forest Service for six years, then at Camp Pendleton and in Coronado. Beginning in 2000, he was the fire chief and public service director in Imperial Beach before coming to Solana Beach. He retired as city manager of Solana Beach on November 28, 2014.

Chief Ott earned a certificate in Public Administration from San Diego State University; Bachelor of Science in Fire Administration and Bachelor of Science in Fire Prevention Technology from Cogswell Polytechnical College in Sunnyvale, California, graduating Magna Cum Laude and Summa Cum Laude; Master of Human Resource Management from the University of Redlands; and a Master of Organizational Management from Grand Canyon University in Arizona. In 2004, he graduated from the National Fire Academy's four-year Executive Fire Officer Program.

In October 2009, Solana Beach, Encinitas, Del Mar, and the Rancho Santa Fe Fire Protection District entered into a two-year cooperative agreement to share management functions for their fire departments to avoid duplicate positions. The Rancho Santa Fe Fire Protection District withdrew from the agreement in 2013. Solana Beach, Encinitas, and Del Mar share the cost of a fire chief, deputy chief, and three battalion chiefs. The senior staff supervise fire suppression operations and emergency medical services; emergency management; fire prevention activities; purchasing of materials, supplies, and fire equipment; management of service contracts; and administrative functions. The department has automatic aid agreements with San Diego and the Rancho Santa Fe Fire District. It provides mutual aid to the Northern San Diego Zone, San Diego County, and as needed throughout California.

Mark Muir became chief of Solana Beach, Encinitas, and Del Mar in 2009. Chief Mark Muir, who served in the fire service for 35 years and the Encinitas City Council for seven years, was chief of the Encinitas Fire Department from 2006 to 2011. He joined the Lemon Grove Fire Department when he was 18 years old, then became a firefighter in Encinitas for most of his career.

Scott Henry was chosen to lead the Solana Beach, Del Mar, and Encinitas Fire Departments in December 2011 after serving as deputy chief. He joined the Encinitas Fire Department in 1980. In 1987 he became a captain. He was active in the Burn Institute.

Jon Canavan served as chief from October 14, 2013, to December 5, 2013. He decided not to keep the job because of the time and energy commitment needed in the position. Previously he served as the Poway Fire Department division chief. He joined the Poway Fire Department in 2003 after spending 13 years with the San Marcos Fire Department.

On December 19, 2013, Deputy Chief Mike Daigle was promoted to chief. He replaced Jon Canavan, who resigned after holding the position for only two months and returned to Poway as fire marshal. Chief Daigle, who was in the fire service fo over 30 years, retired in late 2015.

After serving as acting chief for eight months, Mike Stein was promoted to chief of Del Mar, Solana Beach, and Encinitas in 2016. Chief Stein was hired by Encinitas in September 2013. During his 30-year career in the fire service, he has moved up the ranks from reserve firefighter to chief.

In 2009 as a battalion chief, Stein was assigned to San Diego's Office of Homeland Security where he managed a regional training program for both fire and law enforcement personnel from around the entire county. In 2013, he was given the Major's Award from the U.S. Army Sergeant of the California Emergency Management Agency for his work in Homeland Security.

Chief Stein holds a Bachelor of Science in Business Administration from San Diego State University and a Master of Public Administration from Cal State Dominguez Hills. He is a third generation firefighter with his grandfather serving with the Los Angeles Fire Department and his father serving with the Santa Monica Fire Department for 31 years.

Battalion Chief Dismas Abelman retired on September 19, 2014, after serving Solana Beach, Del Mar, and Encinitas for 10 years. He previously worked at the Coronado Fire Department for 17 years. Chief David Ott said, "His value to the fire service—I have never questioned. He understands what it means to be in the fire service, what a privilege it is to be in the fire service—the ability to help people in sometimes their darkest hour. Dis has always understood that."

The department has 19 personnel. The crews trained 6,475 hours in 2017.

A firefighter/paramedic at the first of five salary steps earns $71,581. A shift captain at the fifth salary step earns $105,518. It can take a firefighter from five to seven years to get a full-time position in a fire department.

Grant Medica joined the department in September 2019. In 2014 he became a volunteer firefighter with the Rainbow Volunteer Fire Department. He was hired by the North County Fire Protection District in December of 2016 as a reserve firefighter/EMT. Grant worked in that role for eight months and then attended Palomar College's Paramedic Class 51. Medica passed his internship with San Diego Fire-Rescue Department and AMR and was promoted to the role of single role paramedic in 2018.

Engineer David Mitchell said: "When I was nineteen years old, standing on a sidewalk, I saw an elderly couple who were crossing the street get hit by a truck and die. It sparked my interest in emergency services and helping people. First I

volunteered as a paramedic at the Mt. Laguna Fire Department, then worked with a great group of guys at the National City Fire Department. In 2012, I joined the Solana Beach Fire Department."

The station, located at 500 Lomas Santa Fe Drive, was built in 1990. It is staffed 24 hours a day with three firefighters on the engine and three firefighters on the ladder truck. There is also an American Medical Response (AMR) ambulance with a paramedic and an EMT. It houses Engine 2411, a 2016 Pierce Arrow XT PUC Detroit Diesel and a Pierce Type 1 105-foot aerial ladder truck. It has retired a 1989 Spartan MS40-2042.

The Solana Beach Firefighters Association (Local 3779) has an annual pancake breakfast at Fiesta del Sol; an annual Guns and Hoses Charity Golf Tournament at the Lomas Santa Fe Country Club to benefit the Iverson Foundation for Active Awareness; an annual toy drive during the Christmas season for Marine Corps

families; and joins other firefighters from throughout the county every year in the Boot Drive to collect money to benefit the Burn Institute.

The Solana Beach CERT (Community Emergency Response Team) members attend a 25-hour training course, free to residents or local employees who are at least 18 years old. They are trained in how to save lives and property during a major disaster to supplement first responders. On July 11, 2013, the Solana Beach CERT received a $2,500 SAFE grant from the San Diego Gas and Electric.

The department received a $34,097 grant of extrication equipment from the Firehouse Subs Public Safety Foundation in July 2019. Firefighter/paramedic Charles Mead said, "This grant will make a huge impact for our fire department and community as the new equipment will allow faster extrication times for our collisions. The new extrication tools will be very effective in our response to traffic collisions."

In 2019, a firewall art sculpture by Betsy Schultz was placed in front of the station. The artwork, 11.5 ft. x 3 ft., is handmade of ceramics, metal, soda ash chunk glass, fused-glass, LED lighting, and a printed Lexan panel. The metal structure contains red, orange and yellow embers of soda ash glass, hand-selected and placed to represent a mosaic of smoldering fire. The front of the sculpture, facing Loma Santa Fe, is a combination of Betsy Schultz's sculptural ceramics and mosaic work using specialty fused-glass created by Solana Beach artist Chris Austin. The back of the sculpture is a steel laser-cut door backed by a Lexan panel with a custom printed photo-composition. The size of the firewall and internal LED lights make it highly visible, day or night, to those walking and passing in cars or on bikes. The lighting of the chunk glass evolves throughout the day, resembling glowing embers with the darkening of the sky. The ceramic shapes that front the firewall transform at night into silhouettes, revealing the abstract shapes of dancing fire. Betsy Schultz worked with VDLA Architects, who designed the landscape plan. The Solana Beach Civic and Historical Society and Garden Club helped to create a coastal native garden and two seating areas complete with boulders and decomposed granite. The artwork is dedicated to the Solana Beach firefighters.

The Solana Beach Fire Department has an ISO rating of 1! It was upgraded to a 1 from a 3 in 2012. ISO surveyed 48,632 communities across the nation. Less than 0.4 percent (only 178 fire departments) of these communities have a rating of 1. In 2011, the department not only excelled in response times but was nearly 40 percent above the national average in cardiac arrest survival rates.

The personnel are committed to delivering a high level of firefighting, rescue, fire prevention, and emergency services.

Engineer David Mitchell

CALLS RECALLED:

*1967:   The San Diego County Fire Chiefs Association invited 27 bomberos from Mexican communities to come to the United States for a four-day training school. Operation Amigo was conducted on the hills above Solana Beach. Training in fire tactics, hose lays, fighting flammable liquid fires, and more was held at the Del Mar Fairgrounds. On the final day of the training school, a banquet was held for the bomberos.

*1988:   Captain Stuart Henrix and firefighter Larry Reigel were overcome with heat exhaustion while fighting a fire in three condominium apartments on South Sierra Avenue. They were treated at Scripps Memorial Hospital in Encinitas. Damage was $500,000.

*2006:   A home on Glencrest Drive was severely damaged during an early morning fire. Twenty-seven firefighters from agencies throughout the area fought the blaze.

*2014:   In April 2014, smoke was reported coming from a roof vent on an apartment building on South Cedros Avenue. A man was given CPR and transported to UCSD Burn Center with serious burns covering 50 percent of his body.

*2014:   On November 2014, Robert Mark Slusarenko of Long Beach veered to the right and went up an embankment on Interstate 5 north of Lomas Santa Fe Drive. The SUV overturned and his 41 year-old passenger died at the scene.

*2017:   On September 23, 2017, a 50-pound poodle was stranded on a bluff near Pacific Avenue. He was trying to climb up the bluff. Two units from Solana Beach Fire Department and one from Encinitas Fire Department responded. John Morgan, a Solana Beach firefighter, was lowered down the steep cliff. He put a harness on the dog and lifted it to safety.

*2017:   Solana Beach Fire Department responded to 1,859 calls in 2017 (fires, 77; EMS/rescue, 1,073; hazardous conditions, 25; service calls, 117; good intentions, 407; false calls; 152, severe weather, 4; and other, 4). The average response time was 4 min. 41 sec. The structure value loss was $645,690. The structure value saved was $32,230,740.

*2017:   The firefighters from Solana Beach, Del Mar, and Encinitas responded to 48 calls for assistance from departments in California fighting wildfires. Solana Beach firefighters had 13 strike team deployments in 2017 on eight different fires.

*2018:   In July 2018, E237 was assigned to the Strike Team 6417A on Division Foxtrot on the West Fire in Alpine.

*2019:   On July 19, 2019, a fire at the Solana Highlands complex destroyed one second-story unit and forced 14 tenants to evacuate.

*2019:   In November 2019, a three-alarm fire destroyed five condominiums at the Del Mar Beach Club at 825 South Sierra Avenue in Solana Beach. The fire spread to the attic and caused the roof of the building to collapse. Two kittens were rescued from under a bed. They were given oxygen and water. The Red Cross helped some of the families displaced by the fire.

*2019:   On November 27, a fire damaged the kitchen of the Pamplemousse Grill on Via de la Valle. Battalion Chief Mike Spaulding said the fire started in the oven. The flames ran up the duct piping to the roof. There were about 40 firefighters who fought the blaze. No injuries.

*2020:   On February 4, 2020, a fire broke out in a detached garage at a home on Santa Helena north of Lomas Santa Fe Drive. A sheriff's deputy suffered smoke-inhalation injuries when she stopped a woman from running back toward the burning structure to get her dogs.

*2020:   In September 2020, Solana Beach firefighters were assigned to the Valley Fire that started in Carveacre, Lawson Valley in east San Diego County. One unit went to the Red Salmon Complex Fire in the Trinity Alps Wilderness area in northern California which burned over 144,000 acres.

SYCUAN FIRE DEPARTMENT

The Sycuan Indian Reservation is located 20 miles from San Diego, off of Interstate 8 East, in Dehesa Valley.

More than 12,000 years before the arrival of Europeans in America, the Kumeyaay Indians inhabited San Diego County. Sycuan is one of 12 Kumeyaay Nation Bands existing today. As an independent, sovereign entity, the Sycuan Band of the Kumeyaay Nation relies on a tribal council of seven officials elected for four-year terms who determine and administer laws for the tribal members. Cody Martinez took office as the council's chairman on January 2, 2019.

The Sycuan Casino originally opened in 1983 as a bingo hall. On March 27, 2019, the Sycuan Casino Resort had a grand opening for their $260 million expansion, including a 12-story hotel. The Sycuan Tribal Development Corporation owns the Singing Hills Golf Resort, the U.S. Grant Hotel, and the Marina Gateway Hotel and Conference Center in National City.

Beginning in 1972, Anna Prieto Sandoval became the chairwoman of the Sycuan Band of the Kumeyaay Nation, bringing members out of poverty to being one of the most successful tribes in the United States. In 1983, California began to allow Native American tribes to have gaming industries. The Pan American International, which ran the first Seminole bingo halls in Florida, proposed building a bingo hall on a site Sandoval and another member owned on the reservation. She accepted the offer over the objections of some of the tribal members. Within 10 years it was replaced with a large casino. In 1987, Sycuan began to run the bingo hall independently. In 1990, the tribe opened a 68,000-square-foot casino. She led the tribe in using revenues from the casino to build new facilities, including a fire department. She attended Gossmont College and later taught the Kumeyaay language at San Diego State University. Anna Prieto Sandoval was born on the reservation on May 14, 1934, and died on October 28, 2010, at the age of 76.

Henry (Hank) Murphy, a member of the Sycuan Band of the Kumeyaay Nation, founded the Sycuan Fire Department on October 11, 1974, and served as its first chief from 1974 to 2010. Without money or training opportunities, he fought to provide the Sycuan Reservation with emergency services. Hank Murphy was born on the Sycuan Reservation and served on the tribal council for more than 30 years and is a tribal elder of the community. He is a United States Marine Corps veteran of the Korean War. From 1995 to 2010, he held 12 wildland fire and aviation academies on the Sycuan Indian Reservation. The academy closed in 2010 because of lack of funding.

William R. (Bill) Clayton was fire chief of the Sycuan Fire Department from 2010 to 2012. He began his 50-year career with the U.S. Forest Service in the Cleveland National Forest. Besides serving as chief of the Sycuan Fire Department, he was deputy chief at the Orange County Fire Department, assistant chief at the Rainbow Conservation Camp, and chief at Cal Fire. He received the most awards of any firefighter in Cal Fire history. In 1998, he received the Medal of Valor for driving through 50-foot flames to save a boy, his mother, and grandfather in 1997 before their home was destroyed in Lake Wohlford. In 2006, he received a second Medal of Valor for saving 200 people at the Valley View Casino during the Paradise Fire in October 2003.

L–R: Captains Juan Medez and Steve Howie.

Sycuan Fire Department's fire chief from 2012 to 2018 was Mitch Villalpando. After serving as captain and deputy chief of the department, Zach Carrillo became interim chief in 2018 and then chief in 2019.

The Sycuan Golden Eagles Hotshots Crew was organized as a Type II hand crew in May 2000. It is one of nine Federal Bureau of Indian Affairs (BIA) Native American Interagency Hotshot Crews in the United States. The Hotshot Crews are hand crews that work in the hottest part of wildfires. The Sycuan Hotshots Crew was funded by the Sycuan Band of the Kumeyaay Nation until it received Type 1 Certified Interagency Hotshots Crew (IAC) status in October 2006. Since 2006, it has been funded by the Bureau of Indian Affairs, Pacific Region. The Sycuan Hotshots Crew consists of many Native American Nations including the Kumeyaay, Paiute, Pomo,

Pima, Karuk, Lakota, Sioux, Zapoteca, Hatuey, Mescalero-Apache, Tule River, Chumash, and Cahuilla. The crew also includes Latino, African American, Filipino, and Anglo firefighters.

Captain Juan Mendez, a Zapoteca Indian, who has worked for the Sycuan Fire Department for 24 years, helped start the Golden Eagles Hotshots Crew and served as its superintendent. He began his career in 1994 as a volunteer firefighter for the Pala Fire Department. In 1995, he graduated from the Sycuan Fire Academy.

On July 1, 2003, the Sycuan Fire Department partnered with the San Diego City Fire-Rescue Department's Air Operations Division to provide a fly crew. The Sycuan firefighting wing is stationed at Montgomery Air Field in San Diego City. The San Diego Fire-Rescue Department's Air Operations Division responds to more than 400 emergencies a year.

The department operates a 75-foot ladder truck, a Type-I structure engine, a Type-III wildland engine, an advanced life support (ALS) ambulance, a Type-I water tender, and a reserve ALS ambulance.

Tribal station 1 is located at 2 Kwaaypaay Court. The department has a fire station located at 5449 Dehesa Road. On August 6, 2019, the Sycuan Band of the Kumeyaay Nation purchased the former volunteer fire station of Dehesa at a county auction for $650,000. In 1976, the site was donated to the county as a volunteer fire station for the Dehesa Volunteer Fire Department, then later transferred to the San Diego Rural Fire Protection District. After the San Diego County Fire Authority was established in 2008, the site went back to the county.

In 1989, Sycuan Fire Department implemented an EMT ambulance service. In 1999, it was the first department in the East County to provide an advance life support (paramedic) engine to the community. Now the ambulance provides emergency services to both the reservation and the communities of Dehesa Valley, Harbison Canyon, Alpine, and other communities.

Between 2003 and 2008, the Native Americans in San Diego County donated $17.5 million to the county's fire protection needs. They continue to donate to fire departments, hospitals, schools, and the San Diego County Burn Institute.

In July 2008, the Sycuan Band of Kumeyaay Indians, the Barona Band of Mission Indians, and the Viejas Band of Kumeyaay Indians awarded the San Diego Fire-Rescue Department $177,898 to help purchase a portable live fire training unit.

In March 2014, the Sycuan and Barona Casinos gave a $45,000 grant to San Miguel Fire Department to help purchase an incident command vehicle. The cost of the vehicle was $65,000.

On June 13, 2018, Tribal Chairman Cody Martinez presented $250,000 to the Dehesa School District. A month later, on July 12, the Sycuan Band of the Kumeyaay Nation donated $20,000 to the victims of the West Fire in Alpine.

Chief Zach Carillo states: "We believe that serving the reservation and community is an honor and we hold ourselves to the highest standards. Duty is not just responding to someone's emergency. It is having the strength to do right, whether someone is watching or whether you are all alone. Without integrity we are hollow, it is our principles that cause us to do our best and help others in need. Finally, commitment. It is the culmination of honor, duty, and integrity. It means we are dedicated to service with faithfulness and loyalty to our community."

CALLS RECALLED:

*2002: On May 31, 2002, Firefighter Robert Broussard, 59, of the Sycuan Fire Department collapsed while participating in an annual process to be recertified to fight wildland fires with the U.S. Forest Service. A medic unit on standby at the certification course was at his side within a minute and began treatment. He was airlifted to a hospital where he was pronounced dead of a heart attack. Firefighter Broussard worked for the Sycuan Fire Department for five years. Broussard was awarded the Medal of Merit and the Life Saving Medal by the Sycuan Fire Department. He served with the U.S. Marines and was a Vietnam veteran.

*2003: The Sycuan firefighters were part of the crews that fought the Cedar Fire in October 2003. In November 2003, the Sycuan Band of Kumeyaay Indians donated $1 million in aid to the Crest and Harbison Canyon communities which were devastated by fire.

*2007: The Sycuan Golden Eagles Hotshots Crew was assigned to the Linville Complex Fire in North Carolina in June 2007. The fire in the Linville Gorge Wilderness that was started by lightning burned 5,400 acres.

*2018: Sycuan firefighters were one of the nine Central Zone agencies (Alpine, Lakeside, San Miguel, Heartland, Barona, Sycuan, Viejas, Santee, and Bonita) responding to the West Fire in Alpine which destroyed 37 homes and burned 505 acres.

*2018: An 80-year-old woman was killed on the reservation when her car went down an embankment and hit several large oak trees.

*2019: In July 2019, crews extinguished a 25-acre brush fire near Sycuan Casino.

*2020: On January 20, 2020, Martin Luther King Day, my 56-year-old son, Kevin, was killed by a drunk hit-and-run driver, Craig Nelson from Julian, on Dehesa Road in front of the Singing Hills Golf Resort at 10:43 a.m. The driver had previous arrests for driving under the influence. Kevin, who had a lifelong love with bicycles, was doing the bicycle loop on Dehesa Road. He was a handsome 6-ft. man who served his community, friends, and neighbors. My life has been crushed by this useless and unnecessary event—losing my child, my only son. It is comforting to me to know that the Sycuan firefighters came to the accident. Jamie Edmonds, who was a firefighter/paramedic for 22 years and knew Kevin for over 20 years, said he had a clear sense of the adage that "any day could be your last" as he rolled out on accident calls regularly. The manager of Sycuan's Singing Hills Golf Resort wrote the following note to Kevin's wife, Nancy: "To die is to stand naked in the wind and melt into the sun. The universe will claim your soul, and then you will truly dance. People who live deeply have no fear of death. Our consolation is that Kevin passed in the moment of doing what he loved. Being outdoors, breathing deep breaths, enjoying nature on a beautiful day, appreciating life. Be kind, forgiving, grateful. Ride your bike, hike your hike, be gentle to animals, love and respect your neighbor. Make a difference as Kevin did. Thank you Kevin."

*2020: In September 2020, homes at the Sycuan Indian Reservation were threatened by the Valley Fire. The fire began off of Spirit Trail and Japatul Road at about 2:15 p.m. on September 5 and burned at a dangerous speed.

UNITED STATES FOREST SERVICE

The U.S. Forest Service was established in 1905. It manages 193 million acres of national forests and grasslands. In 2017, the U.S. Forest Service spent over $2.4 billion on wildfire suppression. The Forest Service spends more than 50% of its budget to manage wildfires. Fire seasons are 78 days longer than in the 1970s, and since 2000, at least 10 states have had their largest fires on record. In 2019, there were 46,000 wildfires in the United States.

"Smokey Bear" was authorized on August 4, 1944, for a fire prevention program. In 1950, a five-pound, three-month-old bear cub was found singed and suffering burns to his paws after the Capitan Gap Fire in the Lincoln National Forest in New Mexico. He was found clinging tightly to a burnt pine tree and was shipped to a veterinary hospital where he was nursed back to health. The cub was named Smokey and was moved to the National Zoo and became an icon of fire safety.

The first USFS fire lookout was in Maine in 1905. In 1913, Haille Daggett became the first female to work at a lookout. She spent 15 years at the Eddy Gulch fire tower at the Klamath National Forest. There were only a few women lookouts until World War II. During the war the fire lookouts were also used as enemy aircraft observation points. At one time, there were over 8,000 lookouts. Most lookout towers have been replaced by better communication systems. However, there are still 1,322 fire lookouts in the country staffed by volunteers and paid personnel. The High Point Lookout on Palomar Mountain is a CL-100 design on a 67-foot tower that was opened in 1964. It is an all metal live-in tower with a 14 x 14-foot cab. The first High Point Tower was constructed in 1935.

The U.S. Forest Service chiefs are: Gifford Pinchot (1905-1910), Henry Solon Graves (1910-1920), William B. Greeley (1920-1928), Robert Y. Stuart (1928-1933), Ferdinand A. Silcox (1933-1939), Earle H. Clapp (1939-1943), Lyle F. Watts (1943-1952), Richard E. McArdie (1952-1962), Edward P. Cliff (1962-1972), John R. McGuire (1972-1979), R. Max Peterson (1979-1987), F. Dale Robertson (1987-1993), Jack Ward Thomas (1993-1996), Michael Dombeck (1996-2001), Dale N. Bosworth (2001-2007), Gail Kimbell (2007-2009), Thomas Tidwell (2009-2017), Tony Tooke (2017-2018), and Vicki Christiansen (2018-).

The Forest Service has five types of hand crews. The crews usually consist of 20 men and women who construct fire lines around wildfires to control them.

Hotshot Crews were first used in the 1940s on the Cleveland and Angeles National Forests. The El Cariso Hotshot Crews were formed in 1948 and the Laguna Hotshots Crews in 1951. The U.S. Forest Service, National Park Service, Bureau of Land Management, Bureau of Indian Affairs, and other agencies operate more than 100 Interagency Hotshot Crews (IHCs). The average days Hotshot Crews spent on fires in 2018 was 106.

Mitchell Edwards, son of Beth and Victor Edwards of Ramona, fought fires in 2017 as part of the Palomar Interagency Hotshots. He fought wildfires throughout California and in Montana. Edwards graduated from Palomar College's 51st Fire Academy on May 25, 2017. He earned an Associate of Fire Technology/General and an Associate of Fire Technology/Emergency Management. Also, he received the Academic Award for being at the top of his class of 40. He missed only eight written test questions out of the 900 that had to be answered during the 17-week academy.

The Palomar Interagency Hotshots in the 2020 crew are: J. Ortega, E. Arrellano, M. Farrell, R. Pina, R. Arroyo, C. Smith, a. Carbajal, B. Terronas, A. Marmolejo, S. Parra, F. Garcia, M. Ortiz, D. Lavering, S. Carvelho, A. Moniz, A. O'Regan, C. Macias, and R, Rodriguez. The hotshots have to be able to do 3 miles in 45 minutes or less with a 45 lb. pack, run 1.5 mile in 10:35 or less, do 40 sit-ups in 60 seconds, do 25 pushups in 60 seconds, and chin-ups based on body weight. Most gain their experience and required qualifications through first working on a Type II hand crew, fire engine, volunteer department, or attending a fire academy.

There are seven smokejumper crews operated by the U.S. Forest Service and two operated by the Bureau of Land Management. The Forest Service has about 320 smokejumpers.

The Forest Service uses planes of many types and sizes to manage wildland fires. Some are owned by the Forest Service, many are leased or contracted during times of high fire activity. The U.S. Forest Service first used helicopters on wildfires in 1947. Small helicopters carry buckets that hold from 100 to 400 gallons of water. Type II helicopters deliver helitack firefighting crews to fires for initial attack. Airtankers are used to drop water and retardant on wildfires. Aerial supervision module/lead planes, Beechcraft King Air 90 and 200 release white smoke to show airtanker pilots where to drop fire retardant. Single Engine Airtankers (SEATs) can deliver up to 800 gallons of fire retardant to support firefighters on the ground. Air Tractor AT-802 aircraft can reload and operate in areas where larger airtankers cannot. Large airtankers (LATs) can deliver from 2,000 to 4,000 gallons of fire retardant. Very large airtankers (VLATs), DC-10s, are capable of delivering over 8,000 gallons of fire retardant.

The air attack planes most commonly used are Twin Commander 500 and 600. The airplanes used for fire detection are Cessna 206, Aero Commander 500, King Air 200, DeHavilland DHC-2 Beaver, Piper Super Cub, and Cessna 185.

The Pacific Southwest Region (Region 5) of the U.S. Forest Service manages 20 million acres of national forest in California. The Cleveland National Forest, one of 18 national forests in this region, covers 465,000 acres. It is divided into the Descanso, Palomar, and Trabuco Ranger Districts. The forest supervisors office for the Cleveland National Forest is at 10845 Rancho Bernardo Road in Rancho Bernardo.

The Trabuco Ranger District Station is located at 1147 East Sixth Street in Corona. The district covers 138,971 acres through Orange and Riverside Counties.

The Palomar Ranger District Station is located at 1634 Black Canyon Road in Ramona. The district covers 128,863 acres of national forest land located in central and northern San Diego County and southern Riverside County.

The Descanso Ranger District Station is located at 3348 Alpine Boulevard in Alpine. The district extends five miles from the Mexican border northward 20 miles to Cuyamaca Rancho State Park.

Clay Howe is the division chief for the Palomar Ranger District. He leads a staff of three battalion chiefs and forestry technicians (fire suppression). The two International Type III engines at the station are each staffed by a crew of seven. Joel Mortier, who has been working at the Palomar Ranger District for 16 years, said he followed in the footsteps of his dad who retired from the U.S. Forest Service. After he graduated from Ramona High School in 1996, he was a member of the Laguna Hotshots and El Cariso Hotshots and worked at the Ramona Air Base.

The motto of the U.S. Forest Service is "Caring for the land and serving people."

Joel Mortier of the USFS Palomar Ranger District.

CALLS RECALLED:

*1871: The Peshtigo Fire on October 8, 1871, in northeastern Wisconsin killed about 2,000 people and burned 1,200,000 acres. Small fires used for clearing land were blown out of control by strong winds.

*1889: In September 1889, the Santiago Canyon Fire burned about 308,000 acres in San Diego County, Orange County, and Riverside County.

*1910: The Great Fire on August 20 and August 21 of 1910 in Idaho and Montana killed 87 people and burned 3,000,000 acres.

*1949: In the summer of 1949, firefighters in Montana's Helena National Forest fought 57 wildfires. On August 5, 1949, 13 smokejumpers died in Mann Gulch in the Helena National Forest.

*1950: The 63,400-acre Conejos Creeek Fire in August 1950 started north of Alpine and passed through Descanso and Cuyamaca Rancho State Park before burning 12 cabins in Pine Valley.

*1956: At 8:05 p.m., Sunday, November 25, 1956, three Forest Service men, a correctional officer, and seven inmates of the Viejas Honor Camp were killed in a fire blowup on the Inaja Fire in the Cleveland National Forest. The men were Albert W. Anderson, 45; Carlton Ray Lingo, 19; Forest B. Maxwell, 30; LeRoy Wehrung, 41; Miles Daniels, 33; William D. Fallin, 22; George A. Garcia, 41; Virgil L. Hamilton, 26; Joseph P. O'Hara, 45; Lonnie L. Shepherd, 26; and Joe Tibbits, 34. The fire was started by a 16-year-old boy on the Inaja Reservation who threw a match into grass to see if it would burn. Before the fire was controlled at 6:00 p.m., Wednesday, November 28, it burned 43,611 acres. More than 2,000 men fought the fire.

*1965: The El Cariso Hotshots lost 12 firefighters on November 1, 1966, at the Loop Canyon Fire in Sylmar. As two crews of the Hotshots were working on containing the fire at a narrow ravine near Sylmar, they were overtaken by flames when the winds changed direction and surprised them. Ten perished almost instantly, two more in hospital care, while the survivors endured serious burns and injuries. The Hotshots who died include Raymond Chee 23; James Moreland, 22; Michael White, 22; John Figlo, 18; William Waller, 21; Joel Hill, 19; Steven White, 18; Carl Shilcutt, 26; John Verdugo, 19; Daniel Moore, 21; Kenneth Barnhill, 19; and Frederick Danner, 18.

*1988: Fires in Yellowstone National Park that burned from June 1988 to November 1988 formed a large wildfire that killed two people and burned 793,800 acres.

*2003: On October 25, 2003, the Cedar Fire started in the Cuyamaca Mountains within the Cleveland National Forest. It killed 14 civilians and 1 firefighter, destroyed 2,232 residences, and burned 273,246 acres. Fire engineer Steven Liss "Steve" Rucker, 38, died while battling the fire. He worked for the Novato Fire Protection District and had travelled down to San Diego County to fight the fire. Three other firefighters were critically injured as the four men fought the blaze near Julian.

*2004: The Taylor Complex Fire in Alaska burned 1,305,592 acres. In 2004, there were 701 fires in Alaska that destroyed 6.6 million acres.

*2007: The large Witch Creek Fire started on October 21, 2007. It began on Witch Creek Road east of Ramona and merged with the Guejito Fire that started in the San Pasqual Valley. It burned 197,990 acres, destroyed 1,141 homes and 587 outbuildings, and killed 2 civilians.

*2013: On August 17, 2013, the Rim Fire started in the Stanislaus National Forest. The fire, which burned 257,314 acres, was human caused. It cost $127 million to contain the wildfire.

*2015: On August 19, 2015, three United States Forest Service firefighters were killed when their vehicle crashed while part of the initial attack on a fire in Okanogan-Wenatchee National Forest in Washington and were overcome by fire. The firefighters were Tom Zbyszewski, 20, Andrew Zajac, 26, and Richard Wheeler, 31. Also in August 2015, Michael Hallenbech, 21, died while battling the Sierra Fire near Lake Tahoe. He was killed when a tree fell on him.

*2017: Twenty-one fires in Montana burned 438,000 acres.

*2020: On September 9, 2020, the U.S. Forest Service's Pacific Southwest Region temporarily closed all 18 national forests in California due to the "unprecedented and historic fire conditions" in the state. By September 11, about 28,000 firefighters and support personnel were assigned to the fires in the West. One hundred large fires burned more than 4.5 million acres in 12 states.

*2020: The Blue Jay Fire in the Yosemite Creek drainage south of 10 Lakes trail and burning on both sides of the Tioga Road was ignited by lightning on July 24. It burned 6,922 acres.

*2020: The Red Salmon Complex Fire in Humboldt County started on July 27 due to lightning. It burned 116,728 acres.

*2020: The Apple Fire in Riverside County started on July 31 in Cherry Valley due to a malfunctioning diesel vehicle. It burned 33,424 acres, destroyed 12 structures, and injured 4 people. There were 1,159 personnel assigned to the fire and 22 hand crews, 42 engines, 7 dozers, 11 helicopters, 2 fixed wing aircraft, 24 water tenders. At the height of the fire, over 2,800 personnel assisted on the incident. The fire cost $51.8 million.

*2020: The Red Salmon Complex Fire started on July 27 in the Trinity Alps Wilderness Area. As of October 12, it burned 144,698 acres and was 55% contained. There were 856 personnel assigned to the wildfire.

*2020: The Wolf Fire in Tuolumne County started on August 11 due to lightning. It burned 1,832 acres.

*2020: The Lake Fire started on August 12 burning on the Angeles National Forest near Lake Hughes and moved northwest towards 100-year-old fuels consisting of big cone Douglas fir, oak, and gray pine. It was contained on September 28. The fire burned 31,089 acres, destroyed 12 homes and 21 outbuildings, and injured 4 firefighters. At its peak, there were 1,500 personnel fighting the wildfire.

*2020: The River Fire in Monterey County started on August 16 and burned 48,088 acres, damaged 13 structures, destroyed 30 structures, and injured 4 people.

*2020: The August Complex Fire started as 38 separate fires started by lightning on August 16 in the Coast range of Northern California. It burned 1,029,605 acres, destroyed 160 structures, damaged 6 structures, and killed one firefighter. There were 1,002 personnel assigned to the fire and 4 crews. It is the largest complex fire in the state.

Diana Jones, the firefighter who died in the August Complex Fire, was a volunteer from Cresson, Texas. She had been with the Cresson Fire Department for five years. Jones and two other firefighters were working on the Tatham Fire within the August Complex when a vehicle crash occurred.

*2020: The North Complex Fire in Plumas and Butte Counties started on August 17 due to lightning. It burned 318,930 acres, destroyed 2,455 structures, and killed 15 people. There were 1,150 personnel at the wildfire. The California Conservation crews sorted through miles of fire hose and refurbished them back into compact rounds to be used for future fire incidents.

*2020: The Holser Fire in Ventura County that started on August 17 in the Holser Canyon area near Lake Piru was caused by a vehicle fire.

It burned 3,000 acres. About 400 firefighters from Los Angeles and Ventura County were assisted by U.S. Forest Service and Cal Fire.

*2020:   The Dolan Fire started 10 miles south of Big Sur on August 18. It burned 124,924 acres before being contained on October 13. There were 546 personnel assigned to the wildfire.

*2020:   The Woodward Fire in Marin County started on August 18 due to lightning. It burned 4,929 acres.

*2020:   The River Fire in Monterey County started on August 16 and burned 48,088 acres, damaged 13 structures, destroyed 30 structures, and injured 4 people.

*2020:   The Woodward Fire, located in the Point Reyes National Seashore, started on August 18 due to lightning. It burned 4,929 acres. It was contained on September 30.

*2020:   The Dolan Fire in Monterey County started on August 18. It burned 124,924 acres and destroyed 14 homes and 5 outbuildings. There were 546 personnel assigned to the blaze.

*2020:   The SQF Complex Fire, consisting of the Rattlesnake Fire and the Castle Fire, started 25 miles north of Kernville in Tulare County on August 19 due to lightning. At the peak of the fire, there were 1,440 personnel assigned to it. One hundred wildland firefighters from 22 states across Mexico assisted with the fire. It burned 167,766 acres, destroyed 184 structures, damaged 11 structures, and injured 15 firefighters.

*2020:   The Moraine Fire in the Sequioa-Kings Canyon Wilderness started on August 21 after lightning occurred. It burned 694 acres.

*2020:   The Sheep Fire in Plumas County started on August 22 as a result of lightning. It burned 29,570 acres, destroyed 26 structures, and injured 1 person. There were 536 personnel, 54 engines, 3 helicopters, 24 water tenders, 10 dozers, and 7 hand crews assigned to the fire.

*2020:   The Slink Fire in Mono County started on August 29 in Slinkville Valley due to lightning. It burned 26,759 acres. It was contained on September 26.

*2020:   The Creek Fire started on September 4 in the Big Creek drainage in the Sierra National Forest. Thirty thousand residents of Fresno County and 15,000 residents of Madera County were evacuated because of the Creek Fire. It burned 341,722 acres, destroyed 856 structures, and damaged 52 structures. There were 3,181 personnel fighting the blaze. On September 8, the California National Guard rescued 120 people who were trapped by the fire. It is the largest single fire in the state. Dan Alpiner, a pilot with Sky Aviation, had a visitor while dropping water from his helicopter on the fire. An owl entered the aircraft and just sat there for several water drops before flying out.

*2020:   The El Dorado Fire, within the San Gorgonio Wilderness, started on September 5 near Yucaipa, California. Over a 23-day period, it burned 22,680 acres, destroyed 10 structures, damaged 6 structures, injured 13, and killed 1 firefighter. At the peak, there were 1,351 personnel assigned to the fire including 17 hand crews, 177 engines, 20 water tenders, 17 dozers, and 10 helicopters.

Firefighter Charles Edward "Charlie" Morton, 39, was killed on September 17 while fighting the blaze. Morton was a 14-year veteran with the U.S. Forest Service who led the Big Bear Interagency Hotshot Squad. He was born in San Diego and grew up in Oceanside. He started his career in 2002 as a corpsman with the California Conservation Corps at the Butte Fire Center in Magalia. He began working for the U.S. Forest Service in 2006 with the Truckee Interagency Hotshots on the Tahoe National Forest, then joined the San Bernardino National Forest in 2007. The memorial service for the fallen USDA Forest Service firefighter was held on Friday, September 25, 2020, at 11 a.m. in San Bernardino. Morton received several honors, including the Posting of Colors, the Hotshot Prayer, a Bell Ceremony, presentations to the family and Charlie's "Last Call," a tradition that honors a firefighter who has fallen in the line of duty with a final radio call, recognizing the end of his watch.

*2020: The Creek Fire started on September 4 in the Big Creek drainage in the Sierra National Forest. Thirty thousand residents of Fresno County and 15,000 residents of Madera County were evacuated because of the Creek Fire. As of October 11, the fire was 55% contained. It burned 333,880 acres, destroyed 856 structures, and damaged 71 structures. At the peak of the fire, there were 3,181 personnel fighting the blaze. On September 8, the California National Guard rescued 120 people who were trapped by the fire.

*2020: On September 5, 2020, the Valley Fire started at Japatul Road and Carveacre Road in the Japatul Valley, southeast of Alpine, at 2:15 p.m. and overnight burned over 4,000 acres and destroyed 10 structures. The fire burned about 500 acres in one hour. Firefighters fought the blaze against high temperatures, low humidity, and wind. It was 95% contained on September 21. The fire burned 17,665 acres, destroyed 30 homes and 31 other structures, and damaged 11 structures. There were 609 fire personnel, 48 engines, 4 water-dropping helicopters, 2 bulldozers, 15 water tenders, and 13 hand crews at the fire. San Diego Gas and Electric (SDGE) sent its SkyMaverick airtanker and Blackhawk helicopter to the blaze. The SkyMaverick holds 2,540 gallons of water and the Blackhawk helicopter carries 860 gallons of water. On September 14, the Cleveland National Forest Type 3 Team took over the management of the fire.

*2020: The Bobcat Fire, Los Angeles County, started on September 6. It had burned 105,345 acres by September 21 and was 15%

contained. There were 1,718 personnel fighting the blaze. Resources included 227 engines, 25 hand crews, 6 helicopters, 18 dozers, and 10 water tenders.

*2020: The Fork Fire in the Crystal Basin near Gerle Creek started on September 8. It burned 1,667 acres.

*2020: The Slater Fire started on September 8 near near Slater Butte Fire Lookout in Siskiyou County on the Klamath National Forest. It burned 156,610 acres, destroyed 440 structures, including 197 homes, and killed two people in the burn area. At the peak of the fire, there were 1,355 personnel assigned to the blaze. Two people died in the burn area.

*2020: The Devil Fire, which was detected on September 9, 2020, was located north of Upper Devil's Peak on the Klamath National Forest. It burned 8,849 acres. By October 12, it was 55% contained.

*2020: The Bullfrog Fire, located 43 miles northeast of Clovis, started on September 9. It burned 1,185 acres.

VALLEY CENTER FIRE PROTECTION DISTRICT

Valley Center is located about 7.5 miles from Escondido and 20 miles from Oceanside with a population of 23,000.

In 1845, Governor Pio Pico gave a 13,000-acre Mexican land grant to Jose Maria Orosco, establishing Rancho Guejito. James Davis became Valley Center's first permanent settler in 1865.

Valley Center was originally called Bear Valley but was changed to Valley Center in 1887. In 1866, a California grizzly bear weighing 2,200 pounds was killed at the ranch of James and Ada Lovett. The owner of the ranch, Edward P. Haskell, created a peach label showing an old oak tree on his property where the bear was found. The tree still stands off of Guejito Road.

On Memorial Day weekend, many visitors come to the city for the Valley Center Stampede Rodeo and Memorial Festival. In 2002, the rodeo was established, and in 2015, a memorial festival was created to pay tribute to the nation's veterans.

Valley Center is home to the Hellhole Canyon Preserve, a 1,907 acre nature reserve that contains 13.5 miles of trails. The Paradise Fire in 2003 burned 95 percent of the preserve and parts of the preserve were burned again in 2007 in the Poomacha Fire.

The Valley Center Fire Protection District (VCFPD) was formed in 1982. The district covers 84.5 square miles, much of it consisting of steep hills and deep canyons.

Governed by a five-member board of directors, the current members are Phil Bell, Steve Hutchison, Mike O'Connor, Charlotte Seaborne, and Jim Wold. In 2013, the board voted to end the 30-year contract service it had with Cal Fire and establish its own independent fire agency.

From September 1, 2013, to November 21, 2014, the San Pasqual Fire Department's chief, Harold Rodriguez, oversaw the Valley Center Fire Department. Chief Rodriguez was the chief of San Pasqual Reservation Fire Department from February 2001 to August 2013. Previously he was a captain at the Barona Fire Department. He attended Moreno Valley Community College, Palomar College, and Fallbrook Union High School.

Josef "Joe" Napier, 54, was appointed the first full-time chief of the Valley Center Fire Protection District on November 21, 2014. Chief Napier, who was raised in Vista, had worked for the Vista Fire Department since January 1986. He was a battalion chief in charge of communications, coordinating the information systems, and supervising six captains. Chief Napier moved to Valley Center in 1998 with his wife and two children. He received his Bachelor in Fire Science from Columbia Southern University, graduating summa cum laude in 2011. From 2005 to 2009, he studied vocational education and professional studies at California State University, Long Beach. In 2015, he was named Male Citizen of the Year by the Valley Center Chamber of Commerce.

Chief Joe Napier leads a staff of one division chief, six captains, six engineers, and six firefighter/paramedics. There are also about 30 firefighters who are employees while in training. The division chief of emergency operations is Jeff Chumbley. The fire marshal/battalion chief is Jim Davidson and the captains are Joe Basinski, Jon Blumeyer, Rick Delaney, Tom Spencer, Dave Loop, and Scott Duncan. The engineers are Robert Westler, Chris Palmer, Ryan Nutt, Jesse Sharpe, Daniel Marquez, and Steve Mandich. The firefighter/paramedics are Michael Urrutia, Jacob Haproff, Brad Perry, Jeremy Randall, and Fritz Eibel. The firefighter/EMT is Ashlei O'Hair. Annie Brown is the accountant bookkeeper and Amy Mayerchik is the administrative assistant.

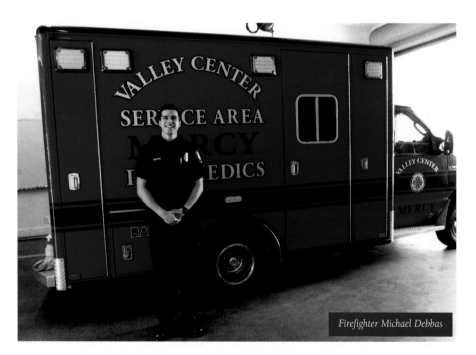

Firefighter Michael Debbas

Jeff Chumbley, 54, was selected as division chief of emergency operations in January 2020. He was born in Minnesota and moved to San Diego County in 1978. Chief Chumbley was inspired to become a firefighter after his brother and mentor, Jim, joined the force. Chumbley served as a firefighter for seven years in Poway, two and half years in San Diego, two and half years in Oceanside, and sixteen years in Carlsbad, retiring as a battalion chief. In 2016, he won the most money for the Firefighters Destruction Derby to benefit the Burn Institute. Out of 1,500 registered volunteers, Chumbley won the Burn Institute's Pamela R. Kelly Volunteer of the Year award for 2009. He served as the chair for every major fundraising event the charity has undertaken, including in 2007 when he chaired all three: "Give Burns the Boot" solicitation drive, "Fire in the Fairways" golf tournament, and the "Burn Run Fire Expo." On December 24, 2020, he was the first in line at the Valley Center Fire Department to receive the COVID vaccine.

Fire Marshal Jim Davidson began working with the department in January 2011 as a fire prevention specialist and was promoted to deputy fire marshal in July 2017. He worked for Hewlett-Packard as an engineer and manager for 16 years. He was a captain with the Palomar Mountain Volunteer Fire Department from January 2009 to July 2013.

Division Chief Gary Funderburk joined the Valley Center Fire Department in February 2015. After serving as captain for two years, he was promoted to division chief in July 2017. Previously he worked for the Huntington Beach Fire Department for 27 years, promoting from firefighter to fire protection specialist to captain. He has a Bachelor of Arts in Vocational Education from California State University, Long Beach, and an Associate of Fire Technology from Santa Ana College. He retired in March 2020.

Division Chief/Fire Marshal Mike Shore retired on January 1, 2019. He worked for the Rancho Santa Fe Fire Protection District for 30 years, retiring in 2015, and a week later began working as a captain for the Valley Center Fire Protection District.

Sadly, Firefighter Chris Thompson, 28, died on July 4, 2020, in a crash on Interstate 5 near Via De La Valle. A car traveling north on Interstate 5 collided with a pickup. Thompson, riding his motorcycle, could not avoid the accident. After serving the country in the US Navy, he became a mentor with a program called Active Valor. The program places military veterans into a mentor position for young children that have lost a parent in combat. He was hired by the Valley Center Fire Department in March 2020 as a probationary firefighter.

The department has two fire stations, each staffed with one captain, one engineer, two firefighter/paramedics, and one firefighter/EMT. Michael Debbas, 23, a reserve firefighter/EMT who attends Palomar College's Fire Academy, said, "I found firefighting interesting, and now I can't imagine doing anything else."

Station 1 is located at 28234 Lilac Road. In front of the station is a piece of steel from one of the World Trade Center Towers with a plaque that states "When the World Trade Center Towers were attacked, the calls were answered by firefighters of the FDNY. Three hundred and forty-one New York firefighters gave their lives in an

effort to save thousands. This piece of steel from one of those buildings will forever serve as a reminder of their sacrifice and our highest calling."

Station 2 is located at 28205 N. Lake Wohlford Road.

There is a Cal Fire station within the district at 14946 Vesper Road.

The department apparatus includes one 2014 Spartan Type 1 engine, one 2008 Smeal Type 1 engine, two 1998 KME engines, and one Type 6 squad. It also houses a OES water tender. In 2010, the department received a flow test machine that cost $14,000.

The department contracts with the county for funding of a paramedic ambulance provided by Mercy Medical Transportation. Emergency medical responses from each station are generally supported by a minimum of five personnel (one captain, one engineer, two firefighter/paramedics and one firefighter/EMT. They respond as a highly trained team to provide advanced life support care on every response with Mercy Ambulance and Valley Center Fire providing advanced life support care and transport. (Mercy Medical donated $1,000 to the district Community Emergency Response Team (CERT) program in 2013.)

Valley Center Fire Protection District, the Greater Valley Center Fire Safe Council, San Pasqual Reservation Fire Department, and Valley View Casino and Resort host an annual wildlife symposium at Valley View Casino Event Center featuring speakers who explain to the community how to be fire safe. Valley View Casino provides a box lunch at the free event.

Tom and Sherrie Ness of Bates Nut Farm were honored with the Valley Center Fire Community Service Award for 2017. In September 2017, Jerome's Furniture donated new mattresses to the department.

Unfortunately, even though the city is in a very high risk area for wildfires, on November 6, 2018, Measure SS, a $180-a-year fire protection parcel tax, was defeated by voters. The vote was 58 percent (3,163) against authorizing the district to enact a parcel tax to fund emergency services to 42 percent (2,296) in favor of the measure.

The board of the fire district put a tax increase on the November 2020 ballot that would require a two-thirds majority, plus one, to pass. The tax is needed to upgrade existing stations and build a third station, buy equipment, and keep fire personnel. A yes vote supports authorizing the district to levy an annual parcel tax of $0.06 per residential square foot. Homeowners would pay 6 cents per square foot of their home size not the entire lot or parcel. A Station 3 would be built at the corner of Cole Grade Road and Cole Grade Lane. The plan was for a country style station to fit in with the community. At the close of escrow on the property, the first building would be the maintenance building, which would house the equipment, with trailers housing the crew. A squad unit would be housed first, followed by a Type 1 engine and an ambulance. As funds were collected from the new housing projects, the main building would be built, and the maintenance shop would revert to the maintenance building. A two-thirds (66.67%) voter was required for the approval of the measure. Measure AA had a yes vote of 57% yes and 43% no vote.

In 2019, the Valley Center Fire Department Foundation was formed so that firefighters can purchase equipment that is not covered in the annual budget. The foundation is a 501(c)3 and donations are tax exempt. Judith and Bahram Shadzi of Cosmic Solar, Inc., made one of the first donations to the foundation.

The mission of the Valley Center Fire Protection District is "to provide exceptional all-risk fire, emergency medical, and community risk reduction services critical to public safety, health, and the preservation of life and property."

CALLS RECALLED:

*1979:   The Valley Center Grocery which was built in the 1880s was destroyed in a fire training exercise.

*2003:   The Paradise Fire in October 2003 killed two people, destroyed 221 homes, and burned 56,700 homes in the county. On October 26, 2003, the fire started along Valley Center Road at 1:30 a.m. Nancy Morphew, 51, died while trying to save her horses from the fire. Sixteen-year-old Ashleigh Roach, also from Valley Center, was with her brother and sister in a car trapped by the fire when she died. Her sister, Allyson, and brother, Jason, escaped the fire. Allyson was burned over 85% of her body and was placed in a medically induced coma for two months. She had to have 30 surgeries.

*2003:   The Valley Center General Store, also known as Corral Liquor, built in 1923, was destroyed by fire.

*2007:   The Poomacha Fire started on October 23, 2007, at 3:13 p.m. in Pauma Valley and was contained on November 9. It was caused as a structure fire spread into vegetation. There were 379 firefighters, 13 fire engines, 7 fire crews, 2 helicopters, and 4 water tenders at the incident. The fire destroyed 138 homes and burned 49,410 acres. The cost of the fire was $20.6 million. The reverse 911 system was used to alert residents in Valley Center to evacuate. Valley Center was the staging area for the crews fighting the fire.

*2016:   Crews responded to 1,720 calls in 2016.

*2018:   In 2018, Captain Joe Basinski and Engineer Ben Thompson saved the life of a 14-year-old teenager in full cardiac arrest.

*2019:   On October 25, 2019, the Miller Fire burned 37 acres and damaged one home. The fire, located at Miller Lane and Cole Grade Road, was contained on October 27.

*2019:   The department responds to about 2,000 calls a year.

*2019:   On February 25, 2019, a garage and barn off of Vesper Road were destroyed. Crews from Valley Center and San Pasqual Reservation responded to the call within seven minutes. The owner suspects a goat may have knocked over a heat lamp which started the fire.

*2020:   In March 2020, an 85-year-old man was killed on Valley Center Road in a crash involving three cars.

*2020:   On May 31, 2020, Peter Bierle, 57, died when his single-engine Carbon Cub airplane crashed on Palomar Vista Drive. His 12-year-old niece, injured in the crash, was transported by Mercy Air to UCSD Medical Center to have her airway evaluated for burns and then transported to Rady Children's Hospital. More than 20 neighbors quickly arrived at the scene to help, pulling the young girl from the plane. Chief Napier said: "There were a few residents on scene who provided amazing leadership and organized the group in order to effect a successful outcome, including Ron McCowan, Sam Beckett and a neighbor named Adam. Ron was the initial CPR certified care provider to check the pulse on the pilot and was saddened that he didn't survive. Bill Dunckell had a pocket knife he used to cut the seat belt off to try to free both. They were leaders in our community who were operating at an amazing level, in harm's way, with fire and aviation gas spilling down. They put that all aside, kept their heads clear to get the little girl out and saved her life." Peter Bierle, who owned Golden Rule Bindery and Churchill Graphics, had scheduled the printing of this book, "Tribute." He was a wonderful man beloved by his wife, Connie, and many, many friends.

VIEJAS FIRE DEPARTMENT

The Viejas Band of Kumeyaay Indians resides on a 1,609-acre reservation in the Viejas Valley, east of the community of Alpine, and 35 miles from San Diego. The reservation has a population of 394.

The 4,200-foot-high Viejas Mountain is a sacred site to the Kumeyaay, a place for religious and cultural ceremonies for more than 4,000 years. Unfortunately, visitors to the mountain have destroyed solstice markers to build campfire rings, constructed stone pyramids using rocks from tribal ruins, formed hiking trails through sacred tribal sites, and attempted to erect communication towers on the summit.

The Kumeyaay were the original native inhabitants of San Diego County. The Viejas Band is recognized as a sovereign government by the United States. The tribe owns and operates the Viejas Casino and Resort, a factory outlet center, and two RV parks.

The Viejas Fire Department located at 1 Viejas Road was established on October 1, 2005. The department is fully funded by the Viejas tribal government with revenues provided by tribal government gaming. The tribal council government

officials are: John Christman, Victor E. Woods, Rene Curo, Samuel Q. Brown, Adrian M. Brown, Kevin M. Carrizosa, and Gabriel T. TeSam. The officials are elected to four-year terms of office.

On March 27, 2008, the Viejas Fire Department and Alpine Fire Department announced that they had entered into a mutual aid agreement. The agreement outlines when and how the two fire departments will assist each other by responding to each department's emergency calls.

In October 2012, the Viejas Band of Kumeyaay Indians and the Heartland Fire Training Authority announced that they have entered into a Joint Powers Agreement. Chief Don Butz said, "This JPA finally allows Viejas to have a seat at the table and have a full and meaningful partnership with other fire agencies that we've worked with for years in a very productive way. Ultimately, this benefits the entire region, since wildfire and other natural disasters do not recognize geographic, political, or other borders. We are all stronger and better protected when we work and train together."

The mobile app PulsePoint was launched in the county in 2014. Residents receive alerts on their phones letting them know of a chance to potentially save someone's life nearby. Chief Don Butz said, "We've encouraged all of our firefighters and paramedics to download the app. It's our way of always being available to save a life, even when we're not on duty. I encourage every resident who has CPR training to download the app and join our effort."

In 2015, the tribal government formed an alliance with REACH Air Medical Services to give their community access to life-saving emergency air transport services. Crews respond to calls from their base located on the Viejas reservation. In addition to serving the residents of the reservation, this collaboration helps provide neighboring rural communities in San Diego County access to 24/7 emergency medical helicopter service.

Viejas Fire Department hosts a basic land navigation for wildland firefighters course. The course is taught over two days and covers the following: introduction to maps, compass and declination, introduction to latitude and longitude, VHF radio communications, hiking in weather and fuels, GPS, data collection and GIS, and the use of ranger beads. The course has been instructed by Damian Guilliani and attended by firefighters from Viejas Fire, Alpine Fire Protection District, Heartland Fire Rescue, Sycuan Fire, and Barona Fire. The classroom instruction provides the necessary skills needed for the field exercises on day two.

Donald Butz served as chief of the Viejas Fire Department from October 2005 to September 2016. Chief Butz has been in the fire service for over 40 years. In September 2014, he became president of the San Diego County Fire Chiefs Association. He was appointed chief of the Lakeside Fire Department in October 2016. From September 1999 to September 2005, he was deputy chief for the Rancho Santa Fe Fire Protection District. From 1988 to 1999, Chief Butz was a fire marshal/fire captain with the San Miguel Consolidated Fire Protection District. He has a Master of Science, Leadership, Disaster Preparedness, and Executive Fire Leadership from Grand Canyon University, a Bachelor of Science in Management from University of Phoenix, and Associate of Fire Science from Miramar College.

Bob Pfohl joined the Viejas Fire Department in 2006, serving as division chief for one year in 2011 before becoming a division chief at the Barona Fire Protection District in October 2012. He became chief of the Viejas Fire Department in October 2016. Previously, he served as fire chief of the Santee Fire Department from 1997 to 2006. In May 2011, Chief Bob Pfohl was selected to receive the 2011 Pamela R. Kelly Volunteer of the Year Award from the Burn Institute of San Diego.

Chief Bob Pfohl leads a crew of 20 firefighters.

The department operates a Type 1, a Type 3, and a Type 6 engines, a truck company, and a paramedic ambulance which is housed at the Viejas Station 25.

In March 2011, the department received a Spartan midpoint pumper with side control pump panel, Hale QMAX 1,750-gpm pump, and a 500-gallon tank.

Through the Spanish, Mexican, and early American periods, the Kumeyaay struggled to keep their heritage. Nowadays, they are thriving once again.

CALLS RECALLED:

*2001: The Viejas Fire started on January 3, 2001, and lasted for six days. The fire was 5 miles wide and 28 miles long. Fifteen homes were damaged or destroyed in the fire as well as 65 outbuildings and 64 vehicles. More than 2,000 firefighters fought the 10,353-acre fire. It cost more than $6.7 million to deploy the resources necessary to put out the fire.

*2003: Five homes were destroyed on the Viejas Reservation during the Cedar Fire.

*2006: During the Horse Fire in 2006, the Viejas Indian tribe's recreation center and the grounds nearby were home to more than 2,100 firefighters battling the fire. Land at the reservation was also used as a command post during the 2001 Viejas Fire and the 2003 Cedar Fire.

*2015: A 5-acre fire broke out near the Viejas Casino and Resort on August 29, 2015. Both sides of Interstate 8 were closed for several hours.

*2017: In July 2017, a Viejas crew was deployed as part of the Central Zone Strike team to San Luis Obispo County to help fight the Alamo Fire.

*2018: In June 2018, the Viejas Fire Department, along with Cal Fire, Barona Fire Department, and Lakeside Fire Protection District, battled a 35-acre brush fire in Ramona. There were about 150 firefighters at the incident.

*2018: In July 2018, the West Fire ignited near the Viejas Casino, burning 505 acres and destroying 34 homes.

*2018: In September 2018, the Fig Tree Fire that started near Viejas Grade Road and Willow Road burned three acres. Two houses were evacuated. An aircraft made several drops over the fire.

*2019: In July 2019, a fire at a two-story abandoned home near the Viejas Casino that spread to brush was fought by the Viejas firefighters as well as crews from Heartland, Santee, Cal Fire, and San Diego.

*2020: On September 5, 2020, the Valley Fire, which started off of Spirit Trail and Carveacre Road, threatened the Viejas Reservation. It burned 16,390 acres, destroyed 30 homes and 31 outbuildings, and injured 3 firefighters.

VISTA FIRE PROTECTION DISTRICT

Vista is located in the northwestern part of San Diego County, seven miles inland from the Pacific Ocean, the city and district covering 36.5 square miles. The population has increased from 337 in 1926 to 123,797 in 2019.

The founding of the San Luis Rey Mission in 1798 brought Native Americans to live at the mission. In 1845 three ranchos were granted to Vista: Rancho Buena Vista Adobe, Rancho Guajome Adobe, and Agua Hediona y los Manos. John Frazier opened the first post office in Vista in 1882. The Vista Irrigation District was founded in 1923. Vista became a charter city on June 13, 2007.

On July 2, 1928, a meeting of the Chamber of Commerce was held at the Vista Irrigation District office to discuss forming a volunteer fire company. The town had a hose cart, some fire hydrants, and several hundred feet of fire hose but not enough to handle a disastrous fire. Five committee members were elected to proceed with the organization of the fire company: Fred D. Pyle, George Black, A.C. Margin, C. E. Lawrence, and C. W. Bissinger. The city of Vista organized a volunteer fire department in July 1928 with 14 members.

The volunteers were: Torp Conteras, Lyle Deardorff, John DeWild, George Green, Charlie Hauslanden, Vince Hovely, John Itzaina, Ernest and Chet Lawrence, Ashley Hinkle, Stephen McGonnell, Paul Michner, Albert Pegg, and George Schneider. The volunteers wore light blue overalls as their uniforms. They shared the job of chief by rotating the position.

By August 1928 the Vista Volunteer Fire Company was ready to practice firefighting. It had 250 feet of fire hose, several ladders, two mules, a nozzle, and a hose cart borrowed from Oceanside. In September 1928, the department bought 200 feet of 1-1/2-in. hose and a large siren that could be heard for several miles. The siren was placed on the roof of the Vista Press.

The fire company held its first annual firemen's ball on September 7, 1928, at the La Granada Hall. The volunteers bought a 1911 Seagrave fire truck from Orange County, which was funded by $511.44 in donations and profits from the fireman's ball. In October 1928, the Vista Development Association agreed to put up a building to house the fire engine and equipment. A 20 x 28-foot structure was built in 1929 and was located at 125 S. Indiana Avenue, housing the fire apparatus and fire equipment. The location was next to the Hart Development Company building, and behind the bank next to the Hanes building, which held the original library, sheriff, and court offices.

A cast iron bell replaced the siren to notify the firemen of an emergency. The bell's original home was in the roof cupola of the Buena School, located on the corner of South Santa Fe and Buena Creek Road. The school closed when the Vista Unified School District opened in 1917. At that time, the fire department was raising funds to buy a fire truck and the bell from the old Buena School was donated to the department. A few weeks later Cave Couts, Jr. of Rancho Guajome offered $25 for the bell and the transaction was accepted.

Couts hung the bell in the water tank tower, located in the

kitchen wing at Guajome. Later, when he was renovating Guajome, he restored the chapel, placing the bell on a buttress next to the reservoir. It stayed there until early in World War II, when Couts loaned the bell back to the Vista Fire Department to use until they could afford to buy a roof siren. After the original chapel burned and a new chapel was made, the bell was never hung again and it now is on a platform at Rancho Guajome. The cast iron bell is 31 inches in diameter and 19 inches high and weighed 380 pounds. The words C. S. Bell Co. Hillsboro, Ohio are in raised letters on the frame. Each part is labeled with the number 32. In 1897 such a bell sold for $33 in the Sears Roebuck catalogue.

The fire company was divided into four districts. District No. 1, northwest of the intersection of Santa Fe Avenue and San Diego Boulevard. Alarm: one whistle of the siren. District No. 2, southwest of the intersection of Santa Fe Avenue and San Diego Boulevard. Alarm: two whistles of the siren. District No. 3, northeast of Santa Fe Avenue and San Diego Boulevard. Alarm: three whistles of the siren. District No. 4, southeast of Santa Fe Avenue and San Diego Boulevard. Alarm: four whistles of the siren. Five whistles of the siren was for practice calls.

The financial statement for the year 1928 was:

Cash received:

Cash contributions		$ 903.99
Receipts from dance		$ 159.70
Women's club card party		$ 24.24
	Total	$1,087.93

Expenditures:

Seagrave fire truck and cost of transportation		$ 511.44
Firemen's insurance for 17 policies		$ 97.75
400 feet of 2 1/2-in. hose, 50 feet of 1 1/2-in. shut-off nozzles, and sundries		$ 267.09
Gas and oil		$ 12.57
Pyreno		$ 19.50
200 feet of 1-1/2 in. hose		$ 117.60
Fire dust		$ 24.33
Siren		$ 115.00
	Total	$ 1,165.28
	Total liabilities	$ 77.35

In 1929, the volunteer fire department bought their first new Ford Model A fire truck from the Oceanside Ford Dealership. Merchants in Vista helped pay for the new truck by donating 50 cents to $1 per month until the truck was finally paid.

The district acquired its own phone number in 1929, so that when a fire occurred the residents would just dial 3000, the fire station's phone number. During World War II a siren was installed on the roof of the small frame Hart Company building and would automatically sound at the station until someone ran to answer the phone. The person who answered the phone would ring the siren to signal:

• 1 ring = building on fire
• 2 rings = grass fire
• 3 rings = medical alert

Volunteers would come at the sound and if the fire was too big for the volunteers, the California Division of Forestry would respond to help. Several men served at different times as chief or acting chief of the volunteer department, among them Chet Lawrence and Charles Hausladen. Lawrence helped later to form the Local Fire Protection District, served on the Board of Fire Commissioners, and was the first fire marshal. The first volunteer fire chief was Ernest Lawrence. He was a tractor driver and night watchman for the Hart Development Company where the firehouse was located.

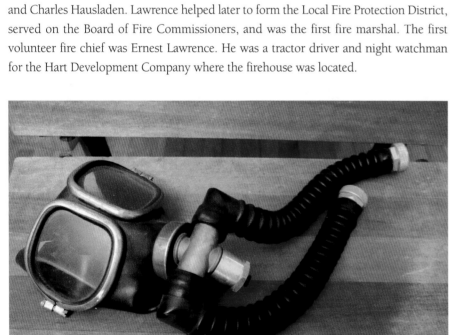

In July 1930, a fire truck and pump were purchased for $1,065.35. In April 1931, the department bought a resuscitator for $356.71. In 1933, the fire department gave out Christmas stockings to the children of Vista paid for from funds from the annual firemen's ball. Stuffed into the stockings: 250 pounds of candy, 100 pounds of walnuts, and 40 pounds of oranges and apples.

Water mains were laid in the downtown area in 1930 with a few fire hydrants from Santa Fe Avenue to Sunset and on East Vista Way to Escondido Avenue. Efforts were made to

formally organize the Vista Fire District in 1934; however, the community, distracted by the Great Depression and the start of World War II, could not meet the state required parameters. In the interim, all equipment was maintained by volunteers. The first ambulance service was from the Foster Bryant Mortuary in 1939. Later, Camp Pendleton gave the volunteer Vista Fire District an old Pontiac ambulance, which they used until 1971 when they acquired a Ford van. A private ambulance service (McCabe's) also helped. The department began buying new Ford ambulances after 1977, when San Diego County began training paramedics.

At the end of the department's fiscal year, September 15, 1935, there was $25.17 in the maintenance fund.

In October 1935, the following officers were elected: Fred Mankin, chief; Albert Pegg, assistant chief; Ashley Hinkle, lieutenant; Mike Gordon secretary; Helmer Johnson, treasurer; A. C. Mankin, corresponding secretary; and Chester Lawrence, chairman of the purchasing committee.

In September 1941, the board of directors of the Vista Irrigation District voted to give $25 per month to the fire department for fire protection, the money to be used by the firemen. Businessmen had been contributing various monthly amounts but in addition the firemen used their own money to help maintain the equipment.

In February 1944, the Vista Volunteer Fire Department contracted to buy the building and the property that it had used for 16 years. The lot was 50 x 45 feet on Indiana Street. The department, led by Chief Chester A. Lawrence, applied to the California Secretary of State to form a corporation.

In March 1944, the California State Office of Civil Defense gave the department a 500-gallon pumper unit, 600 feet of fire hose with connections, ropes, and ladders. On December 20, 1944, an election was held to levy a tax to raise $20,000 to purchase a lot and building for the Vista Fire Protection District. There were 272 votes cast for the tax and 3 against. The commissioners of the fire districts were Ed S. Schank, C. J. Martin, and Charles Hausladen.

In May 1945, the Vista Volunteer Fire Department bought a resuscitator and an inhaler and aspirator machine combination for $500.

At a meeting of the commissioners of the Vista Fire Protection District in June 1945, Chief Chester Lawrence, who had been chief of the Vista Volunteer Fire Department, was appointed fire chief. Sam Martin was named assistant chief and Mike Gordon, fire lieutenant. A fire truck costing $8,000 was ordered. The frontage of the fire station was extended and a second story added which contained living quarters for a paid fireman and his family. The sounding of alarms by telephone over the siren was discontinued. The department received a $4,000 loan from the general reserve fund of the county to be repaid to the county out of revenues of the Vista Fire Protection District. On August 8, 1945, the commissioners decided to hire two men as permanent firemen. In December 1945, Chief Mike Gordon let people in the outlying areas of Vista know that the Vista Irrigation District would supply and install fire hydrants at locations where two to five houses would be served. The cost for installing each hydrant was $20.

In 1955, the the Vista Fire District Board voted to buy a new fire house site at the corner of Broadway and Citrus Avenue at the cost of $30,000.

In May, 1957, the first paid chief was William "Bill" Elder. During this time, the volunteers began to quit. In 1957 the Vista Fire District formed a part-paid fire department. The firemen's average salary was $378 to $460 per month. In 1963, a full-paid department was formed. The second chief of the combined department was Harry Kaylor, formerly of Orange, California.

By 1981 the department had three fire stations and responded to about 2,000 calls a year.

The fire chiefs include: Mankin, Fred (1935); Hausladen, Charles; Lawrence, Chester (1945); Gordon, Mike (1945); Eller, William "Bill" (1957-1971); Kaylor, Harry (1971-1987); Turdie, Roger (1987-2001); Fisher, Gary (2002-2012); Minnick, Rick (2013-2015); Hahn, Jeff (2015-2019); and Vander Pol, Ned (2019-).

Rick Minnick was appointed chief in 2013 and retired in December 2015 at the age of 56. He negotiated agreements with neighboring cities. Chief Minnick considered both the needs of the firefighters and the city in a labor contract that was signed in October 2015. He worked for 34 years with the Vista Fire Department. He began his fire career in Vista in 1981, being promoted in less that six years to captain. Minnick grew up in Monrovia in Los Angeles County. With retirement, he now has more time to spend mountain and road biking. He has a Masters of Public Administration and a Bachelor of Science in Public Administration from San Diego State University.

Jeff Hahn was named chief in December 2015 and retired October 1, 2019, at the age of 55. He completed his paramedic training in Vista in 1984, began his career with the Vista Fire Department in 1986, made captain in 1996, and battalion chief in 2006. He served as deputy chief for four years before becoming chief. He is a member of the International Association of Fire Chiefs, International Association of Firefighters, National Fire Protection Association, International Association of Firefighters Honor Guard, California Professional Firefighters, San Diego County Fire Chiefs, and California Professional Firefighters Pipes and Drums Corps. Chief Hahn travels across the country to play his bagpipes at concerts and fundraisers. His son, Andrew, began playing bagpipes in 2008 as a teenager and has attained professional status.

Ned Vander Pol, 49, became the leader of the department on October 2, 2019. Chief Vander Pol has 21 years of experience in the fire service and over six years of executive level leadership as one of two deputy chiefs of the department. He has been with the Vista Fire Department since 1999. Vander Pol focuses on ensuring that the fire personnel have the best equipment and access to mental health support and providing the resources they need to perform their jobs. Chief Vander Pol has a Bachelor of Science in Fire Service Administration from Cogswell Polytechnical College, an Executive Fire Officer degree from the National Fire Academy, and a Masters of Public Administration from San Diego State University.

On April 11, 2019, Clifford, a two-year-old chocolate Labrador retriever, was introduced to the fire personnel at Station 1 during a 15-minute ceremony. First responders often deal with occupational stress, and Clifford provides comfort to them. The Thor's Hope Foundation, as part of its Firehouse Project, donated the facility dog. Trainer David Green of Performance K9 Training handed the dog to his new handler, Vander Pol. The dog had more than 2,000 hours of training with Trainer David Green beginning in April 2018. He has been trained to be calm and polite in all situations and to be adaptable to interactions with a variety of people in different situations. When at the station, Clifford wears a vest identifying his status, visits the six Vista fire stations, and occasionally goes to educational outreach events.

The Vista Fire Department has a staff of 93 personnel divided into four divisions: administration, suppression, training, and prevention. The executive staff consists of Ned Vander Pol, chief; Craig Usher, deputy chief of administration and fire marshal; Mike Easterling, deputy chief of operations; Danielle Pearson, emergency services officer; Diane Collier, battalion chief of training, health, safety; Brian C. Gregson, battalion chief of "A" shift; Carl Alexander, battalion chief of "B" shift; Jeff Schroeder, battalion chief of "C" shift.

On March 28, 2019, the department welcomed six new personnel: Carl Alexander, battalion chief, and Erik Boisvert, Jacob Donoff, Montana Dye, Michael Saldana, and Ian Wong-Welch, firefighter/paramedics. Also five members of the staff received badges signifying their new rank: Mark Vierow, assistant fire marshal, Eddie Jimenez, captain, and Micah Allen, Jeff Gazdayka, and Mike Romeo, engineers. At the 3rd annual Heroes of Vista event in 2014, Andy Valenta was honored as the Firefighter of the Year; at the 4th annual Heroes of Vista event on April 11, 2015, Captain Eddie Jimenez, who has been a firefighter for 20 years, received the recognition; in 2016, Firefighter Miles Sweeney was recognized; and at the 2019 Heroes of Vista celebration, Emergency Services Officer Danielle Pearson was chosen Firefighter of the Year.

The Vista Fire Department honored captain Matt Kennedy as its 2019 Firefighter of the Year.

Vista Fire has five fire engines, Type 1; one Sutphen platform truck; three brush engines, Type 3; four paramedic units; 1 battalion command vehicle; one regional support vehicle; one OES Type 1 engine; one training chief support vehicle; and six command and prevention staff vehicles. In 2017, three engines were received from Ontario, California. In October 2018, two ambulances built by Lifeline in Sumner, Iowa, were put into service. In 2019, the department received a 107-foot ladder truck which is housed at Station 6.

The fire department operates out of six stations. The stations fly red flags on days the National Weather Service designates as having high temperatures, low humidity, and high winds that could result in a fast-moving brush fire.

Vista voters approved a half-cent sales tax increase in November 2006. After passage of the tax bond measure the city begin the design and construction of two stations simultaneously, Stations 5 and 6. Jeff Katz Architecture led the design of the facilities, and Erickson-Hall Construction Company constructed both buildings.

Station 1 at 175 N. Melrose Drive was renovated in 2009. It is staffed by one battalion chief, one captain, one engineer, and three firefighter/paramedics.

Station 2 at 1050 Valley Drive was renovated in 2009. It is staffed by one captain, one engineer, and one firefighter/paramedic.

Station 3 is located at 1070 Old Taylor Street. It was built in 1963 and remodeled in 1996. The hanger is too small for modern apparatus and engines have to exit the station to an uncontrolled intersection on East Vista Way. The station is staffed by one captain, one engineer, and one firefighter/paramedic.

Station 4 at 2121 Thibodo Road was renovated in 2009. It is staffed by one captain, one engineer, and one firefighter.

Station 5 at 2009 S. Melrose Drive was completed in March 2009. It serves the community in south Vista. The station has 13,600 square feet and cost $6.3 million.

It includes an apparatus room with four bays and three bays respectively, bunk rooms, fitness area, kitchen, dayroom, shop, dispatch, administrative spaces, training rooms, fueling facilities, and emergency generators. The building incorporates stone veneer and stucco materials that are prevalent in the residential neighborhoods surrounding the station. It can house nine firefighters. It is staffed by one captain, one engineer, and one firefighter/paramedic.

Station 6 at 651 E. Vista Way was completed in March 2009. It serves the community in central and north Vista. The station has 11,300 square feet and cost $5,900,000. Areas include an apparatus room with three bays, bunk rooms, fitness area, kitchen, dayroom, shop, dispatch, administrative spaces, training rooms, fueling facilities, and emergency generators. It is staffed by one captain, one engineer, and one firefighter/paramedic.

In 2010, the Vista Fire Department became the first accredited agency in San Diego County through the Commission on Fire Accreditation International (CFAI) and is still the only accredited civilian fire department in the county. For 18 months, the Vista Fire Department underwent a self-evaluation in an attempt to earn accreditation through the Center for Pubic Safety Excellence (CPSE). In 2010, Chief Gary Fisher said, "The accreditation process was certainly a worthwhile investment. Obtaining our accreditation is, by no means, an end goal, but a renewed commitment of the emergency services to the community." The rigorous self-assessment and evaluation model promotes excellence and encourages quality improvement. The department works with a team of peers from other agencies to evaluate their completed self-assessment. Eleven percent of the agencies in the nation (280 agencies) and only 17 in California have achieved accreditation by the commission. The department submits an annual compliance report and undergoes a formal evaluation every five years. The Vista Fire Department completed a re-examination process in late 2015 and was awarded accreditation status in March 2016. Agencies become accredited after peer review of their accreditation documents, completion of an onsite assessment, and participation in a public hearing before the Commission on Fire Accreditation International. There are only 86 agencies in the United States with an ISO rating of 2 from the CFAI!

The Vista Fire Safe Council received a $10,000 Neighborhood Reinvestment Program grant to purchase fire-retardant gel and associated equipment in 2017. The council teaches residents how to reduce the risk of wildfire damage.

The mission of the Vista Fire Protection District is "ensuring the safety and trust of the community."

CALLS RECALLED:

*1927:	There was a large fire at the Vista Irrigation District office.

*1928:	Gus Tomas, a caretaker at the ranch of Harold P. Cooper, was severely burned from a fire caused by smoking a cigarette in bed.

*1931:	A fire at the Shelhoup Department Store at 12:10 a.m. in August 1931 destroyed the stock of dry goods and furnishings. Loss was estimated at $20,000.

*1931:	A house was destroyed by a fire in September 1931. The person who called in the alarm did not give the location of the fire. It wasn't until a second alarm was received that the firefighters knew where the fire was.

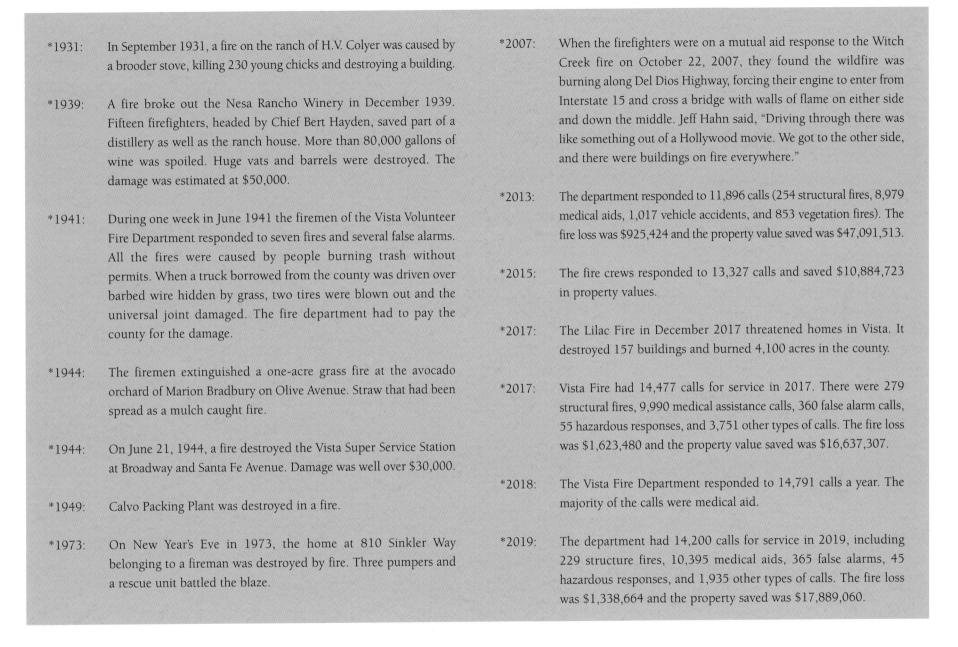

*1931: In September 1931, a fire on the ranch of H.V. Colyer was caused by a brooder stove, killing 230 young chicks and destroying a building.

*1939: A fire broke out the Nesa Rancho Winery in December 1939. Fifteen firefighters, headed by Chief Bert Hayden, saved part of a distillery as well as the ranch house. More than 80,000 gallons of wine was spoiled. Huge vats and barrels were destroyed. The damage was estimated at $50,000.

*1941: During one week in June 1941 the firemen of the Vista Volunteer Fire Department responded to seven fires and several false alarms. All the fires were caused by people burning trash without permits. When a truck borrowed from the county was driven over barbed wire hidden by grass, two tires were blown out and the universal joint damaged. The fire department had to pay the county for the damage.

*1944: The firemen extinguished a one-acre grass fire at the avocado orchard of Marion Bradbury on Olive Avenue. Straw that had been spread as a mulch caught fire.

*1944: On June 21, 1944, a fire destroyed the Vista Super Service Station at Broadway and Santa Fe Avenue. Damage was well over $30,000.

*1949: Calvo Packing Plant was destroyed in a fire.

*1973: On New Year's Eve in 1973, the home at 810 Sinkler Way belonging to a fireman was destroyed by fire. Three pumpers and a rescue unit battled the blaze.

*2007: When the firefighters were on a mutual aid response to the Witch Creek fire on October 22, 2007, they found the wildfire was burning along Del Dios Highway, forcing their engine to enter from Interstate 15 and cross a bridge with walls of flame on either side and down the middle. Jeff Hahn said, "Driving through there was like something out of a Hollywood movie. We got to the other side, and there were buildings on fire everywhere."

*2013: The department responded to 11,896 calls (254 structural fires, 8,979 medical aids, 1,017 vehicle accidents, and 853 vegetation fires). The fire loss was $925,424 and the property value saved was $47,091,513.

*2015: The fire crews responded to 13,327 calls and saved $10,884,723 in property values.

*2017: The Lilac Fire in December 2017 threatened homes in Vista. It destroyed 157 buildings and burned 4,100 acres in the county.

*2017: Vista Fire had 14,477 calls for service in 2017. There were 279 structural fires, 9,990 medical assistance calls, 360 false alarm calls, 55 hazardous responses, and 3,751 other types of calls. The fire loss was $1,623,480 and the property value saved was $16,637,307.

*2018: The Vista Fire Department responded to 14,791 calls a year. The majority of the calls were medical aid.

*2019: The department had 14,200 calls for service in 2019, including 229 structure fires, 10,395 medical aids, 365 false alarms, 45 hazardous responses, and 1,935 other types of calls. The fire loss was $1,338,664 and the property saved was $17,889,060.

WARNER SPRINGS VOLUNTEER FIRE DEPARTMENT

Warner Springs is an unincorporated area in northeast San Diego County with a population of 1,675 people. It is located 50 miles from San Diego between the Cleveland National Forest and Anza-Borrego Desert State Park, east of Mount Palomar.

The Cupeño Indians inhabited Warner Springs more than 4,500 years ago. In 1845, Juan Jose Warner became the owner of the 47,000-acre Valle de San Jose and renamed it Warner Ranch. In 1903, the Cupeño Indians were evicted from their land and sent to live on the Pala Reservation. Renown archeologist Richard Carrico says the valley has been a place of "massacres, insurrections, murder, alleged curses on the land, exploitation of native people, and land development focused on the sulfurous hot springs."

In the 1920s, the 2,500-acre Warner Springs Ranch Resort became popular because of its hot mineral water springs. Pacific Hospitality Group bought the resort in 2013 and is renovating it. The Vista Irrigation District owns 43,000 acres of Warner Springs.

The Warner Springs Volunteer Fire Department had a 1977 GMC Echo I fire engine housed at the Warner Springs Ranch Resort's gas station for many years. From 1989 to 2006, Dennis Parry was chief of the department with a crew of 12 firefighters. When the department was dissolved in 2006, neighboring Sunshine Summit Volunteer Fire Department begin covering Warner Springs under the leadership of Chief Parry until 2015.

When Engineer Chuck Serna of the Sunshine Summit Volunteer Fire Department retired in 2007, he was honored by the community for his six years of dedication to the department. Serna was a mentor to the many volunteers who came into the department and assisted with the Fire Wise Garden in front of the fire station. In 2003, Engineer Serna held the record for most response time to 911 calls; he responded to 135 calls.

In 2015, Warner Springs became part of the San Diego County Fire Authority which contracts with Cal Fire for staffing. Chief Dennis Parry said, "It was a good thing for us because we got paid firefighters and upgraded equipment. The training is the same for all the Cal Fire personnel, all of them are on the same page."

The Sunshine Summit Station (Station 59) is located at 35227 Highway 79. The Cal Fire station (Station 52) is at 31049 Highway 79.

Station 52 opened in March 2011 at a cost of $500,000. The firehouse is 2,200 square feet with a 1,000-gallon backup fuel supply and sleeping quarters. It is open 24 hours a day, 365 days a year.

The firefighters provide fire, rescue, and medical services to the community of Warner Springs. They also provide mutual aid support to the surrounding area.

Cal Fire personnel at Station 52 in Warner Springs: Kenny Wheaton, Moses Alvarez, and Robert McMillen

CALLS RECALLED:

*2003:   The Coyote Fire that burned 18,705 acres in San Diego County was started by lightning near the border of San Diego and Riverside Counties.

*2003:   Warner Springs had one of the first fire engines to respond to San Diego Country Estates in Ramona during the Cedar Fire.

*2007:   Personnel from Warner Springs responded to Palomar Mountain in October 2007 to assist in extinguishing the Poomacha Fire.

*2011:   The Eagle Fire, starting on the Los Coyotes Reservation, burned 14,100 acres between Warner Springs and Anza-Borrego Desert State Park.

*2012:   In August 2012, firefighters fought the 1,650-acre Chihuahua Fire east of State Route 79 which was started by lightning.

*2017:   The Lost Fire burned 255 acres four miles north of Warner Springs near Highway 79 in July 2017. More than 400 firefighters from Cal Fire and the U.S. Forest Service fought the blaze.

*2017:   In November 2017, a truck collided with a motorcycle triggering several small fires. Route 79 was closed while Cal Fire firefighters put out the fires.

*2019:   In July 2019, lightning caused a 2-acre brush fire east of Route 79 below the Hot Springs Lookout. Two airtankers made retardant drops and helicopters from the San Diego County Sheriff's Department, San Diego Gas and Electric, and the U.S. Forest Service made water drops.

*2019:   In October 2019, the Scout Fire burned 12 acres near the Mataguay Scout Camp.

AFTERWORD

More than 1,300 firefighters in

California have died in the line of duty since 1850.

One-third of the firefighters in California are volunteers. Across the United

States almost seventy percent of the firefighters are volunteers—745,000 men

and women who volunteer for the dangerous job of fire and emergency services.

San Diego County has about 800 career firefighters. California has 33,180

career firefighters. The United States has 370,000 career firefighters.